Space, Time and Cosmology

BLOCK 3

Gravitation, Einstein's general theory of relativity and black holes

Unit 9 First steps to a theory of gravitation

Unit 10&11 A metric theory of gravity and the field equations of general relativity

Unit 12 Black holes and other consequences of general relativity

S357 Course Team

Course Team Chair: Raymond Mackintosh

Raymond Mackintosh	Author	Michael Watkins	Course Manager
Russell Stannard	Author	David Tillotson	Course Editor
Bob Zimmer	IET	Peter Twomey	Course Editor
Tony Evans	Author, Assessor	Ian Thomas	Producer, BBC/OUPC
Leon Firth	Author	Liz Sugden	Assistant, BBC/OUPC
Bernard Schutz	Author	Tony Jolly	BBC/OUPC
John Charap	External Assessor	Steve Best	Graphic Artist
Gillian Stansfield	Assessor	Sarah Crompton	Graphic Design
Tom Smith	Reader	Hannah Brunt	Graphic Design
Alan Cooper	Reader	Alison Cadle	Manager OU TEX system

S357 is a revision of a course, S354, first presented in 1979. We should particularly like to acknowledge major contributions of the following original course team members:

John Bolton (OU), David Broadhurst (OU), Paul Clark (OU), Alan Cooper (OU), Tom Smith (OU), Russell Stannard (OU), Andrew Crilly (BBC), Al Saperstein, George Abell, Julian Schwinger

List of Units

The Open University, Walton Hall, Milton Keynes, MK7 6AA.

First published 1997.

Copyright © 1997, 2001 The Open University

Edited, designed and typeset by the Open University using the Open University TEX System.

Printed in the United Kingdom by Henry Ling Ltd, at the Dorset Press, Dorchester, Dorset.

ISBN 0 7492 8160 X

This text forms part of an Open University Third Level Course. If you would like a copy of *Studying with The Open University*, please write to the Course Enquiries Data Service, PO Box 625, Dane Road, Milton Keynes, MK1 1TY. If you have not already enrolled on the Course and would like to buy this or other Open University material, please write to Open University Educational Enterprises Ltd, 12 Cofferidge Close, Stony Stratford, Milton Keynes, MK11 1BY, United Kingdom.

1.2

S357b3i1.2   *Title page photo of Einstein is from the Hulton Getty Picture Company.*

Unit 9 First steps to a theory of gravitation

Prepared by the Course Team

Contents

Aims

In this Unit, we intend to:

1 Provide an argument to show that the description of spacetime given by special relativity, using the concept of an inertial frame as developed in Block 1, is incompatible with the existence of matter in the Universe, especially in large aggregates such as stars.

2 Outline the degree of experimental confirmation of the equivalence principle, which is the pivotal concept used in the argument of Aim 1.

3 Show that a redefinition of the term 'inertial frame', which brings it into accord with the equivalence principle, immediately provides a partial resolution of the incompatibility revealed in Aim 1.

Objectives

When you have finished studying this Unit, you should be able to:

1 Use special relativistic arguments to show that the spatial and temporal properties of a frame of reference in uniform rotation with respect to an inertial frame are not the same as those of an inertial frame as described in Block 2.

2 Discuss, in simple cases, the motion of particles when described in an accelerating frame.

3 Explain the concept of a local region and its significance.

4 State and explain the principle of the universality of free fall and explain the corresponding relationship between gravitational and inertial mass.

5 Explain the new concept of inertial frame and its relations to a freely falling frame.

6 Explain the equivalence principle and the weak equivalence principle; explain the relationship of the latter to the universality of free fall and locally inertial frames.

7 Explain the general consequences of the equivalence principle for the nature of spacetime. In particular, explain how aggregates of matter affect spacetime, the gravitational red or blue shift, and the gravitational bending of light.

8 Explain how the equivalence principle and the universality of free fall have been tested experimentally.

Study comment

1   Principal back references

This Unit builds on a lot of the material introduced in Blocks 1 and 2: in particular, we depend on your having come to grips with the ideas listed in Table 1. Before tackling a particular Section of this Unit, you may wish to review the relevant concepts from this list so that you don't have to interrupt your reading with references to other Units.

TABLE 1   List of key concepts introduced in earlier Units

Concept	Where explained	Where used in this Unit
Lorentz invariant interval	Unit 7, Section 3	Sections 2.2 and 2.4
Data taker and observer	Unit 5, Section 6	Sections 2.3 and 2.4
Instantaneous rest frame	Unit 7, Section 5.2	Sections 2.2 and 5.5
Special motions:		
(i) unaccelerated	Unit 1, Section 4.5	Section 3.1 and following
(ii) uniformly accelerated	Unit 1, Section 4.5	Sections 3.1 and 3.6
(iii) uniform circular	Unit 1, Section 4.5	Sections 2.3, 2.4 and 3.1
Relativistic Doppler shift	Unit 7, Section 5.4	Section 2.3
	Unit 6, Section 2.2	Section 5.5
Galileo's law of constant vertical acceleration	Unit 2, Section 3	Section 3.1 and following
Inertial frame	Unit 2, Section 5.1	Throughout
Setting up an inertial frame	Unit 2, Section 5.1	Section 4.3 and following
Newton's law of gravitation	Unit 2, Section 4.4	Section 3.4
Equation of motion of a pendulum	Unit 2, Section 4.3	Section 5.2
$E = mc^2$	Unit 7, Section 6.5	Section 5.5

2   Strategy if you are behind in your study

Although all of Unit 9 is examinable, the part that can be omitted with least damage to your subsequent study is Section 5.3. It requires familiarity with 'torque' for full understanding.

4

1 Introduction; why spacetime had to change

Band 1 of AC3 introduces
this Unit and this Block.

At the end of the last Block, we had arrived at a new understanding of
electromagnetism. While Coulomb's law gave a perfect account of the
force between two stationary charged bodies, we found that it is wrong to
conclude that the familiar inverse square force law implied *instantaneous*
transmission of force. The fully Lorentz invariant theory implied that *all*
influences of one charge on another were transmitted at the speed of light
(in free space). Indeed, instantaneous forces are impossible in view of the
collapse of the concept of simultaneity as previously understood.

So where does that leave Newton's law of gravity, also an inverse square
law, and also implying instantaneous transmission of force? In trouble,
obviously! Moreover, Einstein, at least, was not content to see that a law
such as Newton's law of gravity is just a 'given' or hypothesis
... unexplained in more fundamental terms. The tremendous achievement
of Einstein's general theory of relativity (GR) is that it provides a deeper
understanding of gravity — Newton's law of gravity emerges naturally
from it. But GR is more than just an explanation of Newton's law of
gravity ... it implies small corrections to it. Several very delicate tests have
confirmed that nature does indeed obey the form of gravity implied by
GR, although for most purposes, especially here on Earth, the difference is
imperceptible. Elsewhere the implications of GR are decisive: black holes
are a famous example and are discussed in Unit 12. Moreover, as we shall
see in later Units, the overall structure of the Universe, its origin and
possible destiny, can only be understood in terms of GR.

General relativity is today commonly referred to as Einstein's theory of
gravitation; this theory was not won cheaply. It entailed a profound
revolution in our understanding of space and time. The first of the
principal aims of Unit 9 is to show that the properties of space and time as
they have been developed in Blocks 1 and 2 simply do not hold true when
we attempt to explain the behaviour of any physical system (matter or
field) that is experiencing the gravitational influence of a large mass such
as the Sun or the Earth. These properties of spacetime were first collected
together in Block 1 as we developed the concept of an inertial frame of
reference. The need to combine space and time in the single
four-dimensional framework of special relativity has been demonstrated in
Unit 7. One would hardly expect that gravity, the longest known but by
far the weakest force in Nature would overturn the basic framework of
spacetime as developed so far. But it does, and this Unit sets out to
demonstrate just that.

A revolution in our understanding of spacetime is not achieved without
new concepts and postulates. In this Unit, we shall have much to say
about *accelerating frames of reference*, *local inertial frames*, and the
equivalence principle.

2   Space and time in a rotating frame

2.1   Introduction

We take our first steps to general relativity by first examining a frame of reference where spacetime is neither that of Newtonian physics nor that of special relativity. The frame in question is a *uniformly rotating* frame. The apparent distortions of spacetime are due to the fact that each point in the rotating frame is accelerating. In succeeding Sections, we explore the relationship between gravity and the force we feel in an accelerating frame; we finally conclude that there is a link between gravity and distortions of spacetime. But first, a reminder of spacetime according to Newton and then according to special relativity.

2.2   Reminder of spacetime in Newtonian physics and in special relativity

In Block 1, we showed that Newtonian mechanics presupposes a specific spacetime framework which was presented as a series of numbered assumptions running from A1 on p. 8 of Unit 1 to A14 on p. 7 of Unit 3.

Time was stated to have the following properties:

1 Time is defined uniquely for all points in space.

2 All observers agree about the rate at which time is observed to flow.

3 The flow of time is not related to any phenomenon involving matter.

Space was described by the following statements:

1 The properties of space are independent of time and have no dependence on any phenomenon involving matter.

2 The properties of space are independent of the place, the orientation or the velocity of the observer.

3 The properties of space may be summed up by the following statement: a Cartesian coordinate system can (in principle) be established to measure distance on any desired scale; the relationship between the 'distance', $|AB|$, between any two points A and B in space and the coordinates (x_A^1, x_A^2, x_A^3), (x_B^1, x_B^2, x_B^3) of these points is given by

$$|AB| = \sqrt{(x_B^1 - x_A^1)^2 + (x_B^2 - x_A^2)^2 + (x_B^3 - x_A^3)^2}. \tag{1}$$

4 All the properties of space contained in the theorems of Euclidean geometry follow from this 'distance formula' (Section 6.4 of Unit 1 gives an example).

5 This distance formula and all the Euclidean properties of space which follow from it would be agreed on by all observers at any point in space, in any orientation and in any state of motion.

Geometry and dynamics are linked in a simple way in Newtonian mechanics. In an inertial frame, the path traced out by a moving particle not subject to any forces is a 'straight line'. In Newtonian spacetime, one measuring rod and one clock would serve to map out all spacetime for all inertial observers regardless of where they are or how they are moving because all inertial observers agree on distances and times.

Special relativity forced us to reconsider this view of space and time: in particular

1 Concepts of space (such as length) depend on the state of motion of the observer.

2 Relationships involving time (such as simultaneity) depend on the state of motion of the observer.

3 To find the quantities that are invariant with respect to a change of inertial observer (i.e. invariant under a Lorentz transformation) in special relativity we put space and time together to form a four-dimensional spacetime. The interval defined by

$$(\Delta S)^2 = c^2(\Delta t)^2 - (\Delta x^1)^2 - (\Delta x^2)^2 - (\Delta x^3)^2 \tag{2}$$

is observer-independent in the same way that $|AB|$ defined by Equation 1 was observer-independent in Newtonian space and time;

4 However, it is still true that, in special relativity, *within one inertial frame* all identical clocks held by observers at various points in the frame run at the same rate, all measuring rods have the same length, and the geometry of space is Euclidean.

In special relativity, it takes one clock and one measuring rod *in each inertial frame* to map out spacetime. By comparing time and length intervals measured with clocks and rods in many different inertial frames travelling with different velocities with respect to each other, we find that the equations of transformation of length and of time intervals between inertial frames are those of the Lorentz transformation. By contrast, one would *not* need a clock and measuring rod in each inertial frame in the Newtonian view of spacetime as it is assumed that all inertial observers agree on any length or time interval.

General relativity demands a new view of spacetime. In this Unit, we shall show that *in the presence of a large amount of matter, the definition of an inertial frame as set up in Block 1 and used in Block 2 breaks down.*

The first step is to show how, once we leave inertial (non-accelerating) frames, the accustomed concepts of spacetime begin to crumble.

2.3   *Measurements of time in a rotating frame of reference*

In Block 1, we explained how an inertial frame may be set up (referring to the Glossary for Block 1 might be a useful reminder). Such a frame is set out in Figure 1. A set of data takers is deployed in the x^1–x^2 plane, each one with a clock to record the times of events in a small region of the plane, as discussed in Section 4.3 of Unit 5. We are using here the precise definitions of 'data takers' and 'observer' explained in Section 6 of Unit 5, which we quote immediately below.

> ...the term 'observer', as used in a technical sense, can be taken to mean a whole array or system of data takers ...arranged at fixed points, each with an identical synchronized clock...

A procedure for synchronizing all the clocks is also discussed in Unit 5. Our example here only needs the x^1–x^2 plane, so a three-dimensional array of clocks is unnecessary.

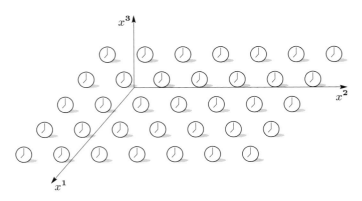

Figure 1   An inertial frame, X, with a grid of clocks spread out through the x^1–x^2 plane.

uniformly rotating frame of reference

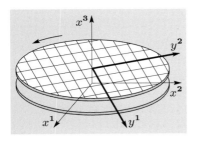

Figure 2   A uniformly rotating frame of reference, Y, mounted on a turntable which rotates about the x^3-axis of X.

Now imagine the situation shown in Figure 2: a turntable that can rotate about the x^3-axis, with a coordinate system y^1–y^2 inscribed on it. It is set into rotation with uniform angular speed, ω. At each crossing point on the y^1–y^2 grid marked on the turntable, a data taker can be installed with his clock, just as in the inertial frame of Figure 1. Any event taking place in the plane defined by $x^3 = 0$ and within a distance R of the x^3-axis, where R is the turntable radius, can be specified in two ways. The first is by the triplet (x^0, x^1, x^2), where $x^0/c = t$ is the time of the event measured by one of the clocks of Figure 1; the second is by the triplet (y^0, y^1, y^2) where $y^0/c = t'$ is the time of the event measured by one of the clocks in the array aboard the turntable of Figure 2. We now ask: in what ways does the uniformly rotating frame of reference (which we shall label Y) differ from the inertial frame of reference (which we label X)?

We shall show that the Y-frame of reference differs from the inertial frame, X, in two ways:

1 Identical clocks at different points in the Y-frame run at different rates so that they will not stay synchronized. (By 'identical' we mean clocks of identical construction that run at the same rate when they are placed next to each other.)

2 The spatial geometry of the frame, as measured by rigid measuring rods, is not Euclidean. (See Section 2.4.)

Now a point in the Y-frame *is* accelerating with respect to the inertial frame, X. A point stationary with respect to the Y-frame, say

$$y^1 = r \qquad y^2 = 0$$

is moving around the circle

$$(x^1)^2 + (x^2)^2 = r^2$$

in the X-frame, with constant angular speed, ω. This motion is analysed in Unit 1, Section 4.5, and the acceleration of the point P, ($\mathbf{a} = -\omega^2 \mathbf{x}$), is non-zero at all times: all points fixed in the Y-frame except the origin, $y^1 = y^2 = 0$, are accelerating with respect to the X-frame.

Objective 1   **SAQ 1**   How do the equations for $\mathbf{v}(t)$ and $\mathbf{a}(t)$ in Section 4.5 of Unit 1 show that the origin of the Y-frame is at rest with respect to the X-frame?

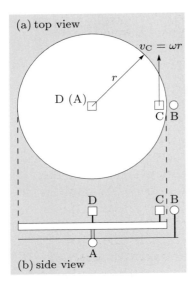

(a) top view

$v_C = \omega r$

r

D (A)

C B

D   C B

A

(b) side view

Figure 3   The comparison of clocks on the turntable with those in the frame X. (a) Top view. (b) Side view.

To prove property 1 above, concerning the rates of running of identical clocks in the Y-frame, we compare clocks in the Y-frame with identical clocks at the same spatial points in the X-frame. Consider a clock labelled C (with square face in the top view of the turntable in Figure 3a) that has been placed at a distance r from the origin in the Y-frame, as it passes a clock labelled B (with round face), with its data taker, at the same distance from the origin in the X-frame. Clock C is moving with speed $v_C = \omega r$ with respect to clock B as it passes. Although clock C is accelerating, we can apply the formulae of special relativity to it by considering that, for a small time interval as clock C passes clock B, it is in the 'instantaneous rest frame' of clock C. This application of special relativity to an accelerating system was explained in Section 5.2 of Unit 7. Thus, using Equation 26 in Section 3.2 of Unit 6, we can relate the rate of ticking of clock C to that of clock B. A data taker sitting with clock B in the X-frame will see that, as clock C passes him, it appears to run slow compared with clock B, which he is holding. Equation 26 of Unit 6 tells us that if τ_B and τ_C are the intervals between ticks of clocks B and C respectively, as measured in the X-frame, then

$$\tau_C = \frac{\tau_B}{[1 - (\omega r/c)^2]^{1/2}}$$

which means that $\tau_B < \tau_C$. Clock C appears to run slower than clock B because the interval of time, τ_C, between two ticks of clock C is greater than the interval of time, τ_B, between two ticks of clock B, according to a data taker in the X-frame. Observers in either frame will agree that in one complete revolution, clock B will have advanced further than clock C.

If we look at the side view of the turntable in Figure 3(b) we can make some interesting comparisons. We have just seen that clock C runs slow with respect to clock B. Clock B and clock A are in the same inertial frame, X and therefore run at the same rate. Also clock A in X and clock D in Y are at rest with respect to each other — they're at the origin. So they also run at equal rates. Putting these relationships together in terms of the time intervals between ticks measured in the X-frame, gives us

$$\tau_D = \tau_A = \tau_B < \tau_C.$$

Thus, the clock at a point of radius r in the Y-frame is running slow with respect to a clock at the origin *in the same frame*.

Objective 1   **SAQ 2**   Suppose you put a clock, A, at a distance of 10 cm from the centre of the turntable of an old (vinyl) record player, which revolves at $33\frac{1}{3}$ r.p.m. By how much would its rate of running differ from that of an identical clock B sitting beside the turntable as seen by a data taker sitting at rest with clock B?

Objective 1   **SAQ 3**   Using Equation 26 of Unit 6 and the same reasoning as before, prove that a clock in Y at radius r is running slow compared with a clock at radius $r/2$ in Y.

Generalizing the results of SAQ 3, we can say that, in the Y-frame, all clocks at a given distance from the origin run at the same rate. However, any two clocks that are at different distances from the origin will run at different rates. As a result, the synchronization procedure described in Unit 5, Section 4, for all the clocks in a frame of reference would be pointless in the Y-frame; even if they were all put into synchronization at one instant, they would immediately become unsynchronized.

Although we have used the inertial frame, X, to elucidate a property of the rotating frame, Y, this desynchronization of clocks can be observed from within the Y-frame, without appealing to any other reference frame. For example, a testable consequence of the fact that, in the Y-frame, a clock at a point (y^1, y^2) (not $(0,0)$) runs slow, with respect to a clock at $(0,0)$, can be observed by putting light sources at these two points on the turntable. These light sources emit a specific pattern of spectral lines (such as the yellow light that comes from sodium vapour lamps). The atoms in the light source behave like a clock. If they emit light of a precise frequency, they emit a specific number of vibrations per second. So the time interval ('period'), τ, of one vibration can be taken as a time standard. Since all atoms of a given element are identical, they can serve as 'identical clocks'. In an experiment, if light of a given frequency $f(y^1, y^2)$, emitted at the point (y^1, y^2), is observed at the origin, the frequency will be observed to be lower than the frequency $f(0,0)$ of an identical lamp situated at the origin and undergoing the same physical process of light emission. That is,

$$\frac{f(y^1, y^2)}{f(0,0)} < 1.$$

To see that this must be so, recall that an atom at a finite radius emits less oscillations in a complete revolution than one at the origin. We can interpret the frequency change as follows. Since frequency f is $1/\tau$, where τ is the period,

$$\frac{f(y^1, y^2)}{f(0,0)} = \frac{\tau(0,0)}{\tau(y^1, y^2)} < 1$$

or

$$\tau(0,0) < \tau(y^1, y^2).$$

The observed period of vibration of the light waves coming from the point (y^1, y^2) is longer than the period of the reference light at the origin; the 'clock' at (y^1, y^2) is seen to be running slow.

This effect is really just the relativistic transverse Doppler shift (Unit 7, Section 5.4). The light source at the origin of the turntable is at rest with respect to the inertial frame, X. The light source at (y^1, y^2) is instantaneously moving with speed ωR, where $R = [(y^1)^2 + (y^2)^2]^{1/2}$, in a direction perpendicular to the line connecting the two light sources. The formula of SAQ 19 of Unit 7 applied to light sent from (y^1, y^2) to the origin is (with $f_0 = f(0,0)$ and $f = f(y^1, y^2)$)

$$f(0,0) = \frac{f(y^1, y^2)\left(1 - \frac{\omega R}{c}\cos\frac{\pi}{2}\right)}{\left[1 - \left(\frac{\omega R}{c}\right)^2\right]^{1/2}} = \frac{f(y^1, y^2)}{\left[1 - \left(\frac{\omega R}{c}\right)^2\right]^{1/2}}. \tag{3}$$

Thus

$$f(0,0) > f(y^1, y^2).$$

Notice that in these arguments concerning the rates of running of clocks we have used only ideas developed within special relativity (to be specific, instantaneous rest frames, the time-dilation effect or the transverse Doppler effect) to analyse the rotating frame of reference.

Objective 1   **SAQ 4**   Three identical clocks, O, A and B, are fixed to a turntable which rotates with constant angular speed, ω, with respect to an inertial frame, X, as illustrated in Figure 4. A and B are at opposite ends of a diameter, D, of a circle with centre O. When the reading on O is $-D/2c$, light signals are sent from O to arrive at A and B. When these signals arrive, A and B are set to read zero. How would the following questions be answered by data takers in the X-frame?

(a) Are O, A and B synchronized when O reads zero?

(b) Are O and A synchronized subsequently?

(c) Are O and B synchronized subsequently?

(d) Are A and B synchronized subsequently?

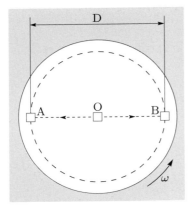

Figure 4   Illustration for SAQ 4

2.4   Measurements of space in a rotating frame of reference

We now turn to statement 2 on p. 7 to the effect that spatial geometry is not Euclidean in a rotating frame. More specifically, we apply the length contraction of special relativity to demonstrate that the spatial geometry of the Y-frame, as mapped out with rigid rods, is not Euclidean. In an *inertial* frame the spatial distance, |AB|, between two points A and B with Cartesian coordinates

$$A = (y_A^1, y_A^2); \qquad B = (y_B^1, y_B^2)$$

would be given by Equation 1, as applied to the **1–2** plane, as

$$|AB| = \sqrt{(y_B^1 - y_A^1)^2 + (y_B^2 - y_A^2)^2}. \tag{4}$$

But this Euclidean formula does *not* give the spatial distance between points in the Y-frame in terms of their coordinates, when this distance is mapped out with rigid rods. The following SAQ reviews the situation in the X-frame.

Objective 1   **SAQ 5**   A rigid rod of length l is set into place with one end at the origin of the X-frame. The events $\mathscr{E}_a$ and $\mathscr{E}_b$ associated with the end-points of the rod at the time, t, are thus

$$\mathscr{E}_a = (ct, 0, 0) \quad \text{and} \quad \mathscr{E}_b = (ct, x^1, x^2)$$

(a) What is the square of the Lorentz invariant interval associated with these events?

(b) How is it related to the distance, as given by the Cartesian distance formula, between the spatial points $(0,0)$ and (x^1, x^2) in the X-frame?

(c) Why can we say that, in special relativity, the spatial geometry of an inertial frame as mapped out with rigid rods is Euclidean?

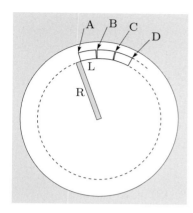

Figure 5 A determination of the spatial geometry of the rotating frame of reference

Instead of proving statement 2 on p. 7 by showing that Equation 4 does not apply in general, we simply show that one property of Euclidean geometry does not hold in the Y-frame. This property is that the ratio of the circumference to the diameter of *any* circle is constant, namely π. We shall take a particular class of circles in the Y-frame and show that this property does not hold for them, implying that the *spatial geometry* of the Y-frame is not Euclidean.

Figure 5 illustrates the procedure. The rotating turntable is represented by the continuous outer circle, and on this turntable we lay out a circle of a given radius, R. To do this we take a rigid rod, R, of length R and, keeping one end fixed at the origin, we mark a large number of equally spaced points, A, B, C, D .... The equal spacing is assured by using a small rigid rod, L, of length L as shown in the Figure. Then we carry out the following four-step procedure.

1 We gather many replicas of the small rigid rod, L, at the same place in the Y-frame and check that they are all of the same length.

2 By laying a number of small rods end to end along the large rod, R, we measure the length of R in units of L. This gives us a number N_R, the length of R.

3 By laying small rods between the points A, B, C, D ... we get a measure of the circumference of the circle; N_C is the number of small rods it takes to go around the circumference. We can make this as accurate as we like by using rods of small enough length, L, for any given circle.

4 The ratio $N_C/2N_R$ is computed. It will not be equal to π.

The above procedure all takes place in the Y-frame and no appeal to any other frame is necessary to test experimentally that $N_C/2N_R \neq \pi$. But we can prove it by using the inertial frame, X, as well as the rotating frame, Y.

We begin by comparing the circle of radius R, in Y, with a circle of the same radius in X. The key point is that, in a rotating frame, the direction of motion of any point is always perpendicular to the line drawn from that point to the origin. This means that if, as one places the rod of length R to mark a point on the circumference in Y, one places an identical rod in the inertial frame X alongside it, then the respective ends of both rods will coincide. So the circle in the Y-frame is 'lying on top of' a circle of identical radius in X. This means that $N_R = \widetilde{N}_R$, where $\widetilde{N}_R$ is the number of small rods, L, spanning the rod R in the X-frame.

Now we consider the circumferences of the two circles. In the X-frame we can lay the small rods, L, around the circumference and obtain a number $\widetilde{N}_C$. The ratio $\widetilde{N}_C/2\widetilde{N}_R$ *will* equal π because the spatial geometry of X is Euclidean. But if a data taker in the X-frame compares the length of a small rod along the circumference in X with an identical rod along the circumference in Y, the Y rod will appear shorter than the X rod because it is moving with speed ωR with respect to the rod in X. (Again we consider the Y rod to be in an 'instantaneous rest frame' to use the length contraction concept of special relativity.) It will therefore take more than $\widetilde{N}_C$ rods to go all the way round the circumference in the Y-frame. Since $N_C > \widetilde{N}_C$ and $\widetilde{N}_C/2\widetilde{N}_R = \pi$, then

$$\frac{N_C}{2N_R} > \pi \qquad \text{(remember } N_R = \widetilde{N}_R\text{)}.$$

To make sure the small rods in X and Y are identical, orient the small rods in a radial direction and compare them.

Notice that although we have used a data taker in the X-frame to deduce this result about the Y-frame, data takers in X and Y must agree on N_C, the number of rods arranged around the circle on the rotating turntable, just as they must agree as to how many times a clock, fixed to the rim, will tick in one revolution.

Objective 1   **SAQ 6**   How will the ratio N_C/N_R vary as R is increased?

Objective 1   **SAQ 7**   How does the result of SAQ 6 relate to the expectations of Euclidean geometry for the properties of concentric circles?

By applying special relativity to the rotating frame of reference, we have found that spatial geometry in the rotating frame is *not* Euclidean, unlike the spatial geometry in an inertial frame such as frame X.

Objective 1   **SAQ 8**   Is there any region of a rotating turntable within which the spatial geometry, as evidenced by the ratio $N_C/2N_R$, becomes Euclidean?

Summary of Section 2

In this Section, we have seen that using special relativity to analyse a rotating frame of reference produces some strange (but correct) consequences. We know from Block 1 that Newton's first law would not apply in such a frame, but now we see that the basic properties of space and time are not what they would be in an inertial frame. A single concept of time for the whole frame has disappeared, to be replaced by clocks that run at different rates at different spatial points. The Euclidean spatial geometry of the inertial frame has also disappeared as has the property that all regions of space have identical geometries.

What about accelerating frames in general? The argument of this Section is based entirely on one example, the uniformly rotating frame. But curious properties of the kind associated with the rotating frame are, *we assert*, characteristic of all accelerating frames of reference. Each point on the rotating frame had a different acceleration, and we assert that strange things also happen in frames with uniform acceleration. It would therefore seem that the message of this Section should be to keep away at all costs from rotating frames of reference and any other accelerating frames of reference that give rise to similar problems. Why spend Section 2 analysing rotating frames, and, the next Section, accelerating frames in general?

The reason lies in the relationship between acceleration and gravity. As we are about to see, the effects of being stationary in the gravitational field of a large body, such as the Earth or the Sun, are the same (with certain qualifications) as those observed in an accelerating frame of reference. The study of accelerating frames of reference therefore provides a means of going to the heart of Einstein's theory of gravitation.

3 Gravity and acceleration; introducing local inertial frames

3.1   Acceleration simulating gravity

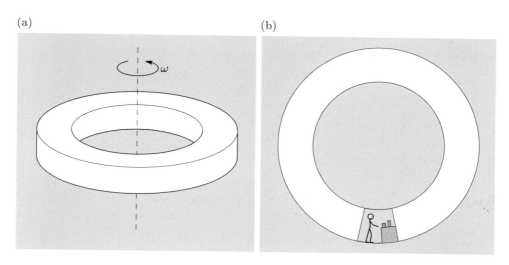

(a)   (b)

Figure 6   A rotating space-station. (a) General plan. (b) A small laboratory inside it.

Let us now think about what we would actually experience in a rotating frame. Consider a large space-station built in the form of a mammoth doughnut, as pictured in Figure 6(a). The station has a small angular speed, ω, with respect to the fixed stars, about the central axis of symmetry. The people who inhabit the station live in cabins built along the outer rim (Figure 6b). Imagine the way in which they would experience their environment inside the station. They would not float around feeling weightless; they would feel their feet pressed firmly to the outer wall (which they would probably call the 'floor'). If a marble were gently pushed off a desk in one of the cabins, it would move in the general direction of the legs of the table; one would say that it 'fell to the floor'. In short, those dwelling on the station would feel that everything was behaving much as it does on Earth, where the force of gravity keeps things in their places — books on tables, coats on coathooks, etc.

Now suppose that these astronauts decide to see if they can tell whether the forces that keep them and their belongings in place are the result of (i) the gravitational attraction of some large body outside their laboratory or (ii) the result of being uniformly rotated as we have described. They push objects of differing masses and of differing compositions off the edge of the table and watch how they move, estimating the resulting accelerations by measuring how long they take to fall to the floor. What will they find?

To answer this question, we view the situation from a non-rotating, inertial frame. In such a frame, Newton's laws apply, and since there is no force on the marble, it will proceed in a straight line. It is just a matter of geometry to transform back to see how the motion appears in the rotating frame. We shall not go through the details, but the results are not surprising. The astronaut initially sees the marble accelerate 'straight

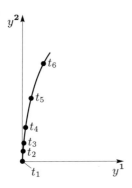

Figure 7 Expanded-scale representation of the path of a particle released at rest as viewed in the rotating frame of the space-station. Times $t_1, t_2, \ldots$ are at equal time intervals, so an initial acceleration in the y^2-direction is evident. Note that positive y^2 is what the astronaut would call 'down'.

local measurements

down' in his frame. However, over time, the path would deviate as is shown in Figure 7, where the y^2-axis is in the radially outwards direction ('down') and the y^1-axis is in the direction along which the astronauts align the tops of their dinner tables. The path deviates to the side because, while the object moves in what an inertial observer would call a straight line, the space station is rotating.

The initial acceleration of the object is just minus that which an inertial observer would ascribe to the astronaut's dining room. Looking at this from an inertial frame, we know that the acceleration of a point $\mathbf{x}$ from the axis of rotation is $-\omega^2\mathbf{x}$, and thus depends on where in the room point $\mathbf{x}$ is. If the astronaut's dining room is small enough, a *local* acceleration can be ascribed to it — in other words $-\omega^2\mathbf{x}$ doesn't vary much for different $\mathbf{x}$ within the room. The magnitude of the downward acceleration shown in Figure 7 is $|\omega^2\mathbf{x}|$, and will be well defined if the astronaut's dining room is a *local* region, i.e. small enough that variations in $\mathbf{x}$ within it are small compared to $\mathbf{x}$ itself.

If, then, the astronaut drops the marble, and watches its motion, can he distinguish what happens from the effect of gravity? In general, yes, as Figure 7 makes clear. But, if he is in a small enough room, the answer is *no*. The room will have a well-defined acceleration, and the marble will fall 'straight down' with that acceleration. The deviations from this, shown in Figure 7, increase with the size of the region over which measurements of the ball's motion are made. If he wants to convince a colleague that the spaceship is at rest on a planet, all he has to do is reduce the size of the region over which the measurements are made. However precise the measuring instruments his colleague produces, he only has to induce his colleague to look at the motion in an appropriately small region to convince (delude) him into believing that the marble falls under the gravity of a planet. But as soon as his colleague takes a more global view, perhaps watching the marble move over a longer distance, or watching the fall of many marbles at different points around the spaceship, he will be able to distinguish consequences of rotation from effects of gravity.

The composition of the marble evidently yields no clues as to whether gravity or acceleration is involved. If acceleration is responsible for its motion, as in a rotating spaceship, then *the motion of the marble seen by the astronaut is determined by a purely geometrical transformation of uniform motion in an inertial frame* and hence is independent of its composition. But, according to Galileo, see Unit 2 Section 3, this composition independence is a property of motion under gravity too; this is a subject we return to soon.

If, then, motion is observed over *a large enough volume of space*, one can distinguish being in a rotating (or accelerating) frame of reference from being in a gravitational field. Moreover, as we demonstrate later, we could also make this distinction in a smaller laboratory if we ran the experiments over *a longer period of time*. However, if one is confined to observing motion in a small enough region of space and over small enough intervals of time then one cannot use observations to make this distinction. What we mean by 'small enough' is related to the precision of the measuring equipment. The more accurate the measuring equipment, the smaller the spacetime volumes have to be to maintain indistinguishability. We shall refer to measurements in 'small enough' regions of spacetime as 'local' measurements.

3.2 Gravity simulating acceleration

We could sum up Section 3.1 as follows:

1 An observer is placed in an accelerating frame of reference, in fact a uniformly rotating frame of reference.

2 He does 'dropping experiments' with objects of differing masses and compositions.

3 If he confines his experiments to a 'small' region of spacetime, he finds that he cannot tell that he is not stationary in a gravitational field.

4 If he enlarges the spacetime region in which he performs his experiments he *can* tell that in fact he is in an accelerating frame of reference. Gravitational attraction can be simulated by the effects of a rotating frame of reference *only* in a 'small' region of spacetime.

We now show with another example that the converse is also true:

1′ An observer is placed stationary in the gravitational influence of some large body.

2′ He does 'dropping experiments' with objects of differing masses and compositions.

3′ If he performs 'local' experiments, i.e. experiments in a 'small' region of spacetime, he finds that he cannot tell that he is not in an accelerating frame of reference in empty space.

4′ If he enlarges the spacetime region in which he performs his experiments he *can* tell that in fact he is in the gravitational influence of some large body.

Let us verify that this does work with a simple example, but using this time a different type of accelerating frame of reference.

Suppose that you are in a small cabin, such as a lift, and that you are stationary in the gravitational field of a large body such as the Earth as in Figure 8(a). You release from your hand a small object. Galileo's law of constant vertical acceleration applies to a very good approximation so the body accelerates straight to the floor as in Figure 8(b). There is nothing surprising in that; the implications are less obvious. Without looking outside the cabin, can you distinguish the situation of Figure 8(b) from that of Figure 8(c)? In the latter case, instead of being at rest in a gravitational field, you are out in 'empty space' in a rocket-ship with the motors turned on to provide a constant acceleration. Just as in the space-station, you don't float around the cabin but are pressed to the back end (the 'floor'). When you let go of the object it is under the action of no forces so it proceeds at constant velocity. You and the rocket, however, are still accelerating. So you and the cabin accelerate away from the object — what you would *observe* is that the object accelerates away from your hand towards the floor. This is exactly the same behaviour that you would observe in the situation of Figure 8(b).

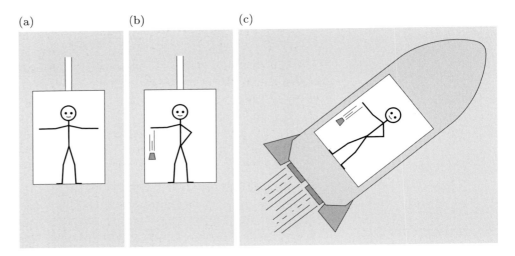

(a)   (b)   (c)

Figure 8   Comparison of a small laboratory stationary in the gravitational field of a large body, and a similar laboratory in an accelerating rocket. (a) Stationary laboratory. (b) A 'dropping experiment' done in this stationary laboratory. (c) A 'dropping experiment' done in the laboratory aboard an accelerating rocket.

This completes steps 1, 2 and 3 as applied to a gravitational field. To find the corresponding step 4, we enlarge the laboratory: Figure 9(a) shows a gigantic exaggeration of the situation. Two masses are simultaneously dropped by the experimenter. The (almost) spherical Earth acts like a point mass situated at its geometric centre so that as the two masses accelerate toward the floor they also accelerate towards each other. This acceleration of the two particles towards each other is called 'lateral acceleration' in discussions to follow.

lateral acceleration

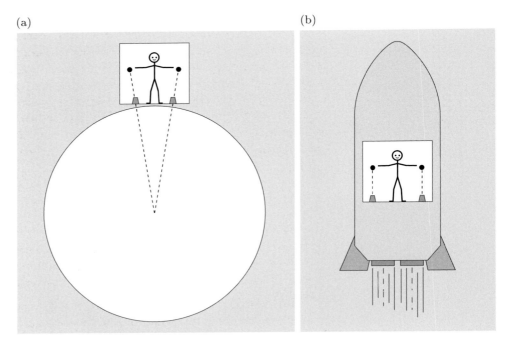

(a)   (b)

Figure 9   The differentiation of the effects of gravity from those of an accelerating frame of reference. (a) A 'dropping experiment' performed in a mammoth laboratory on the Earth. (b) A 'dropping experiment' performed in the accelerating frame of reference of a rocket-ship.

Now, no such lateral acceleration occurs in the uniformly accelerating frame of reference provided by the rocket-ship with its engines firing. The two masses held by the experimenter in Figure 9(b) are subject to no forces from the instant they are released from his hands. (The mutual gravitational attraction of the two masses can be neglected in this argument because we can make it arbitrarily small by making the two masses as small as necessary). They therefore move with constant velocity thereafter and stay at constant separation from one another. Since the rocket is still accelerating under the action of its engines, the floor accelerates to meet the two masses. The observer in the rocket simply sees the two masses accelerate to the floor, when released, with no change in separation.

The relative size of the lateral and downward accelerations depends on the initial separation of the two masses whose motions are observed in a stationary laboratory. Clearly, in the extreme case of a laboratory stretching around the world with the masses on opposite sides of the world, their mutual acceleration would be very large!

local region

We now use these ideas to define a 'local region'. This concept will enable us to give a concise definition of the equivalence principle in Section 4. A *local region* is a region of spacetime which is small enough that any effects of the non-uniformity of a gravitational field cannot be detected. Of course, if you have more sensitive instruments, or the gravitational field has steeper gradients, the actual size of the region would have to be smaller. The idea is that whatever the degree of sensitivity of your instruments, there is always a region which is small enough in spatial extent and time interval that no 'lateral acceleration', for example, can be detected; that region would be a local region in the context of such measurements.

Objective 3

SAQ 9 Consider an experimenter, working in a small isolated windowless laboratory stationary on the surface of the Earth. He wishes to confirm that he is indeed under the gravitational influence of the Earth and is not in an accelerating rocket out in space. To do this, he observes the paths of small objects within the laboratory, which are subject to no electromagnetic or nuclear forces. However, he finds that if he drops two objects from opposite sides of the top of the laboratory, as sketched in Figure 9(a), his equipment for measuring distances is not accurate enough to detect any change in separation of the two particles as they fall.

(a) Since the experimenter cannot expand the spatial size of his laboratory, can you suggest a way in which he could double the time interval over which he observes the paths?

(*Read the answer to part (a) before continuing to part (b).*)

(b) If the experimenter were in a uniformly accelerating rocket, how would you expect the separation of the two particles to behave in the course of the experiment described in the answer to part (a)?

(c) How would you expect the separation between the two particles to behave in the experimenter's laboratory on Earth during the course of the experiment described in the answer to part (a)?

(d) How can the expansion of the time of observation of the particles within the same spatial region help to distinguish between the effects of a gravitational field and an accelerating frame of reference?

3.3   The universality of free fall

In Section 3.1, an astronaut attempted to distinguish between the effects of the rotating space-station and those of a gravitational field by dropping objects of differing masses and compositions. The different compositions of the dropping bodies could not help. If the apparent motion was due to rotation, then it would simply be a geometrical transformation of inertial motion and thereby clearly independent of composition or mass; if it were gravitational, the astronaut would surely recall experiments showing that the same acceleration occurs for objects of differing masses or compositions moving under the gravitational influence of some body. This composition-independence of motion under gravity was known to Galileo and has been the subject of experimental tests of increasing precision ever since. Whether or not Galileo actually dropped different objects from the leaning tower of Pisa, he did perform more controlled experiments such as the rolling of balls of different materials down inclined planes. All such experiments support a general principle known as the 'universality of free fall' which says that in any situation involving only gravitational attraction, the motion of a body is independent of its mass or chemical composition. The only qualification recalls the analogous situation for the electric effects of a charged body described in Unit 4: in defining the electric field $\mathbf{E}(\mathbf{x})$, we stipulate that the charge that tests the field must be small enough not to modify the distribution of the other charges that create the field. In the same way, we assume that the bodies we are talking about are 'test-bodies' in the same sense — they are small enough to 'test' the gravitational influence of a massive source of gravitational field without disturbing it. We can now state the principle of the universality of free fall.

test-body

general form of the principle of the universality of free fall

THE UNIVERSALITY OF FREE FALL

If a test-body is placed at a given point in space and is given an initial velocity there, then its subsequent motion will be independent of its internal structure or composition, provided it is not subject to any external electromagnetic or nuclear forces.

Note that in the last resort, air resistance or other forms of friction boil down to the result of electromagnetic forces when considered on the atomic scale.

It is very important to be clear as to what is meant by the term 'free fall'. You might be tempted to say that a sky-diver falling from an aeroplane, before he opens his parachute, is in free fall, whereas an astronaut in an orbiting satellite is not falling at all — he is swinging around the Earth in an elliptical orbit. In terms of what is meant here by free fall you would be wrong on both counts. *To be in free fall according to our definition is to be freely moving subject to gravitational influences only.* Thus the astronaut 'floating' in his space-station is only under the gravitational pull of the Earth, the Sun and the Moon, as long as the rockets are not being fired. The motion he executes is described as free fall.

free fall

Objective 4   SAQ 10   Why is the sky-diver *not* in free fall?

Objective 4   SAQ 11   A team of astronauts fly a mission from the Earth to the Moon, as
illustrated in Figure 10. For what part, or parts, of the journey could they
be said to be in free fall?

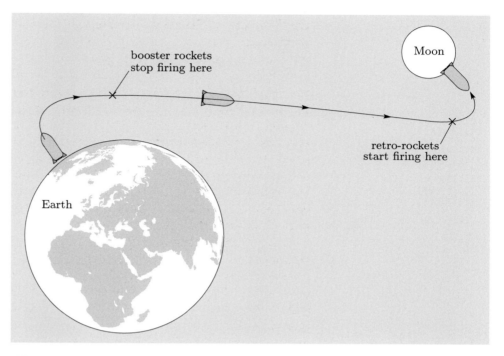

Figure 10   Illustration for SAQ 11.

It is clear from the answers to SAQs 10 and 11 that the idea of free fall
must be extended beyond the common notion of 'falling' down, say, a
mineshaft. One can travel in a circle, ellipse or parabola and be in free fall
the whole time; one can 'fall' down a mineshaft and, technically speaking,
not be in *free fall*. It is in the technical sense explained above that the
term 'free fall' will subsequently be used.

3.4   The universality of free fall in Newtonian mechanics

If we express the universality of free fall within the conceptual framework
of Newton's mechanics and theory of gravity, then we find that it leads to
a very simple equation which suggests experimental tests. To derive it, we
recall from Block 1 that Newtonian theory involves two different concepts
of mass:

1 *Inertial mass*, m, which gives the ratio of the magnitudes of the force
and the acceleration in Newton's second law; that is $m = |\mathbf{F}|/|\mathbf{a}|$.

2 *Gravitational mass*, μ, which determines the force that a given piece of
matter experiences from, or exerts on, another piece of matter as a result
of gravity. It is defined through Newton's law of universal gravitation for
the force on a body a, mass μ_a, due to a body b, mass μ_b:

$$|\mathbf{F}_{ab}| = G\frac{\mu_a \mu_b}{|\mathbf{x}_a - \mathbf{x}_b|^2}. \tag{5}$$

Because of its importance, we review here the derivation given in Unit 2 of
the relationship between m and μ that follows from the universality of free

fall. Imagine two different bodies with masses (μ_1, m_1) and (μ_2, m_2) placed at the *same* point in a gravitational field. From Newton's law of gravitation, Equation 5, the force on either body is proportional to its gravitational mass, μ:

$$|\mathbf{F}| \propto \mu \qquad \text{or} \qquad |\mathbf{F}| = \mu|\mathbf{g}|.$$

(If $\mathbf{g}$ is due to the proximity of some other large body (a planet, say) mass μ_{planet} a distance r away, then $g = G\mu_{\text{planet}}/r^2$.) Thus,

$$|\mathbf{F}_1| = \mu_1|\mathbf{g}| \qquad \text{and} \qquad |\mathbf{F}_2| = \mu_2|\mathbf{g}|.$$

Each of the bodies accelerates according to Newton's second law:

$$|\mathbf{F}_1| = m_1|\mathbf{a}_1| \qquad \text{and} \qquad |\mathbf{F}_2| = m_2|\mathbf{a}_2|$$

so

$$m_1|\mathbf{a}_1| = \mu_1|\mathbf{g}| \qquad \text{and} \qquad m_2|\mathbf{a}_2| = \mu_2|\mathbf{g}|$$

or

$$\frac{m_1|\mathbf{a}_1|}{\mu_1} = \frac{m_2|\mathbf{a}_2|}{\mu_2}.$$

We now invoke the universality of free fall: this tells us that $|\mathbf{a}_1| = |\mathbf{a}_2|$, since these accelerations control the subsequent motions, which have to be identical.

It follows that

$$\frac{m_1}{\mu_1} = \frac{m_2}{\mu_2}$$

and this will be true for any pair of masses. Thus

$$\frac{m}{\mu} = \text{constant}$$

and by choosing the constant to be equal to 1,

$$m = \mu \qquad \text{for any substance.}$$

Thus, the universality of free fall implies that $m = \mu$, and from Newton's day to the present, tests of this principle have been based on tests of the equality $m = \mu$, as we shall see in Section 5.

3.5 *Falling freely in the Space Shuttle*

The Space Shuttle, or indeed the Skylab of the 1970s or a space station of the future, falls freely around the Earth when in orbit. In effect, it is a freely falling frame. Within the Shuttle, everything appears to be weightless. Why? Here is one way of seeing the answer which brings out a particular feature of local frames which has not had due emphasis. The orbital period of an Earth satellite depends on its distance from the centre of the Earth (it is sufficient for the argument to consider just circular orbits). Thus, two adjacent satellites at the same height and on the same orbit could remain perfectly in step and the same distance apart *for ever*, as they encircle the Earth. Similarly, if an astronaut lets go of a spanner in the Shuttle, it will circle the Earth in step with the Shuttle ... or will it? Obviously, two spanners in the space shuttle at (slightly) different orbital radii will have different orbital periods and must eventually move apart. Indeed, any object released within the shuttle at a different height above the centre of the Earth than the centre of mass of the shuttle will eventually move apart from the shuttle, hitting one of the walls, perhaps even the ceiling!

The word to stress in what we have just said is *eventually*. We have mostly stressed that 'local' means 'local in space', but 'local in time' is important too. Indeed, it could hardly be otherwise since we know that space and time have become intertwined in Einstein–Minkowski spacetime. But the Shuttle example makes clear that however small the Shuttle is, if you wait long enough you will find that gravity and acceleration are distinguishable, and within the Shuttle, cannot precisely cancel to give exact weightlessness. Conversely, however accurate your timing instrument or precise your position measurements, you can make departures from apparent weightlessness unmeasurable by making the spacecraft small enough and the time interval of the measurement short enough.

tidal force

Incidentally, the fact that two satellites at different heights must move apart implies that the Shuttle must 'feel' a force acting to pull it apart. Obviously, the force becomes unobservably small in the limit of small size of spacecraft. This force is an example of a *tidal* force, since the differential force of the Moon on the oceans at different parts of the Earth's surface is largely responsible for the tides. The lateral acceleration in Figure 9(a) can be viewed as the result of a tidal force. Tidal forces are important for a body, or important within a region, in proportion to the extent that gravity is non-uniform over the body or across the region. They are a consequence of the inhomogeneity of the gravitational field. Tidal forces are believed to be responsible for the rings of Saturn, either by breaking up a planet that got too close, or by inhibiting the formation of a planet from 'planet-stuff'. Tidal forces can be huge near black holes, as we shall see in Unit 12. Their significance in this Unit is that, roughly speaking, a 'local' frame is a frame where there are no detectable tidal effects.

3.6 'Freely falling frames are locally inertial frames'

Given the provisos about 'locality', a spanner thrown across the Space Shuttle appears to move within the Shuttle with exactly constant velocity until it strikes a wall of the Shuttle, or another astronaut catches it. It appears to obey Newton's first law; the Shuttle appears to be, locally at least, an inertial frame. We make this idea more precise with a simpler example.

Imagine that you are standing with a marble in your hand in the closed cabin of an elevator at the top of a mineshaft from which the air has been evacuated. At the instant that you release the marble from your hand, without throwing or pushing it in any direction, someone cuts the cable to the elevator. Instead of panicking, you calmly observe the subsequent motion of the marble, using the edges of the walls of the cabin as a Cartesian coordinate system. Now the marble obviously starts to accelerate in the direction of the centre of the Earth but so do you and the cabin (your coordinate system). So, relative to this coordinate system, the marble, released at rest, stays at rest.

If we use Newtonian mechanics to describe this situation, a striking facet of this new, 'freely falling' coordinate system emerges. We set up an inertial frame as described in Unit 2 (Section 5.1), with origin far from any matter, and extended to all space so as to be able to describe the motions of the elevator and the particle in it (Figure 11). We choose an inertial frame in which the Earth is momentarily stationary (the 'instantaneous rest frame of the Earth') and ignore the Earth's rotation.

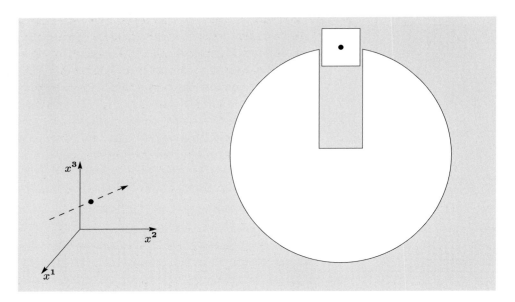

Figure 11   Establishment of the inertial frame that is the 'instantaneous rest frame of the Earth'.

We describe the motion of a particle in the elevator by the position vector $\mathbf{x}_1(t)$, as shown in Figure 12. Because the particle is near the surface of the Earth, we invoke Galileo's law, which says that the particle experiences a constant acceleration in the negative x^3-direction; that is, the acceleration vector $\mathbf{g}$ is

$$\mathbf{g} = (0, 0, -g).$$

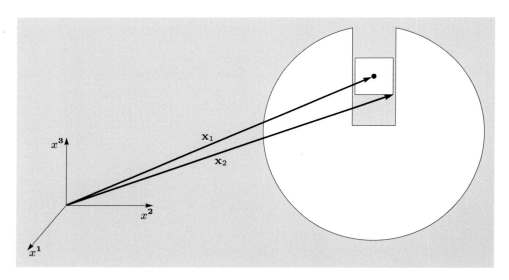

Figure 12   The motion of a freely falling particle in a freely falling elevator, both described in the 'instantaneous rest frame of the Earth'

Now, instead of simply releasing the particle at rest at a position

$$\mathbf{x}_1(0) \equiv \mathbf{s}_1 = (x_1^1(0), x_1^2(0), x_1^3(0))$$

(where (0) indicates $t = 0$), we also give it an initial velocity

$$\mathbf{v}_1(0) = (v_1^1(0), v_1^2(0), v_1^3(0))$$

in some arbitrary direction. In this situation of constant acceleration, Equation 14 in Unit 1 tells us how the particle will move:

$$\mathbf{x}_1(t) = \tfrac{1}{2}\mathbf{g}t^2 + \mathbf{v}_1(0)t + \mathbf{s}_1. \tag{6}$$

In addition, we can describe the motion of one of the corners of the elevator cabin, which we label $\mathbf{x}_2$. It starts from rest at an initial position, $\mathbf{s}_2$, and accelerates with the *same* constant acceleration, $\mathbf{g}$; it is here that the argument depends on the universality of free fall. Equation 14 of Unit 1 says that its subsequent motion will be given by

$$\mathbf{x}_2(t) = \tfrac{1}{2}\mathbf{g}t^2 + \mathbf{s}_2. \tag{7}$$

But how does the separation, $\mathbf{x}_1 - \mathbf{x}_2$, behave with time? Subtracting Equation 7 from Equation 6 gives

$$\mathbf{x}_1(t) - \mathbf{x}_2(t) = \mathbf{v}_1(0)t + (\mathbf{s}_1 - \mathbf{s}_2).$$

This says that the separation varies linearly with time; it does not exhibit accelerated motion. As we see in Figure 13, by subtracting $\mathbf{x}_2(t)$ from $\mathbf{x}_1(t)$, we move from our inertial frame of reference to a frame of reference with its origin in the corner of the elevator — a freely falling frame of reference. We see that in *this* frame of reference, any particle sent off with an initial velocity moves in a straight line with constant velocity thereafter!

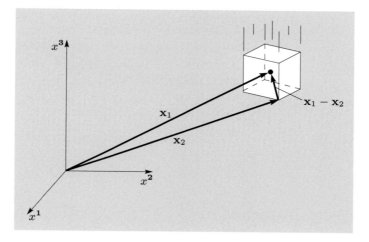

Figure 13   The instantaneous rest frame of the Earth and the freely falling frame of the elevator.

We conclude that, in a freely falling frame of reference in the gravitational field of the Earth:

1 a particle set at rest remains at rest;

2 a particle set in motion with an arbitrary initial velocity $\mathbf{v}(0)$ executes straight-line motion with the constant velocity $\mathbf{v}(0)$.

This is just the behaviour that you would see in an *inertial frame* — in the presence of gravity, a non-rotating freely falling frame is an inertial frame! *We then have a new way of defining an inertial frame.* Instead of going far out into space to set up our origin and orientation of axes, *we set up our origin on a freely falling particle at any point in space that we choose, near a large mass or not, and orient the axes so that other freely falling particles stay at rest or move in straight lines.*

This realization that (non-rotating) *freely falling frames behave like inertial frames* fundamentally changes our conception of an inertial frame of reference. This change is inevitable since we have just defined one inertial frame in which the Earth is stationary and another inertial frame accelerating with respect to the first according to the formula

$$\mathbf{x}_2(t) = \tfrac{1}{2}\mathbf{g}t^2 + \mathbf{s}_2.$$

In the Newtonian scheme, *two frames of reference that are accelerating with respect to each other cannot both be inertial frames.*

What changes in our conception of an inertial frame is the size of the region of spacetime over which an inertial frame can be considered to extend. In Blocks 1 and 2, an inertial frame was defined by observations on particles far out in space. Having defined an origin and orientation of coordinate axes by means of these observations, we then imagined these axes extended throughout all space to define a global inertial frame. This is how we defined an inertial frame in which the Earth is stationary at the outset of this discussion. But the new way of defining an inertial frame, i.e. fixing the origin and orientation of axes by means of observations on freely falling particles anywhere in space (close to large masses or not), implies that such an inertial frame exists only in a limited region of space and for a limited extent of time. It is a 'locally inertial frame' where 'locally' means 'of limited extent in space and time'. The impossibility, within the Newtonian scheme, of having two inertial frames accelerating with respect to each other no longer applies to *local* inertial frames.

locally inertial frame

That the freely falling elevator gives an inertial frame only for measurements performed within a local region of spacetime can be seen by doing a 'dropping experiment' with two marbles held at arm's length. As illustrated in Figure 14(a), the marbles fall along lines that intersect at the centre of the Earth.

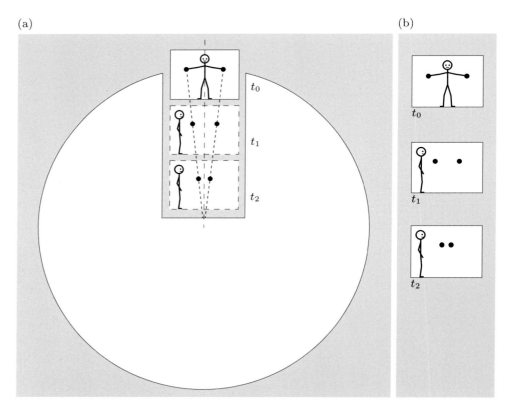

(a)   (b)

Figure 14   The locally inertial nature of a freely falling frame. (a) Lateral acceleration of particles released at rest, viewed in the instantaneous rest-frame of the Earth. (b) Lateral acceleration of particles released at rest, viewed in the freely falling frame.

Viewed from the freely falling frame of the cabin (Figure 14b), when the two marbles are released at rest, they move closer to one another. Thus an object set free at rest, at an arbitrary point in the freely falling cabin, will not stay at rest. (Within a small cabin, this 'lateral acceleration' will be much smaller than the 'vertical' acceleration of the particles towards the centre of the Earth that has been cancelled out by moving to the freely falling frame.) With measuring instruments of a given standard of precision, there are regions of space small enough and lengths of time short enough such that experiments carried out in this spacetime region will not reveal deviations (in this case the convergence of test-particles released at rest) from the behaviour that is expected in an inertial frame.

From Figure 14 we see that both the space and time dimensions of the experiment must be limited. The region might be small enough for the behaviour to seem inertial over short times, but deviations might still be noticeable over long time intervals. Once again we note that it is not space alone, but 'spacetime' that must be considered. The variation in space of the acceleration **g**, in both magnitude and direction, is at the core of the need to restrict the experiment to a local region: a local region is one where **g** is effectively uniform, i.e. tidal forces are negligible.

Objectives 3 and 5   **SAQ 12**   Suppose an inertial frame is established out in space by the usual methods of Unit 2. Why would you expect the spatial extent, in a given direction, of this inertial frame not to be fixed for all time? Under what circumstances would the spatial extent of the frame contract with time and expand with time?

Objective 5   **SAQ 13**   If a marble is released above the surface of the Earth, it accelerates towards the Earth.

(a) How is this explained in a Newtonian picture?

(b) How does one describe this motion using Newton's first law and our new method of defining inertial frames?

In answering SAQ 13, you may have noticed how the redefinition of inertial frame begins to undermine the idea of gravity as a force. Other phenomena that we have called forces, such as electromagnetic forces, can still be used to explain why objects set free at rest begin to accelerate. But whereas, in the old view, gravity is appealed to in exactly the same way, the new view says: 'No, it's not that the gravitational force is acting, it is that the motion is being viewed from the wrong frame of reference. Transform to the freely falling frame. Gravity will disappear and motion without gravitational effects will be observed.' Einstein postulated that *gravity is not a force like others. It disappears as a force if you pick a freely falling frame of reference within which to view physical phenomena.*

Summary of Section 3

We began with an example of a frame of reference where there is acceleration, the rotating space-platform, and considered experiments based on studying the paths of objects dropped from rest. We found that there exist regions of spacetime small enough that such experiments done within these regions give results indistinguishable from those which would be found for a similar object dropped in an appropriate gravitational field. Similarly, we took one example of a frame of reference stationary with respect to a large mass and showed that, for similar experiments performed within small enough regions of spacetime, the behaviour is indistinguishable from that observed in a uniformly accelerating rocket-ship.

From these examples emerged the idea of a local region.

In Section 3.3, we defined a test-body as an infinitesimally small piece of matter that reacts to the gravitational influence of other, larger bodies without in its turn affecting them. With this definition, we stated the *universality of free fall*:

> If a test-body is placed at a given point in space and is given an initial velocity there, then its subsequent motion will be independent of its internal structure or composition, provided it is not subject to any electromagnetic or nuclear forces.

Within the conceptual scheme provided by Newton's theory of gravity (which comprises Newton's laws of motion and the law of universal gravitation) the universality of free fall implies that the inertial mass of any body is equal to its gravitational mass,

$$m = \mu.$$

This equality leads to experimental tests of the universality of free fall.

A consequence of the universality of free fall is that a (non-rotating) freely falling frame is a *local inertial frame*. Within such a frame, gravity apparently disappears, as in the orbiting Space Shuttle.

4 The equivalence principle and the properties of spacetime

4.1 Introduction

In Section 2, we saw that acceleration distorts spacetime, and in Section 3 we saw that in a local region, gravity and acceleration could not be distinguished. We now take the first step toward a theory of gravity as an effect of spacetime distortions.

A consequence of the equality of inertial and gravitational mass, and the discussion of Section 3, is that if we are sealed in a suitably small ('local') space laboratory, then we shall not be able to distinguish the effects of being adjacent to a concentration of mass large enough to have an appreciable gravitational pull or, on the other hand, undergoing an acceleration, far from the influence of matter in space. We could not distinguish the two possibilities by dropping a lump of lead and a feather ... any effects of air resistance would be the same in each case.

In 1907, Einstein declared that one could *not* distinguish gravity from acceleration (we shall refrain from *always* adding, 'in a local region', but it is implicit!) and elevated this to a formal principle, the 'equivalence principle', which we shall often write EP. The EP was to be Einstein's guiding principle for the next eight years over which he developed the general theory of relativity.

4.2 The equivalence principle

Let us imagine a local region which is stationary with respect to an *arbitrary* distribution of matter, or located in *any* uniformly accelerating frame of reference. We consider experiments which are completely general except that they do not involve electromagnetic or nuclear forces — in other words, generalizations of the dropping experiments we discussed in the last Section. Such experiments will reveal *either* that the motion is like that of free particles ('inertial') *or* that it is 'non-inertial' i.e. the bodies behave in the sort of way we identify with motion under gravity. If the motion is non-inertial, it might be caused *either* by the gravitational attraction of nearby matter, *or* by the fact that the frame is accelerating with respect to an inertial frame. **But we cannot tell which by 'local' experiments.**

We state this more formally as the 'weak equivalence principle', weak EP:

> **THE WEAK EQUIVALENCE PRINCIPLE**
>
> The motion of bodies within a local region adjacent to a concentration of mass cannot be distinguished by any experiment from the motion of bodies within a local region of appropriate uniform acceleration.

But what about experiments which *do* involve electromagnetic or nuclear phenomena? Could such experiments (still confined to the local region, of course) discriminate between the effects of acceleration or of a nearby mass? It is just this which is denied in the second step of generalization.

Imagine attempting to distinguish the effects of being near a mass (i.e. source of gravitational field) from the effects of being in a frame with an appropriate uniform acceleration. It might seem that one could always devise an experiment of *some* kind to do so. The equivalence principle asserts otherwise:

the equivalence principle

THE EQUIVALENCE PRINCIPLE

The physical behaviour within a local spacetime region resulting from a concentration of mass cannot be distinguished by *any* experiment from the physical behaviour within a local spacetime region resulting from an appropriate uniform acceleration.

The words 'local region' signals the fact that however great the gradient of the gravitational field and however sensitive the equipment, there is always a small enough region of spacetime over which the non-uniformity has no detectable consequences.

Colloquially speaking, the equivalence principle, EP, says that we can find situations in which the effects of gravity on any physical system are the same as the effects of acceleration provided that:

1 We do not look at the system for too long a time.

2 We do not let the physical phenomena spread over too large a region in space.

3 We do not examine the physical phenomena too precisely.

What, now, is the relationship of the universality of free fall to the equivalence principle? To answer this, we first note that the EP really has two aspects: (i) the laws governing the motion of falling bodies are the same in (a local region) near a gravitating mass and in a uniformly accelerating frame far from mass; and, (ii) *all* laws of physics are the same in (a local region) near a gravitating mass and in a suitable uniformly accelerating frame. Clearly, statement (ii) is stronger than statement (i) which is the special case we have called the weak EP. The full EP, statement (ii), is more general, and could conceivably be wrong even if the weak EP were somehow proved exactly.

It is the less general statement (i), i.e. the weak EP, that is closely related to the universality of free fall. The universality of free fall, however, *appears* to be more general than statement (i) in one respect. This is that it applies to the *whole path* of an object in free fall, whereas statement (i) applies only in a local region. But to see that this supposed greater generality is not real, consider the free fall of a body point by point; if at *each point* its acceleration is 'independent of its internal structure or composition' then its subsequent motion as a whole must also be 'independent of structure or composition', i.e. universality of free fall will apply. But if statement (i), the weak EP, is true, then the effect of gravity at each point (i.e. within a local region at each point) is equivalent to the effect of being in a local accelerating frame at that point. And certainly, the effect on a body of being in an accelerating frame is indeed 'independent of the structure or composition' of the body. The universality of free fall is therefore logically equivalent to the weak EP, but we shall keep it as a named principle since it represents an important aspect of the weak EP, and is often referred to in the literature.

Finally, we note that the core physics of the universality of free fall and the weak EP is the equivalence of gravitational and inertial mass, $m = \mu$. It was this fact which gripped the imagination of Einstein, with momentous consequences. Einstein felt that the relationship $m = \mu$ should emerge *naturally* from a proper theory of gravity. In Newtonian mechanics, the concepts of inertial and gravitational mass arise in completely different conceptual situations and are defined in separate laws. It seemed unsatisfactory that such a remarkable fact as the universality of free fall should be explained by the arbitrary equating of two unrelated constants, m and μ.

In Section 5, we discuss at length the experimental corroboration of the equivalence principle, EP. Meanwhile, in Section 4.3 we *use* the EP, to make the last link in the chain of arguments to show that *the picture of spacetime presented by special relativity must be modified in the presence of gravity.*

Objective 6   **SAQ 14**   State in your own words the difference between the EP and the weak EP.

4.3   Spacetime in the presence of matter

We now demonstrate the power of the equivalence principle (EP). We have seen that in a uniformly rotating frame of reference, identical clocks located at different radii run at different rates. In Section 5.5, we shall show that this effect also takes place in a uniformly accelerating frame. We now apply the EP in such a frame. The EP guarantees that all effects observed in (a local region of) such a frame could just as well be due to matter generating the same gravitational acceleration. But from the study of rotating frames of reference, we know what acceleration does to clocks. *Hence identical clocks placed at rest at different spatial points in the vicinity of a large mass must run at different rates.* This argument is significant for three reasons:

(i) It is typical of the way the EP allows us to infer the behaviour of physical systems (e.g. clocks) in a gravitational field from the behaviour of the same systems in an accelerating frame of reference.

(ii) It has produced a statement, about clocks placed at different points in a gravitational field, which can be *experimentally tested*. Such experimental tests tell us if we should continue to accept the EP. (We discuss such tests in Section 5.)

(iii) It tells us something very important about the properties of time as measured by identical clocks spread out through a frame containing matter. The presence of matter causes the behaviour of the clocks to differ from that described in Blocks 1 and 2 for an inertial frame.

This last observation leads to the most important conclusion of the Unit so far. It is so important that we recall the key points:

1 In Section 2.3 and Section 2.4, we showed that the properties of space and time as described in an inertial frame in special relativity do not continue to hold when described from a frame of reference uniformly rotating with respect to an inertial frame.

2 At the end of Section 2.4, we asserted that the statement of point 1 holds for accelerating frames of reference in general.

3 The equivalence principle tells us that the non-inertial effects that we see in a uniformly accelerating frame of reference will also be seen in a local region of spacetime in a frame at rest with respect to a large aggregate of matter.

These three statements together show that *the properties of space and time in a frame of reference that contains a large aggregate of matter cannot be the same as those described by special relativity as applying to an inertial frame.*

A 'large aggregate of matter' simply refers to enough matter to generate an 'appreciable' gravitational field, where what is appreciable may depend on the context. This phraseology reflects the fact that the concept of 'matter' begs less questions than that of 'gravitational field'.

global frame of reference

Now consider how we defined inertial frames in Unit 2. An origin of coordinates is chosen far out in space, away from all large aggregates of matter such as stars or planets. The origin of the frame is set on one freely moving particle and the orientation of the axes is controlled so that a second freely moving particle, whose path never meets the origin, moves in a straight line. Then these axes *are extended through all space* to provide an inertial frame for the study of physical phenomena throughout the Universe. We therefore describe such an inertial frame as a 'global' frame of reference. Any other non-rotating frame of reference whose origin is at constant velocity with respect to the one we have initially set up is also an inertial frame. Hence we can pick an inertial frame in which the instantaneous velocity of some large mass, such as the Sun, is zero. Since inertial frames are defined to extend throughout all space, this 'instantaneous rest frame' of the Sun should be appropriate for describing the properties of space and time, as well as the behaviour of physical systems, in the vicinity of the Sun.

But we have just seen that the properties of space and time in a frame at rest with respect to a large mass *cannot* be the same as those described in an inertial frame. Clearly, if inertial frames as defined in Blocks 1 and 2 extend throughout all of space (i.e. if they are global frames of reference) they must encounter large masses. But we have seen that the properties of spacetime in the vicinity of these masses are *modified* by the masses so that these global frames must have spacetime properties that are non-inertial, i.e. differ from those required by special relativity! Therefore *global inertial frames of reference defined in Block 1 and refined in Block 2 are incompatible with the existence of large aggregates of matter.* This important conclusion corresponds with Aim 1 of this Unit.

Motion of bodies is most simple to describe in an inertial frame — free motion of material particles is in straight lines and the spacetime properties don't vary from point to point. If we were asked to analyse some physical system in an accelerating frame, it would make sense to transform the coordinates to an inertial frame (where the physics is simpler), do the analysis, and then transform the results back into the accelerating frame. The question then arises: can we do the same thing for gravity? That is, instead of looking at physical phenomena in a frame of reference that is stationary with respect to an aggregate of matter (the Earth, or the Sun) can we transform to some other frame of reference in which the effects of gravity have disappeared, just as the effects of acceleration disappear in an inertial frame?

The answer is a qualified *yes*. The qualification is the familiar restriction to *local* regions. In other words, as long as we restrict ourselves to a suitably small region of spacetime, then we can indeed 'eliminate gravity' by transforming our frame of reference. In effect, the equivalence principle says there do exist *local* inertial frames. *They are the freely falling frames we saw in Section 3.* This leads to a new statement of the EP: at any event in spacetime, there always exists a local inertial frame — it is the freely falling frame which passes through the point of spacetime in question. (Strictly speaking, one should specify a non-rotating local frame.) We suspend discussion of whether it is the full EP or the weak EP until Section 6.

Objective 6   **SAQ 15**   Suppose you are in a small laboratory at rest on the surface of the Earth. Suppose also that you have two small objects of the same size and shape but made of different materials, and that every time you drop the two of them simultaneously from rest, from the same height, one of them hits the floor before the other. If you accept the equivalence principle, what are you forced to conclude about the forces causing the motion you observe?

Study comment

The next SAQ is important and you might be asked to explain the answer.

Objectives 6 and 7   **SAQ 16**   A rocket-ship contains a laboratory.

(a)   (b)

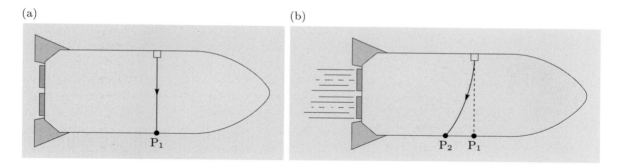

Figure 15   (a) The rocket in empty space (far from matter) has its engines off. (b) The rocket engines are switched on.

A laser is set up to shine a fine beam of light across the laboratory to an array of photosensitive cells which detect exactly where the beam of light arrives. The direction of the light beam is roughly perpendicular to the direction of thrust of the rocket.

The rocket is flown out into empty space and the rocket engines are switched off. The laser is shone across the laboratory and the point of arrival, P_1, of the beam is noted, see Figure 15(a). The rocket engines are then switched on to give an acceleration of the magnitude of the acceleration due to gravity near the surface of the Earth. The point of arrival of the laser beam is observed to change to a new position, P_2, when the thrust is switched on, a consequence of the finite speed of light, see Figure 15(b).

The rocket is then flown back to Earth and lands in the same orientation in which it took off. The motors are shut off and the laser beam is shone across the laboratory.

(a) Reasoning on the basis of equivalence principle, can you say whether the light beam, in the experiment carried out after the rocket has returned to Earth, hits the point P_1 or not? Explain your reasoning.

(b) Under what conditions could we predict that, in fact, the light beam hits the point P_2 in this experiment.

(c) If, in the experiment on the surface of the Earth, the light beam actually did hit point P_1, what would we have to conclude?

So light is bent by gravity! Light crossing a freely falling laboratory (spacecraft, perhaps) travels in a straight line (since the laws of special relativity, including Maxwell's equations, hold in a local inertial frame.) Light emitted in the same direction across a spacecraft which is not freely falling (e.g. by virtue of accelerating far from any mass) will *not* reach exactly the same spot on the other side of the spacecraft. The EP then says that light *must* therefore be bent by gravity in a non-accelerating frame. This bending is too small to be detected on Earth, but has important astronomical consequences which we will explain after we have introduced general relativity in the following Units.

Summary of Section 4

1 In Section 3, we had found examples of similar effects due to: (i) the gravitational influence of nearby matter, or, (ii) being in an accelerating frame of reference (even in the absence of gravity). Now, in Section 4 we have generalized to any natural phenomenon observed within a spacetime region of appropriate size, arriving at the equivalence principle, EP. In a nutshell, the EP says that in a local region of spacetime, the effect of gravity cannot be distinguished by any experiment from a suitable uniform acceleration. In other words, the effects of gravity on any physical system are the same as the effects of viewing the system, in the absence of gravity, from a uniformly accelerating frame of reference provided that

— We do not observe the system for too long a time;

— We do not let the physical phenomena spread over too large a region in space;

— We do not examine the physical phenomena too precisely.

2 A less general form of the EP (namely the weak EP) was also introduced, which contains the same essential physics as the principle of universality of free fall.

3 It had been shown in Sections 2.3 and 2.4 that the properties of spacetime found in a rotating frame of reference differ from the properties of spacetime described in an inertial frame. This was seen as an effect of acceleration. The EP therefore guarantees that the properties of space and time found in a frame of reference which is stationary with respect to an aggregate of matter also differ from those of an inertial frame. In particular, identical clocks at different locations in such a frame may not run at the same rate.

5 Experimental tests of the universality of free fall and the equivalence principle

5.1 Introduction

The equivalence principle has been used in Section 4 to show that gravity fundamentally changes the properties of space and time. Clearly, if the universality of free fall were to be disproved, the EP would thereby also be disproved. Obviously, these principles must be tested by experiment.

5.2 Tests of the relationship $m = \mu$

Tests to check whether the ratio m/μ is the same for all materials date back to Newton who made many measurements of the ratio using an ingenious experimental arrangement of two pendulums set up side by side, see Figure 16. The lengths of the two strings are made equal; the two weights have the same gravitational mass, μ, as determined by balancing them against each other on a beam-balance. Without doing any calculation, one can reason that if the two weights are released from rest, side by side, at the same instant, and if they are to exhibit the same subsequent motion as the universality of free fall says they should, then they should swing back and forth together and not get out of step. Because they can be made to swing for quite a long time, Newton could compare much longer sections of their respective world-lines than would be possible on Galileo's inclined plane.

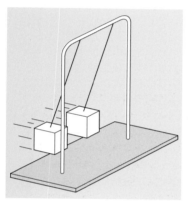

Figure 16   Representation of Newton's experiment to test $m = \mu$.

We can apply the general method explained in the last paragraph of Section 3.4 to this particular experiment by using the results of SAQ 12 of Unit 2. In SAQs 8–12 of Unit 2, you were asked to analyse the motion of a pendulum using Newtonian mechanics. The results of SAQ 12 showed that the angle, θ, that the pendulum makes with the vertical, changes in time according to the equation

$$\theta(t) = \theta_{\max} \sin\left[\sqrt{\frac{F_0}{ml}}(t - t_0) \right]$$

where F_0 is the magnitude of the force applied to the plumb-bob by the gravitational attraction of the Earth. The force on the bob is $F_0 = \mu g$, where g is approximately constant, as explained in Section 4.4 of Unit 2. Therefore the expression for $\theta(t)$ becomes

$$\theta(t) = \theta_{\max} \sin\left[\sqrt{\frac{\mu g}{ml}}(t - t_0) \right]$$

and the ratio μ/m, which appears in the right-hand side, tells us how to use the pendulum to test the universality of free fall. If this ratio were to change from substance to substance, then the variation of θ with t would not be the same for the two pendulums of Newton's experiment. Two plumb-bobs released at the same instant at the same angle would not stay in step. How quickly they got out of step would vary from sample to sample of material used for the bobs.

Objective 8   SAQ 17   Why should the shapes and sizes of the two plumb-bobs be as similar as possible?

Objective 8   SAQ 18   If, as is quite likely, the two strings of the pendulum are cut to slightly different lengths, the two pendulums will go out of step as they swing. Explain how this will not spoil the experiment, that is, how one can still look for a variation in μ/m with composition, using the two pendulums of unequal lengths.

Newton performed the experiments with sound insight as to what was required for an accurate result. His pendulums were quite long, 11 feet or so. This would allow him to keep the amplitude of the swing fairly small. More importantly, he enclosed the different samples in containers that were externally the same, and positioned the different samples carefully at the centre of mass of the containers. Together, these measures allowed him to minimize the effect of air resistance. With measurements made on his system of two pendulums, Newton convinced himself that $m = \mu$ for a range of materials including lead, silver, glass, sand, wood, and wheat, within an accuracy of one part in a thousand.

'Eöt' rhymes with 'hurt', 'vö' rhymes with 'aver' and 's' is pronounced 'sh'.

The modern era of high-precision tests of the universality of free fall was initiated by the Hungarian Baron Roland von Eötvös. It was his experiments, performed on a range of materials first in 1889 and refined over the next three decades, that showed that the equation

$$m = \mu$$

was true to within five parts in 10^9. Eötvös's experiment is described in Section 5.3. Einstein was unaware of this experiment when, in 1907, he adopted the EP as his starting point in his search for a theory of gravitation. But he did become aware of it around 1912 and henceforth cited it extensively.

5.3   How Eötvös compared m and μ

The experiment performed by Eötvös exploited the fact that at the latitude of Hungary, see Figure 17(a), the effective gravitational force on a body, as measured by a pendulum or plumb-bob for example, is a vector sum of two forces. One is the true gravitational force $\mathbf{F}_g$, directed toward the centre of the Earth, and the other is a centrifugal force $\mathbf{F}_c$, normal to the Earth's axis of rotation, as shown in Figure 17(a). For a body of gravitational mass μ and inertial mass m we have $\mathbf{F}_g = \mu\mathbf{g}$ and $\mathbf{F}_c = m\mathbf{a}$ where $\mathbf{g}$ and $\mathbf{a}$ are the gravitational and centrifugal accelerations where the experiment is performed. The key point is that the two forces depend on the two kinds of mass, in particular the centrifugal force depends on the inertial mass, since this force has its origin in the inertial tendency of a body to continue in a straight line. 'Centrifugal force' is the name given to the force which appears in the rotating (non-inertial) frame due to the rotation; in the case of the Earth it is, as far as our everyday experience is concerned, overwhelmed by the much stronger gravitational force. It is crucial for the experiment that the two forces are not parallel (the experiment would therefore be impossible at the equator). See Figure 17(a).

(a)   (b)

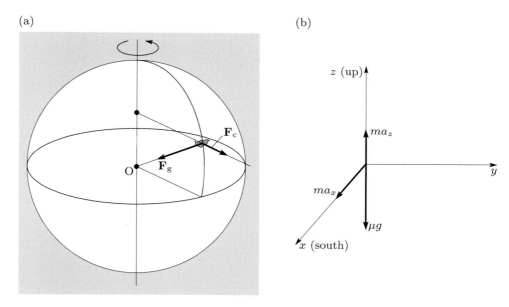

Figure 17 (a) The Earth, showing the gravitational and centrifugal forces near Hungary, not to scale (the gravitational force is by far the larger in magnitude.) (b) The coordinate system in Hungary, as lined up with the local forces.

'Up' is not, we note, the direction of a plumb-line; the difference is small but all important in the context of this experiment!

We now adopt a frame of reference, based, let us say, in Hungary, in which the z-axis is 'up', i.e. away from the centre of the Earth, the x-axis points south and the y-axis points east; see Figure 17(b) (in this Section only, we use the more conventional x, y, z coordinate system for simplicity). The purely gravitational force on our body is in the negative z-direction, and has magnitude μg, whereas the centrifugal force $m\mathbf{a}$ has two components, ma_z in the z-direction, and ma_x in the x-direction.

Clearly, we are going to require two bodies (more, ultimately) made of different materials if we are to compare m/μ for different substances. So, let us say we have two bodies, 1 and 2, of masses m_1, μ_1 and m_2, μ_2. But how do we contrive an arrangement which picks out the (presumably tiny) differences in response to $\mathbf{a}$ and $\mathbf{g}$?

Eötvös exploited a sensitive apparatus originally designed for a gravity

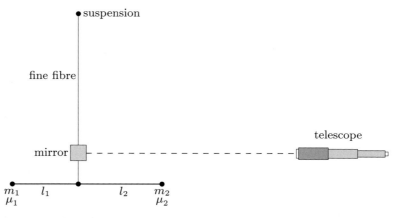

Figure 18 Schematic diagram of Eötvös's apparatus, showing two masses suspended from a long delicate fibre.

survey (one can locate ore beneath the surface of the Earth from minute fluctuations in local gravity) the key component of which is a light but rigid rod with two balls made of the materials 1 and 2 at each end, suspended at the centre by a long and delicate fibre, see Figure 18, which can twist measurably under a minute torque. Near the end of the fibre is fixed a small mirror which can be examined by a fixed telescope in order to register any slight twisting of the fibre, as would be occasioned, for example by an unequal lateral force on the two masses.

Indeed, there will be a lateral force on the masses. In Figure 19 we show the axis of the suspended rod in the y-direction and the forces acting on the masses.

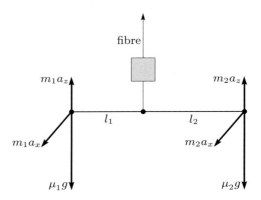

Figure 19   The two suspended masses with the forces acting on them resolved into x (south) and z (up) components.

The masses are positioned in such a way that the rod is exactly horizontal; the condition for this is that the net torque about the x-axis is zero i.e.

$$l_1(\mu_1 g - m_1 a_z) = l_2(\mu_2 g - m_2 a_z)$$

from which we can deduce an expression for the ratio l_1/l_2. The torque about the axis of the fibre is entirely due to the inertial force; it is

$$\tau = l_1 m_1 a_x - l_2 m_2 a_x.$$

Using the expression for the ratio l_1/l_2 we can, with some straightforward algebra, arrive at the following expression for τ:

$$\tau = l_1 a_x m_1 \frac{\dfrac{\mu_2}{m_2} - \dfrac{\mu_1}{m_1}}{\dfrac{\mu_2}{m_2} - \dfrac{a_z}{g}}.$$

The important point is the condition for zero torque: $\mu_2/m_2 = \mu_1/m_1$ which is, of course, the condition for the universality of free fall, or the equality of inertial and gravitational mass. The experiment was therefore a 'null' experiment. It had to be shown that there was no twisting of the fibre. While the mirror arrangement was extremely sensitive for looking at small 'extra' twists, the only way it was possible to be sure there was no measurable twist was to turn the whole apparatus through 180°. If there were a twist, it would now be in the opposite direction. In this way, Eötvös was able to show that indeed there was no twist to such remarkable precision, that he could say that μ/m was the same for all of the great variety of substances he tested, to within one part in 10^9 or so. Of course, showing that μ/m is constant permits one to define the masses by setting $m = \mu$.

Later developments by Dicke and others used very similar basic ideas, but (remarkably, it might seem) they compared the inertial force of an accelerating body in orbit around the Sun, with the gravitational force due to the Sun.

5.4 Implications and further tests of $m = \mu$

It is worth considering briefly some implications of the fact that $m = \mu$. For a start, the wide range of materials tested encompassed materials with widely varying proportions of protons (and electrons) and neutrons. It might simply imply that all these particles move in gravity in the same way, but it is more complicated (and more interesting) than that. The mass of a hydrogen atom is not simply the mass of an electron plus the mass of a proton: it is slightly less. As we mentioned towards the end of Unit 7, the difference is the mass equivalent of the *binding energy*, the energy released when a proton captures an electron to form a H atom, and conversely the energy that has to be added to a H atom in order to ionize it. If the binding energy is E, then the H atom has a mass E/c^2 less than the combined mass of a proton and an electron. The fact that $m = \mu$ for a wide variety of chemical substances, *each with a different proportion of binding energy*, shows that as far as gravity is concerned, the mass equivalent of electrostatic energy (that binds an atom) is mass like any other: the wide variety of elements for which $m = \mu$ show that the same must be true for nuclear binding energy which also varies from element to element, and even isotope to isotope. (Nuclear binding energies are typically a factor of 10^6 greater than chemical or atomic binding energies, which is why one can arrange to extract much more energy from a lump of uranium than from a lump of coal or TNT.)

If atomic and nuclear binding energy E has equal gravitational and inertial mass E/c^2, what about the *gravitational* binding energy that binds the Moon to the Earth, for example? Does gravitational energy weigh? Indeed, in 1991 Müller and collaborators showed, using lunar ranging experiments, that gravitational energy contributes equally to the combined m of the Earth and Moon and the combined μ of the Earth and Moon with an accuracy of about one part in a thousand ... a very difficult experiment. As we shall note in later Units, it is the fact that gravitational energy has mass that makes the equations of general relativity 'non-linear' and very difficult to solve in general.

Since the time of Eötvös, and principally since the 1960s, the universality of free fall has been subjected to even more stringent testing. P. G. Roll, R. Krotkov and R. H. Dicke developed a variant of Eötvös's technique in 1964 which verified $m = \mu$ to one part in 10^{11} for aluminium and gold. In 1972, V. B. Braginsky and V. I. Panov have claimed an accuracy of one part in 10^{12} with aluminium and platinum. One variation in Eötvös-like experiments is to consider the gravitational attraction of the Sun, or even the galactic centre. In 1992, Smith, Adelberger, Heckel and Su in Seattle showed that beryllium, copper and aluminium fall toward the galactic centre with accelerations that are equal to a few parts in ten thousand. Since it is believed that the Galaxy is mostly 'dark matter' (see Units 13–15) this (very difficult) experiment shows that the only significant long-range interaction between dark and ordinary matter is EP-obeying gravitation. Over the next few years, we can expect ever more sophisticated experiments putting ever tighter limits on any possible deviation from the universality of free fall.

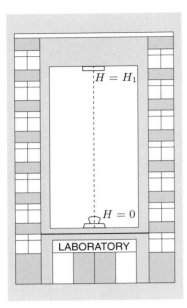

Figure 20 Experimental set-up of the gravitational redshift experiment.

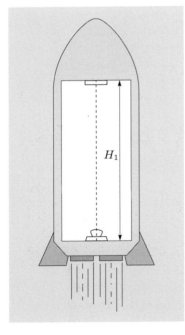

Figure 21 Equivalent accelerating frame set-up for the redshift experiment.

5.5 *The gravitational redshift as a test of the EP*

A second experimental confirmation of the equivalence principle (EP) is based on the effect predicted in Section 4.3: clocks at different points in a gravitational field run at different rates. An atom emitting light (or other electromagnetic waves) of a precise frequency is, in effect, a clock. So, one can look for this effect by comparing the frequencies of light emitted by identical atoms emitting light at different points in the gravitational field of a large body, such as the Earth or a star. Using the EP, we can derive an expression for the difference ('shift') in frequency of the light emitted by atoms at different points in a gravitational field.

We shall now deduce a formula for the frequency shift (called a 'gravitational redshift' or a 'gravitational blueshift' according to how it is observed) and then compare our prediction with the results of experiments.

For small distances above the Earth's surface, the gravitational field can be assumed to be uniform, exerting a constant force, μg, vertically downward on any object of mass μ. The type of experiment envisaged is illustrated in Figure 20, where electromagnetic radiation (γ-rays) is emitted at height $H = 0$ and received at $H = H_1$. How does the received frequency, f', differ from the frequency, f, generated in an identical process at height H_1?

The EP says that what takes place in a uniform gravitational field also takes place in a uniformly accelerating frame of reference. That is, the process of Figure 20 in a gravitational field has an exactly equivalent process, in the absence of gravity, in a uniformly accelerating frame. By thinking about a 'dropping experiment', you can easily convince yourself that the required accelerating frame of reference is one of constant vertical acceleration upwards of magnitude g, as could be provided by a rocket in outer space. The situation is illustrated in Figure 21, and we can imagine the rocket to be initially at rest. At the moment that a particular wavefront of the light, of frequency, f, is emitted at the rear of the rocket, the rocket motors are switched on to give the thrust required to produce the acceleration g. The wavefront travels the distance H_1 to the receiver in time Δt given by

$$\Delta t = \frac{H_1}{c}.$$

We must now make use of the idea, introduced in Unit 7, of an 'instantaneous rest frame' (we also used it in Section 2.3). We assume that the source and receiver are not affected by acceleration (our arguments hold however small the acceleration is). When the wavefront is emitted, the source is instantaneously at rest. The wavefront could equally have been emitted by a source stationary in a rest frame, F_S, of speed zero as depicted in Figure 22. By the time that the wavefront has reached the receiver, the receiver is moving at instantaneous speed

$$v = g\,\Delta t = \frac{gH_1}{c}$$

with respect to the frame F_S. Since the receiver is not affected by the acceleration, the wavefront could equally have been received by a receiver moving at constant speed gH_1/c in frame F_S; this is the instantaneous rest frame of the receiver, F_R, depicted in Figure 22. We now continue the argument in terms of a source in F_S, and a receiver in F_R, with the actual rocket being ignored. If the receiver is moving away from the source with speed gH_1/c, as viewed in F_S, at the instant of reception of the wavefront, then a source in F_S is moving away from the receiver with the same speed,

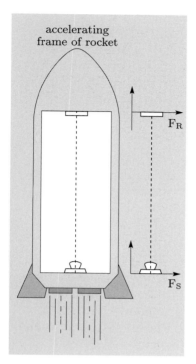

accelerating
frame of rocket

F_R

F_S

Figure 22 Representation of instantaneous rest frames of the source, F_s, and the receiver, F_g, in the gravitational redshift experiment.

as viewed in F_R at this instant. If we now view things from within frame F_R, we can use the relativistic Doppler shift, as discussed in Unit 6, to evaluate the frequency shift to be expected.

As described in Unit 6, if a source of light of frequency f is moving away from a receiver at speed v, the frequency f' of light observed at the receiver will differ from f according to the equation

$$f' = f \left(\frac{1 - v/c}{1 + v/c} \right)^{1/2} = f \frac{(1 - v/c)^{1/2}}{(1 + v/c)^{1/2}}$$

$$= f \frac{(1 - v/c)^{1/2}}{(1 + v/c)^{1/2}} \times \frac{(1 - v/c)^{1/2}}{(1 - v/c)^{1/2}}.$$

$$f' = \frac{f(1 - v/c)}{[1 - (v/c)^2]^{1/2}}. \tag{8}$$

If v is much smaller than c, then

$$\left(\frac{v}{c} \right)^2 \ll \frac{v}{c} \ll 1$$

and we can neglect the $(v/c)^2$ term in the denominator of Equation 8 to get

$$f' \approx f \left(1 - \frac{v}{c} \right)$$

which we can rewrite as

$$\frac{f' - f}{f} \approx -\frac{v}{c}$$

or

$$\frac{\Delta f}{f} \approx -\frac{v}{c}. \tag{9}$$

From Equation 9, one can see that the light received at the top of the rocket will have a lower frequency; the light is said to be 'redshifted'. The size of the shift in frequency is given by

$$\Delta f \approx -f \frac{v}{c} = -f \frac{gH_1}{c^2}. \tag{10}$$

Notice that if the light were sent in the opposite direction, that is, down the page in Figure 21 and 22, then the source would be moving towards the receiver (in the receiver's instantaneous rest frame) and not away from it. This would change the sign of v in Equation 8 and thus Δf would be positive; we would have what is called a 'blueshift'.

The EP tells us that Equation 10 must also be the formula for the gravitational field situation of Figure 20, and this gives us a quantitative formula that can be tested in the Earth's gravitational field.

Objectives 7 and 8   **SAQ 19**   Work out the value of $\Delta f / f$ to be expected for a height H_1 of 20 m.

It is clear from the answer to SAQ 19 that detection of redshift over a distance of 20 m would require very highly tuned sources and receivers. Such sources and receivers became available in the late 1950s with the discovery by R. Mössbauer of a means of rendering the frequencies of gamma rays emitted and absorbed by certain nuclei extraordinarily well defined (see the end of this section and the start of Section 5.6 for more details). This discovery opened up the possibility that small shifts in frequency corresponding to laboratory-scale differences in height could actually be measured. Using instruments based on Mössbauer's discovery, R. V. Pound and G. A. Rebka (and later Pound and J. L. Snider) detected the redshift of γ-rays travelling up a tower 22.5 m in height and the corresponding blueshift of γ-rays travelling down the tower. When all the experimental difficulties had been resolved, the results agreed with those predicted by Equation 10 to within 1 per cent.

The Rebka and Pound experiment suggests the following derivation of the gravitational red- or blue-shift. Consider an atom with energy levels E_1 and E_2. For reasons that will be apparent, we consider these to be the energy levels at sea-level. When the atom falls from the excited state E_2 to E_1, it emits light of frequency f given by $hf = E_2 - E_1$, where h is Planck's constant. Now, we know that the mass of the atom in these two states is, respectively, E_1/c^2 and E_2/c^2, so that if the atom is now lifted to a height H above sea-level, the gravitational potential energy must be added to each state, so the energies are respectively $E_1' = E_1 + (E_1/c^2)gH$ and $E_2' = E_2 + (E_2/c^2)gH$, so that a photon emitted when the atom jumps from the upper to lower states is f' where $hf' = E_2' - E_1' = hf(1 + gH/c^2)$ i.e.

$$\frac{f'}{f} = 1 + g\frac{H}{c^2}, \tag{11}$$

the same energy shift we saw before. Hence, if one had sufficiently accurate atomic clocks, one could simply put them at different heights, and wait for a time difference to appear! Notice how the EP comes in through the fact that differences in binding energy lead to differences in mass which are 'seen' by gravity in exactly the same way as any other mass. Also, this derivation of the red/blue-shift invokes *only* the $m = \mu$ aspect of the EP, i.e. the weak EP.

Notice from Equation 11 that if we observe at sea level a photon emitted at height H *above* us, then we will see it *blueshifted*, with fractional change in frequency

$$\frac{\Delta f}{f} = \frac{gH}{c^2}. \tag{12}$$

This result is sometimes interpreted as saying that a photon in a gravitational field has 'energy' hf and potential energy $hfgH/c^2$. In this picture, a photon 'climbing up' a gravitational field loses energy and is hence redshifted. This is a useful way to remember the sign of the redshift, but it is not a rigorous proof. As we emphasize later, the red- or blue-shift is an effect of spacetime distortion.

In more recent years, the accuracy of gravitational redshift experiments has improved with the increased precision with which electromagnetic waves of a controlled frequency can be generated. In 1976, a microwave generator whose frequency can be controlled to one part in 10^{14} was put in a rocket which took it from ground level to 10 000 km. The difference between the observed frequency of this oscillator and that of an identical oscillator kept at ground level was monitored continuously. The position and velocity of the rocket were determined throughout the flight.

There are two major effects which compete to change the frequency of the oscillator in the rocket with respect to the one kept on the ground; the special relativistic Doppler effect induced by the velocity of the rocket with respect to the ground and the gravitational frequency shift (in this case a blueshift). By monitoring the velocity of the rocket, the Doppler shift can be evaluated and hence subtracted from the experimental data, leaving the gravitational blueshift. By monitoring the position of the rocket, the blueshift can be correlated with the rocket's height to check the predictions of the EP. From this experiment the EP has been verified to within two parts in 10^4.

The obvious way to test the prediction about clocks in a gravitational field is to put one clock on a mountain-top, another at sea-level and compare their rates of running. Equation 10 can be used to show that the fractional change, $\Delta\tau/\tau$, in the rate of ticking of two clocks separated by $3\,000\,\text{m}$ of height is extremely small; three parts in 10^{13}. (From $\tau = 1/f$, one can show (see marginal note) that $\Delta\tau/\tau = -\Delta f/f$.) That is why we do not notice the effect on our wrist-watches of spending a holiday in the mountains. But the state of the art in precision time-keeping has now reached the point where such a simple experiment is feasible and has produced results in agreement with the prediction of Equation 10. Although the present accuracy of these results does not compare with that of the Pound–Rebka experiment or the rocket experiment, the simplicity of the technique makes it worth mentioning and indicates that we are now in an age where the effects of matter on the definition of time have to be taken into account, even in the manner of terrestrial time-keeping.

$$\frac{\mathrm{d}\tau}{\mathrm{d}f} = \frac{\mathrm{d}}{\mathrm{d}f}\left(\frac{1}{f}\right) = -\frac{1}{f^2} = -\frac{\tau}{f}$$
hence the result

You might be tempted to think that the direct effect of gravity on the mechanism of the clock is responsible for the different rates at which time appears to pass at different heights. This is not so. The argument based on the EP involves a *local* region in which gravity is uniform (so that the force on an object of mass μ anywhere in the region is μg), yet still clearly predicts that clocks go at different rates at different heights (where there are different gravitational potential energies). It is also true that very strong tidal forces (i.e. gradients in gravitational force) do not affect the intrinsic rate of clocks. (An example of extreme gravitational gradients is on the surface of a neutron star or pulsar.) Gravitational time dilation or redshift is a property of spacetime itself!

For completeness, we briefly indicate the basis of the Mössbauer effect. Normally, when a nucleus emits a high energy photon in gamma decay, the energy of the photon is shifted by the random thermal motion of the nucleus, which also recoils during the emission process. Remarkably, as Mössbauer discovered, if the emitting nucleus is part of certain crystal structures, it is the crystal as a whole which recoils during emission rather than the emitting nucleus, and the effect of the thermal motion is also markedly reduced. The result is that certain gamma rays have an energy spread of only about one part in 10^{13}, making possible experiments such as those of Rebka and Pound, and of Hay and co-workers described in the next section.

5.6   *The experiment of Hay, Schiffer, Cranshaw and Egelstaff*

In 1960, Hay and his colleagues at Harwell published an interesting experiment which nicely links the beginning of the Unit to Section 5.

Recall that the experiment of Rebka and Pound was made possible by the Mössbauer effect which makes the spectral lines of certain gamma rays emitted by certain nuclei (^{57}Fe in particular) extraordinarily 'narrow', i.e.

well defined in energy (i.e. frequency). In the inverse process, ^{57}Fe nuclei in their ground states also absorb gamma rays with the same extreme selectivity in energy (frequency).

Now, imagine a turntable which can be made to rotate very rapidly. At the centre, there is some ^{57}Fe in its excited state emitting gamma rays of precisely defined energy. Around the edge of the disk is a narrow cylindrical film of ^{57}Fe, and beyond that is a gamma ray detector. When the disk is not rotating, the outer ^{57}Fe absorbs the gamma rays, so the gamma ray detector show a small counting rate. But when the disk rotates, the characteristic frequency of the outer ^{57}Fe changes. It therefore becomes increasingly ineffective as an absorber as the rotational speed is increased and the frequencies become mismatched. The count rate at the detector therefore increases.

Now the interesting thing for us is that there are two different interpretations. This is essentially the situation in Section 2.3 brought to life, and as in that Section the shift in frequency can be interpreted purely in terms of special relativity, through the transverse Doppler shift (or, equivalently, in terms of time dilation.) But, we now see an entirely different way of looking at it: an ^{57}Fe nucleus fixed to the disk is subject to a centrifugal acceleration the magnitude of which increases with radius. But the EP assures us that acceleration must have the same effect on an ^{57}Fe nucleus as gravitation. As a ^{57}Fe nucleus moves out, it is as if it moves down through a gravitational potential well. The ^{57}Fe is subject to the gravitational redshift, and indeed, it can be shown that this line of reasoning leads to exactly the same frequency shift as one finds from the arguments of Section 2.3. As of course it must, Nature being consistent. Hay *et al.*, by the way, found the expected result.

The rotating disk provides a way to remember the *sign* of the gravitational blue/red-shift: if one sits with a clock (or light emitting atom) at the centre of the disk watching an identical clock (or atom, etc.) on the rim, one receives fewer ticks (or light wave maxima) per revolution of the wheel than one receives from the adjacent fixed identical clock (atom). That is, the incoming light is redshifted. This was interpreted in Section 2.3, using arguments based on special relativity and the idea of instantaneous rest frames, as time dilation or the transverse Doppler shift. But, on a rotating disk, bodies tend to 'move outward', so that 'further out' is equivalent to 'down'. Thus the *lower* clock in a gravitational field runs slower. Light received from it by a receiver which is higher will seem reddened, just as the ticks from a clock on the rim of a wheel will be more widely spaced as seen from the centre of the wheel, or equivalently, light from a source on the rim is reddened as seen from the hub.

Summary of Section 5

1 The universality of free fall has a long history of experimental examination. The Newtonian method of testing the ratio m/μ for departures from unity has been used by Newton, Eötvös, Dicke and Braginsky with increasing levels of precision. The present belief is that

$$\left| \frac{m}{\mu} - 1 \right| < 10^{-12}.$$

Recently, the equality $m = \mu$ has been shown to apply even to the mass corresponding to gravitational energy.

2 The prediction that clocks at different points of a gravitational field run at different rates has been tested both directly with atomic clocks and in terms of the shift in frequency of the radiation from atoms (or nuclei) undergoing the identical process of emission at different points in the Earth's gravitational field. This is the 'gravitational redshift'. The fractional shift in frequency, $\Delta f/f$, is related to the difference, H, in height of two atoms in a uniform gravitational field producing a gravitational acceleration g, by

$$\frac{\Delta f}{f} = \frac{gH}{c^2}$$

This equation is derived by an argument based on the equivalence principle. The present best test of the gravitational redshift indicates that it agrees with this prediction to within two parts in 10^4.

6   The equivalence principle in contemporary physics

We are soon to meet general relativity — a theory which goes far beyond the equivalence principle. So what is the present status of that principle within physics?

What is certain is that, as the distinguished relativist J. L. Synge put it, the EP played a critical role as midwife to general relativity, GR. However, in modern developments of GR, the position of the full EP is somewhat less clear. For a start, the EP as stated has never been tested precisely. On closer analysis, it turns out that the various tests are really tests of the weak EP. Worse: it is now understood that the EP cannot be *precisely* true for at least two reasons:

– It can be shown that the ideal 'local' region in which gravitational effects (as distinct from effects of acceleration) are undetectable, does not exist. As stressed by Ohanian and Ruffini, for example, one can in principle measure the gradient of a gravitational field even as one approaches the limit of zero experimental volume.

– Quantum field theory shows that even in a local region, strong gravitational field gradients will mean that the physics in a local inertial frame is not exactly that of special relativity, as implied by EP. This was shown in 1980 by Drummond and Hathrell and further explicated by Daniels and Shore in 1994.

It should shock you to know that a consequence of the second point is that in such regions (perhaps near a black hole) light can actually go faster than c, although causality will not be broken. This effect is unlikely ever to be observed, however, but seems to be a firm consequence of our modern understanding.

So does general relativity collapse as a consequence? No. It appears that the full EP is not required as a foundation of GR. Even where the EP is taken as the starting point for GR, it turns out on closer examination that only the weak EP is used. The key ingredient can be stated in various equivalent ways: the weak EP; the universality of free fall; the fact that $m = \mu$; the fact that at any point there is indeed always a local inertial frame.

What, then, is the status of tests of the EP? There is no problem with tests of $m = \mu$ and this remains an essential test. In particular, the fact that gravitational potential energy (e.g. the 'binding energy' of the Earth and the Moon) itself has gravitational mass equal to its inertial mass is seen as crucial. If this were to fail, then it would falsify GR; in this sense, tests of $m = \mu$ are tests of GR. The arguments for the gravitational redshift can be made in such a way that they depend on $m = \mu$, or at least the weak EP applied to the motion of light considered as photons. In any case, the gravitational redshift does, as we shall see in Units 10 & 11, follow directly from GR itself, so the tests remain vital; a disproof of the predicted gravitational redshift, and the related gravitational time dilation, would be a disproof of GR. It does seem that although the full EP is not strictly true, it is nevertheless the case that all consequences of EP that are not strongly dependent on the vanishing of tidal forces (due to strong gradients of the gravitational force) are true. Although the EP is a useful guide and source of insight, the fact is that it is general relativity itself that is now the reliable guide and arbiter. The next two Units introduce this profound and revolutionary theory for which the EP was a stepping stone.

By revealing certain contemporary qualifications concerning the (full) EP, we show that physics is not all cut and dried. Nevertheless, a permanent transformation of our understanding of spacetime has emerged in this Unit, a transformation we shall build on in the following Units.

Objective 6   SAQ 20   Explain why a candle or paraffin lantern placed on the floor of a freely falling lift will soon go out. (This has nothing to do with what might happen if the lift hits the bottom of the lift shaft!)

7 Unit Summary

1 Einstein saw that Newton's law of gravitation could not be the final truth. His starting point for a theory of gravitation was the observation, going back to Galileo and Newton, that we have summed up as $m = \mu$. In this Unit, we have set out to pave the way for Einstein's theory of gravitation, general relativity. Along the way we have glimpsed deep changes in our view of spacetime.

2 We found that in a rotating frame of reference, identical clocks at different spatial points may run at different rates, and the spatial geometry as mapped out by rigid rods will not be Euclidean. We noted that the effects on clocks fixed in a rotating frame applied also to uniformly accelerating clocks.

3 We saw that experimenters in a sufficiently local region of an accelerating frame would not be able to distinguish gravity from acceleration by means of 'dropping' experiments.

4 All objects fall the same way, independently of composition, a fact expressed as $m = \mu$. The composition-independence implies that the mass equivalent of chemical or nuclear energy 'gravitates' like any other mass; the same even applies to gravitational binding energy, a fact to be of deep significance for general relativity.

5 Freely falling frames are locally inertial frames; they can be defined at every point in spacetime.

6 The last three points can be formalized as the weak equivalence principle.

7 The equivalence principle, EP, is a stronger statement: in a local region, one cannot by *any* type of experiment distinguish effects of uniform acceleration from proximity to mass, and in that region, the laws of physics are those of special relativity, independently of the strength or gradient of the gravitational field there.

8 Alternative statements: the weak EP says that at any point there exists a freely falling local inertial frame. The EP says that at any point there exists a local inertial frame, *and* the laws of physics in that frame are exactly those of special relativity (i.e. independently of the gradient of any gravitational field at that point.) The idea in each case is that at any point there is, in general instantaneously, some freely falling frame.

9 The EP has striking consequences: (i) in the presence of matter, spacetime is *not* that of Newtonian physics *nor* that of special relativity; (ii) clocks run at different rates at different points in gravitational fields in a precisely defined way that has been verified by experiment.

10 The equality $m = \mu$ has also been verified to high precision. As we shall see in the next Units, a falsification of either of these results would be a falsification of general relativity as well as a falsification of the EP.

11 Although the EP is thought to be true in most circumstances, and remains a useful guide, it is actually the weak EP which is a starting point in modern treatments of general relativity. Of course, the EP implies the weak EP but not the reverse.

Band 2 of AC3 comments on this Unit.

Self-assessment questions — answers and comments

SAQ 1 The equations for $\mathbf{v}(t)$ and $\mathbf{a}(t)$ in Section 4.5 of Unit 1 are:

$$\mathbf{v}(t) = (-\omega r \sin \omega t, \omega r \cos \omega t, 0) \tag{13}$$

$$\mathbf{a}(t) = (-\omega^2 r \cos \omega t, -\omega^2 r \sin \omega t, 0). \tag{14}$$

The origin of the Y-frame is specified by the equation

$$r = 0. \tag{15}$$

Putting Equation 15 into Equations 13 and 14 gives

$$\mathbf{v}(t) = (0, 0, 0)$$
$$\mathbf{a}(t) = (0, 0, 0)$$

for all values of t. So the origin of the Y-frame is always at rest, and therefore not accelerating, with respect to the origin of the X-frame.

SAQ 2 Equation 17 of Unit 6 relates the period τ_0 between ticks of a clock in the rest frame to τ, the period of an identical clock in a frame moving at speed v:

$$\tau = \frac{\tau_0}{[1 - (v/c)^2]^{1/2}}. \tag{16}$$

For our problem, we consider the clock, A, on the turntable to be an 'instantaneous Lorentz frame' with speed $v = \omega r$ when the comparison is made with clock B in an inertial frame. Then Equation 16 gives

$$\tau_A = \frac{\tau_B}{[1 - (\omega r/c)^2]^{1/2}}. \tag{17}$$

Now $33\frac{1}{3}$ r.p.m. is

$$\frac{33\frac{1}{3}}{60} \times 2\pi \text{ radians per second}$$

and 10 cm is 0.1 m. Thus

$$\frac{\tau_A}{\tau_B} = \frac{1}{\left[1 - \left(\dfrac{33\frac{1}{3} \times 2\pi \times 0.1}{60 \times 3 \times 10^8}\right)^2\right]^{1/2}}$$

$$\approx \frac{1}{\sqrt{1 - 1.4 \times 10^{-18}}} \approx 1 + 0.7 \times 10^{-18}$$

so

$$\frac{\tau_A - \tau_B}{\tau_B} \approx 0.7 \times 10^{-18}.$$

SAQ 3 We use Equation 16 above as adapted from Equation 26 of Unit 6.

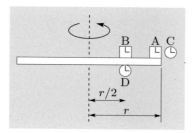

Figure 23 The comparison of clocks on the turntable with those in the inertial frame: illustration for the answer to SAQ 3.

The distribution of clocks in this problem is illustrated in Figure 23. Square clocks are in the rotating frame, Y; round clocks are in the inertial frame, X. We consider clocks A and B to be in 'instantaneous Lorentz frames' with speeds ωr and $\omega r/2$ respectively in order to apply Equation 16 to them. By this equation

$$\tau_A = \frac{\tau_C}{[1 - (\omega r/c)^2]^{1/2}} \tag{18}$$

$$\tau_B = \frac{\tau_D}{[1 - (\omega r/2c)^2]^{1/2}} \tag{19}$$

and since C and D are in the inertial frame, X,

$$\tau_C = \tau_D. \tag{20}$$

Solving Equation 18 for τ_C and Equation 19 for τ_D and applying Equation 20, we get

$$\tau_A \left[1 - (\omega r/c)^2\right]^{1/2} = \tau_B \left[1 - (\omega r/2c)^2\right]^{1/2}.$$

Therefore

$$\tau_A = \tau_B \left[\frac{1 - (\omega r/2c)^2}{1 - (\omega r/c)^2}\right]^{1/2}.$$

Therefore

$$\tau_A > \tau_B.$$

The clock at radius r runs slow with respect to the clock at radius $r/2$ in the frame Y.

SAQ 4 (a) Yes. According to data takers in X, the signals arrive at A and B simultaneously, after a time $D/2c$, and the clock at O runs at the same rate as the clocks they use, because it is at rest in X. Thus all three clocks are synchronized to zero when the signals arrive.

(b) No. A runs slower than O, because it is moving with speed $\omega D/2$ in X.

(c) No. B runs slower than O, because it is moving with speed $\omega D/2$ in X.

(d) Yes. when O reads T, *both* A and B read

$$T \left[1 - (\omega D/2c)^2\right]^{1/2}.$$

SAQ 5 (a) As in the thought-problem of Section 4.2 of Unit 5, we use the rigid rod to define two simultaneous events with its end-points. At any arbitrary time, t, as measured in the frame in which the rod is at rest, the events defined by its end-points are

$$\mathscr{E}_a \equiv (ct, 0, 0) \quad \text{and} \quad \mathscr{E}_b \equiv (ct, x^1, x^2).$$

The square of Lorentz invariant interval (Equation 6 in Section 3.2 of Unit 7) for a frame with only two spatial dimensions is

$$(S_{ab})^2 = (ct_b - ct_a)^2 - (x_b^1 - x_a^1)^2 - (x_b^2 - x_a^2)^2. \tag{21}$$

So, inserting the coordinates of the events $\mathscr{E}_a$ and $\mathscr{E}_b$ in Equation 21, we get

$$(S_{ab})^2 = -[(x^1)^2 + (x^2)^2].$$

(b) The length, l, of the rigid rod, as given by the distance between its end-points, is determined with the Cartesian distance formula:

$$l \equiv \sqrt{(x^1 - 0)^2 + (x^2 - 0)^2} = \sqrt{(x^1)^2 + (x^2)^2}$$

using Equation 4. Therefore, the relationship between the Lorentz invariant interval between events $\mathscr{E}_a$ and $\mathscr{E}_b$ and the length of the rigid rod that defines these events is

$$-(S_{ab})^2 = l^2.$$

(c) *The spatial geometry of an inertial frame of reference is the study of invariant relationships between simultaneous events.* $(S_{ab})^2$ between simultaneous events in an inertial frame turns out to measure the same thing as the 'length' of a rigid rod placed between the events, where 'length' is defined by the Cartesian distance formula (Equation 4). The geometry defined by the Cartesian distance formula is Euclidean geometry (see Unit 1, Section 6). Therefore the spatial geometry of the inertial frame in special relativity is Euclidean.

SAQ 6 We use the technique of comparing the quantities N_C and N_R in the Y-frame with the corresponding quantities $\tilde{N}_C$ and $\tilde{N}_R$ in the X-frame to obtain our answer. As R increases from an initial value, R_1, to a final value, R_2, the instantaneous speed, ωR, of a measuring rod on the circumference increases with respect to that of the corresponding rod in the X-frame. The Lorentz contraction will be greater; so the ratio $N_C / \tilde{N}_C$ will increase. In symbols,

$$\frac{N_{C_2}}{\tilde{N}_{C_2}} > \frac{N_{C_1}}{\tilde{N}_{C_1}}. \tag{22}$$

Now, the radial measurements are not affected by the rotation, as we explained on p. 11. In symbols, this means

$$N_{R_1} = \tilde{N}_{R_1} \tag{23}$$

$$N_{R_2} = \tilde{N}_{R_2}. \tag{24}$$

Since the X-frame is inertial, we have

$$\frac{\tilde{N}_{C_1}}{\tilde{N}_{R_1}} = 2\pi \tag{25}$$

$$\frac{\tilde{N}_{C_2}}{\tilde{N}_{R_2}} = 2\pi. \tag{26}$$

Applying Equations 24 and 26 together to the left-hand side of Equation 22, we get

$$\frac{N_{C_2}}{\tilde{N}_{C_2}} = \frac{\tilde{N}_{R_2}}{N_{R_2}} \times \frac{N_{C_2}}{\tilde{N}_{C_2}} = \frac{N_{C_2}/N_{R_2}}{\tilde{N}_{C_2}/\tilde{N}_{R_2}} = \frac{N_{C_2}/N_{R_2}}{2\pi}. \tag{27}$$

Applying Equations 23 and 25 to the right-hand side of Equation 22, we get

$$\frac{N_{C_1}}{\tilde{N}_{C_1}} = \frac{\tilde{N}_{R_1}}{N_{R_1}} \times \frac{N_{C_1}}{\tilde{N}_{C_1}} = \frac{N_{C_1}/N_{R_1}}{\tilde{N}_{C_1}/\tilde{N}_{R_1}} = \frac{N_{C_1}/N_{R_1}}{2\pi}. \tag{28}$$

Putting Equations 27 and 28 together with Equation 22, we get

$$\frac{N_{C_2}/N_{R_2}}{2\pi} > \frac{N_{C_1}/N_{R_1}}{2\pi} \quad \text{or} \quad \frac{N_{C_2}}{N_{R_2}} > \frac{N_{C_1}}{N_{R_1}}.$$

So as the radius R of the circle in the Y-frame gets larger the ratio N_C/N_R gets larger; it deviates more from the Euclidean value of 2π.

SAQ 7 In Euclidean geometry, the ratio of circumference to radius is equal to 2π for any circle of arbitrary radius about a given centre. That the ratio N_C/N_R should vary with the size of the radius of a circle is in direct conflict with the properties of circles in Euclidean geometry.

SAQ 8 Consider a circular region surrounding the origin of the turntable. As the radius, R, of this region is made smaller, the maximum speed, ωR, of points in the region gets smaller. Length contraction (and time dilation) effects get smaller. At some degree of precision of measurement these effects are always there for any region of finite size. Hence, in principle, there is no finite region of the turntable in which the spatial geometry is exactly Euclidean. However, departures from Euclidean geometry can be made arbitrarily small by choosing small enough regions around the origin.

SAQ 9 **(a)** He can double the time interval over which he can observe the paths of the objects by throwing them 'up' from the floor to which they would move if released from rest anywhere in the laboratory. The two objects are given initial velocities that are parallel and equal in magnitude. If the initial speed is chosen appropriately they will rise almost to the ceiling and then fall back to the floor. This will double the time interval within which the objects are not subject to electromagnetic or nuclear forces (at an atomic level it is electromagnetic forces that keep you from falling through the floor).

(b) The paths of the particles when thrown against the thrust in an accelerating rocket would be the same as those drawn in Figure 9(b). The two objects would rise along the dashed lines of that Figure, almost to the 'ceiling', and then retrace their steps exactly to hit the 'floor' at the points from which they were launched. The separation between them would stay constant throughout the experiment.

(c) The motion of the two objects, A and B, in a typical situation in the gravitational field of the Earth is shown, in exaggerated scale, in Figure 24. The object A is thrown directly against the pull of the Earth: it rises almost to the ceiling and then retraces its steps exactly to the floor. The object B is thrown with initial velocity parallel to the initial velocity of A. But as you can see from Figure 24, the pull of the Earth on B is towards the centre, which is not directly in the opposite direction to the initial velocity of B. Not only is there a vertical force on B (drawn as $\mathbf{F}_v$ at the centre of the Earth for convenience) but a small horizontal force $\mathbf{F}_h$. This causes B to move towards A as it goes up and as it comes down.

(d) Doubling the time of observation of A and B increases the possibility of distinguishing the effects of gravity from those of acceleration because it increases the time during which the force $\mathbf{F}_h$ operates on particle B. Particle B thus moves farther towards particle A in moving from the floor to the ceiling and back than it would in merely dropping from the ceiling to the floor. It may be that this increase in the change in separation of A and B is enough to bring it within the limits of observation of the apparatus available to the experimenter. This would be an example of distinguishing the effects of gravity and acceleration by staying within the same spatial volume but expanding the time of observation. He has expanded the spacetime volume, as is suggested in point 4 on page 15 and point 4′ on page 15, by expanding the time dimension.

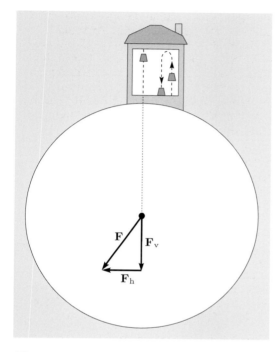

Figure 24 Illustration for the answer to SAQ 9. The gravitational force acting on the object B and its resolution into horizontal and vertical components is shown at the centre of the Earth for convenience.

SAQ 10 The sky-diver is not in free fall according to our definition because a force other than gravitational force is acting on him. This is the frictional drag of the air (even though his parachute is not yet open) and it is the cause of the fact that he will not continue indefinitely to accelerate as he falls but will reach a 'terminal speed' of about $55\,\mathrm{m\,s^{-1}}$. For our technical definition of free fall to apply, *only* gravitational forces can be acting.

SAQ 11 The astronauts are in free fall for that portion of the journey between the shutting off of the booster rockets and the firing on the retro-rockets. For the other two parts of the mission, the astronauts and their space-ship are under the influence of a non-gravitational force provided by their rockets. Although one might say that they are 'falling towards the Moon' when the retro-rockets are on, they are not in free fall as we have defined it.

SAQ 12 One establishes the origin of an inertial frame by following the motion of a particle set free in outer space. The spatial extent of the frame in any given direction is governed by how far one can go in that direction before a significant amount of matter (a star, perhaps) comes into close proximity. Its influence will disturb the directions of free fall and signify that new freely falling frames will be needed to define the locally inertial frames in its vicinity. But the particle originally set free in outer space may be moving at constant velocity towards such a large mass. Then the spatial extent of the inertial frame it defines, in the direction of its motion, changes with time; it gets smaller as the particle gets closer to the star. If the particle were moving away from a star, the spatial extent of the frame it defines would get larger with time.

SAQ 13 (a) The Newtonian prescription deals in a very easy way with the fact described. It says that the particle should not stay at rest because there is a force acting on it — the gravitational force. Newton gives a prescription of how to calculate this force, and we find that the resultant acceleration agrees very well with his prescription.

(b) Our new method deals with this problem by saying that the marble does not remain at rest because we are not viewing it from an inertial frame. We must transform our frame of reference to one freely falling towards the Earth; then that marble and any other object released from rest will remain at rest, as long as no electromagnetic or nuclear forces act on it.

SAQ 14 The EP says that a local region near a concentration of mass and a uniformly accelerating frame (of appropriate acceleration) are indistinguishable as far as *all* laws of physics are concerned. The weak EP is equivalent to the universality of free fall and states merely that the two situations are indistinguishable on the basis of the motion of falling bodies (including photons).

SAQ 15 If we accept the equivalence principle, we accept that whatever takes place in a small laboratory in the gravitational field of the Earth will also take place in a rocket-ship whose motor is providing a constant acceleration, **g**. In such a rocket-ship, two objects that are not experiencing electromagnetic or nuclear forces and are released at rest at the same distance from the 'floor' will hit the floor at the same time, regardless of their masses or compositions. If as a matter of experimental fact, one object in the rocket-ship consistently hits the floor before the other, we would have to conclude that some force, either electromagnetic or nuclear, was present and was affecting the two objects differently. Using the equivalence principle, we will have to draw this same conclusion in the case of the laboratory on Earth (provided that the spacetime volume of the experiment was of an appropriate size).

SAQ 16 (a) The light beam does not hit the point P_1. The equivalence principle says that only the experimental behaviour observed with the spacetime volume V in the accelerating frame of acceleration g will be observed in the same spacetime volume around an event $(x^0, \mathbf{x})$ where the acceleration due to gravity is g. Since the light beam did not hit the point P_1 in the accelerating rocket, it will not hit P_1 in the gravitational situation.

(b) The condition that must be fulfilled for us to be able to predict that the light beam will hit the point P_2 is that the spacetime volume V (which is a product of the width of the laboratory in the rocket and the time of travel of the light beam across the laboratory) is of the appropriate size. This could be checked by doing other experiments that are designed to detect the difference between acceleration and gravity. If they yield no result that distinguishes acceleration from gravity, then we can predict that the laser beam will hit the point P_2.

(c) If the laser beam actually hit the point P_1 and no experimental fault were found to explain this result, then we would have to conclude that the equivalence principle is wrong.

SAQ 17 The two plumb-bobs should have shapes and sizes as similar as is possible so that the inevitable effects of air friction will slow them down equally. They would then still keep in step if μ/m is independent of the material of the bob.

SAQ 18 Suppose that the lengths of the two strings were slightly different so that in the time the first pendulum swings 17 times, the second swings 18 times. If the two pendulums start together from rest, they will get progressively further out of step from swing 1 to swing 9 of the second pendulum; from swing 10 to swing 18 they will return progressively into step, matching up at the end of swing 18. This will repeat itself between swings 19 to 36 and so on. We can check that this 'in step, out of step' oscillation is caused by the inequality of the lengths by putting two bobs of the same material on the strings and observing the pattern of oscillations. If μ/m is independent of material, this same pattern (in step at 0, 18, 36,... swings; out of step at 9, 27, ...swings) should occur with any combination of plumb-bobs of differing materials. (It will, of course, be difficult to change the plumb-bobs without altering the effective lengths of the pendulums.)

SAQ 19 The formula for the fractional change in frequency (Equation 10) is

$$\frac{\Delta f}{f} = -\frac{gH_1}{c^2}.$$

In SI units, $g = 9.81 \, \mathrm{m\,s^{-2}}$ and $c = 3 \times 10^8 \, \mathrm{m\,s^{-1}}$. Therefore

$$\frac{\Delta f}{f} = \frac{-9.81 \times 20}{(3 \times 10^8)^2} = -2.2 \times 10^{-15}.$$

SAQ 20 There will be 'no gravity' in a freely falling lift; it will be a local inertial frame. Gravity is essential for convection currents (hot air rises as colder air falls) and without convection currents to carry off the hot burned gas, the flame will rapidly asphyxiate itself.

Unit 10 & 11
A metric theory of gravity and the field equations of general relativity

Prepared by the Course Team

Contents

Aims

In this Unit we intend to:

1 Explain what is meant by the phrase 'general relativity is a metric theory of motion under gravity'.

2 Explain the way in which the principle of equivalence leads us towards a metric theory of gravity and how the universality of free fall is incorporated into general relativity.

3 Explain what is meant by the phrase 'spacetime is curved in the presence of matter'.

4 Outline in qualitative terms how the distribution of matter controls the curvature of spacetime; and hence explain how the specific geometric features of spacetime in the presence of matter become part of the 'problem of motion under gravity'.

5 Sketch the history of the experimental testing of the general theory of relativity.

Objectives

When you have finished studying this Unit, you should be able to:

1 Explain, with examples, how to give a geometric solution to the mechanical problem of finding the path of a particle.

2 Recognize and use the parametric description of curves.

3 Identify the metric of the plane, in Cartesian coordinates and in plane polar coordinates, and explain what it describes.

4 Give expressions for

(a) the length of a small segment of a curve in the plane (in two forms),

(b) the length of a curve in the plane,

in Cartesian coordinates and in plane polar coordinates and use them to solve problems.

5 Explain the difference between a flat two-dimensional surface and a curved two-dimensional surface using the different geometric properties of figures drawn on those surfaces.

6 Identify (i) the metric of a spherical surface of radius R, (ii) the length of a small segment of a curve drawn on a sphere and (iii) the length of a curve on a sphere, and use them to solve problems.

7 Show that the metrics of the sphere and the plane lead to different geometric properties of figures drawn on these surfaces.

8 Explain and use a uniform notation for the description of metrics of two-dimensional surfaces.

9 Explain the concept of a geodesic equation, and use specific forms of geodesic equations to identify geodesics of a two-dimensional surface.

10 Identify the metric of the two-dimensional spacetime of special relativity and the expressions for (i) the proper time elapsed along a small segment of a world-line and (ii) the proper time elapsed along any world-line, in two-dimensional spacetime.

11 Explain the role that proper time plays in a metric theory of free-particle motion in special relativity, and quote the basic postulate of such a theory.

12 Quote and discuss the central ideas of a metric theory of gravity.

13 Relate the concepts of (i) locally inertial frames and (ii) the geodesics of two-dimensional curved surfaces to those aspects of spacetime in the presence of gravity identified by the principle of equivalence and the universality of free fall.

14 Give four definitions of the curvature of a two-dimensional surface and relate the terms 'flat' and 'curved', as applied to two-dimensional surfaces, to properties described in these four definitions.

15 Explain the importance of the fourth definition of curvature (curvature$_4$) for the understanding of the phrase 'curved spacetime'.

16 Explain, with examples, how curvature$_4$ determines the geometric properties of a two-dimensional surface without uniquely specifying the metric.

17 Give a sketch of the role that Einstein's field equations play in the general theory of relativity. Give a qualitative account of the difference between Ricci curvature and Riemann curvature.

18 Discuss the Schwarzschild solution to Einstein's field equations, explaining the properties of it that make it a reasonable solution. Explain also the meaning of the phrase 'loss of metrical significance' as applied to the r- and t-coordinates in the Schwarzschild metric.

19 Explain the meaning of the sentence 'the structure of spacetime has become as much a part of the *solution* to the problem of motion under gravity as the trajectories or world-lines of particles are part of the solution'.

20 Give a sketch of the history of the experimental testing of the general theory of relativity.

Study guide for Unit 10 & 11

1   General advice

The first bit of advice has to be: don't panic! Unit 10 & 11 is presented as one double Unit containing twice the work of a normal unit. This is done because the natural break in the story that it tells comes somewhere between 60 and 70 per cent of the way through. If you are going to study it in two approximately equal parts, then the end of Section 8 could be a dividing line between them. There is also quite a lot of optional material in this Unit (see below).

Sections 4, 6 and 12 contain extensive mathematical derivations of formulae that express two of the major concepts of the Unit: the metric of a surface, and its curvature. Although the derivations are important steps to the understanding of these concepts, it is the concepts themselves and their uses that are the most important objectives of your study. You will not be expected to reproduce the derivations from memory. The summaries at the ends of Section 4.2, 4.4, 6 and 12 should help you estimate the effectiveness of your study. If you understand the concepts, symbols and equations that you find there and can use them to answer the SAQs, you can be satisfied with your progress.

2   Plan of the Unit

From the *Oxford English Dictionary*: 'Allegory — [The] description of a subject under the guise of another subject of aptly suggestive resemblance'.

Much of this Unit can be considered to be an allegory of general relativity told in two dimensions. We set out below the plan of this Unit to show which sections are setting up the allegory and which sections are dealing with general relativity more directly.

1 Section 2 describes non-mathematically the radical difference between Einstein's way of explaining the motions of objects under gravity and Newton's explanation of the same phenomena. We work with two-dimensional examples but we are aiming at the elucidation of aspects of general relativity (in four dimensions).

2 Sections 3 to 9.1 set up the two-dimensional part of the allegory; that is, they describe the other 'subject of aptly suggestive resemblance'. If you are impatient to get to general relativity, your patience will be most sorely tried in these pages. We can only ask you to persevere, because with one exception, all the major mathematical concepts are set out in their two-dimensional forms in these sections.

3 Sections 9.2 to 10 relate the two-dimensional developments of the proceeding six sections to four-dimensional spacetime to give the first glimpse, in mathematical form, of Einstein's theory of motion under gravity.

4 Section 11 works with both two- and four-dimensional situations to explain how the principle of equivalence and the universality of free fall point the way to the general theory of relativity.

5 Sections 12.1 to 12.4 go back to two dimensions exclusively to develop the last major concept needed for the allegory of general relativity that we are presenting in this Block.

6 Sections 12.5 to 14 all concern themselves with general relativity as such. Although we cannot show a derivation of Einstein's field equations, we can show you a solution of these equations which enables us to derive the gravitational redshift, and give an account of why planets move the way they do around the Sun.

3   Principal back references

This unit builds on much that has been the subject of earlier Units. In particular, there are specific sections of earlier Units of which we make detailed use. They are listed in Table 1 so that you may, if you wish, revise them before working through this Unit.

TABLE 1   List of key concepts introduced in earlier Units.

Concept	Where explained	Where used in this Unit
the development of geometry from a 'distance function'	Unit 1, Section 6	Section 2 and following
Newton's explanation of motion under gravity	Unit 2, Sections 4.3 and 4.4	Section 2 and following
the use of a differential equation to find a desired function	Appendix to Unit 3	Sections 8, 9 and 12
the Lorentz invariant interval S_{ab} and ΔS in two dimensions and four dimensions	Unit 7, Sections 3.1, 3.2, 4.2, and 5.2	Sections 2, 9 and following
proper time elapsed along a world-line	Unit 7, Sections 5.2 and 5.3	Sections 2, 9 and following
the resolution of the twin 'paradox'	Unit 7, Section 5.3, especially Theorem II	Section 2
τ is the argument of $x^0(\tau)$, $x^1(\tau)$	Unit 7, Section 5.3	Sections 2, 9 and following

4   Tapes

Some bands of Audiocassette AC3 form an integral part of the teaching material of this Unit. In Sections 9.1 and 12.4, the most efficient way for you to absorb the information is to look at a visual display while a course team member talks about it. In Section 9.1 the display is a large table of ideas and equations; in Section 12.4, it is a series of figures or 'frames'. When you study these sections you will need your audiocassette player.

5   Optional material

We wish to stress that any part of this Unit that is marked optional *is truly optional*. We would not have put it there if we did not want you to read and understand it, but no development in the main text depends on the ideas or methods explained therein. Nor is any optional material assessable in this Course.

6   Emergency study strategy

First of all, rest assured that the extensive passages marked 'non assessable' will indeed not be examined, and later parts of the course do not depend upon them. The optional Appendix 1 does derive certain equations which are used elsewhere in the Unit, but you would not be expected to reproduce the derivation. Indeed the equations in question would always be quoted in any assessment. In this connection, note that in an exam, the geodesic equations of Section 8 and the expression for curvature$_4$ in Section 12.4 would be provided; although they are important you are *not* expected to memorize them.

You should *not* skip most of Section 13 where the Schwarzschild solution is introduced, since the rest of the Unit and most of Unit 12 would then be unintelligible. However if you are really behind, Section 13.2 could be skimmed, though you should be aware of the final conclusion stated as a single italicized sentence near the end.

If you are seriously behind, and willing to forego the possibility of writing about the tests of general relativity in essay questions, then little in the remainder of the course rests upon Section 14 except for the brief subsection on gravitational lenses in Unit 12.

1 Introduction

Band 3 of AC3 introduces this Unit.

In considering the equivalence principle in the last Unit, we saw that certain treasured illusions concerning space and time had to be relinquished. In this double unit, as we present Einstein's theory of general relativity (theory of gravitation), we must begin by looking again at the ways in which we describe the geometric properties of spacetime.

The core of Einstein's theory of gravitation can be summed up in two complementary statements:

1. the presence of matter (or anything with mass) causes spacetime to become curved rather than flat, as it was in Units 4–7.
2. bodies move in curved spacetime along paths ('geodesics') which are for curved spacetime what straight lines are for flat space.

In this double unit we explain these two statements. In particular we explain what it means for spacetime to be 'curved' and what 'geodesics' are. To give you a glimpse here of what is involved, recall that Newton's first law says that a body not subject to forces travels in a straight line at constant speed. Roughly speaking, what Einstein's theory says is that in the presence of mass, a body (assuming it has no rocket motor and is not subject to electric forces, etc.) still travels in a particular sort of straight line through spacetime which has been distorted by the mass. This is seen as a deeper explanation of the phenomena described otherwise by Newton's gravitational force and Newton's second law. By some measures, the departure of spacetime from flatness in the region of even a heavy body like the Sun is rather small. But not that small: the planets, after all, do not pass the Sun on straight lines, but are in orbit about it. The distortion of spacetime near the Earth keeps you in your chair as you read this.

Having said that Einstein's geometrical theory of gravity is 'deeper' than Newton's, does this mean that in some sense it is truer? In fact, in certain fine details it makes predictions which differ from those of Newton's theory. Thus Einstein's theory can be tested and the unit concludes with an account of certain tests which verify the theory. In doing so, they imply that the entire Newtonian framework of space and time must be replaced. Later in the course, we shall find other consequences of the theory which are nothing less than momentous: the existence of black holes and the way the Universe evolves in time.

Einstein's theory of gravitation is a profound achievement; before we can present a true glimpse of it we must first prepare the way with a number of technicalities, mostly concerned with achieving a mathematical description of the geometry of spacetime.

A mathematical note on straight lines in the plane

The following definition of straight lines in the plane will be of use to you throughout this Unit.

In Unit 1, Section 6, a straight line between two points, A and B, with Cartesian coordinates

$$A = (x_A^1, x_A^2, x_A^3) \quad \text{and} \quad B = (x_B^1, x_B^2, x_B^3)$$

in three-dimensional space is defined to be the set of points, such as

$$C = (x_C^1, x_C^2, x_C^3)$$

that satisfy the constraint:

$$|AC| + |CB| = |AB|. \tag{1a}$$

$|AB|$ is the 'distance function' for points in three-dimensional space and is defined in terms of Cartesian coordinates for points A and B as

$$|AB| \equiv [(x_B^1 - x_A^1)^2 + (x_B^2 - x_A^2)^2 + (x_B^3 - x_A^3)^2]^{1/2} \tag{1b}$$

In this Unit we use the notation [ ]$^{1/2}$, rather than $\sqrt{\ }$, to represent 'the square root of'.

and likewise for $|AC|$ and $|CB|$. In Unit 10 & 11 we shall be principally concerned with lines in the (x^1, x^2) plane, that is, lines made up of points whose x^3-coordinate is zero. The distance function $|AB|$ then reduces to

$$|AB| = [(x_B^1 - x_A^1)^2 + (x_B^2 - x_A^2)^2]^{1/2}$$

which can be similarly used to define a straight line in the (x^1, x^2) plane via Equation 1a.

In later sections we shall want to make use of the more common definition of a straight line in the plane, which says that any set of points in the plane whose Cartesian coordinates obey the equation

$$x^2 = ax^1 + b \tag{1c}$$

definition of a straight line

is a straight line. It is not hard to show that, indeed, a *straight line* under this definition obeys Equation 1a. Thus, any line that is 'straight' according to Equation 1c is also 'straight' under the definition of Unit 1, Section 6. Therefore, any property of straight lines deduced in Unit 1, Section 6, using the definition based on Equations 1a and 1b is also true of a straight line defined by Equation 1c.

2 What is a 'geometric theory of gravity'?

Before we develop the key mathematical concepts, we shall sketch out in words the new way in which general relativity explains why one body moves as it does under the gravitational influence of another body. The ideas used in this explanation are much more like the ideas involved in solving geometric problems than those used in Newtonian mechanics, so we first show how geometry can be used to solve a problem in mechanics.

Here is a basic problem of mechanics: if the forces acting on a particle are known, how will the particle move in response to these forces? In the terminology of Block 1 the answer will be given as a set of three coordinate functions, $x^1(t)$, $x^2(t)$ and $x^3(t)$, of the time t. For a particular instant t_0, the position vector

$$\mathbf{x}(t_0) = (x^1(t_0), x^2(t_0), x^3(t_0))$$

trajectory of a particle in three-dimensional space

represents the instantaneous position of the particle. The way in which the position vector $\mathbf{x}(t)$ varies with t gives a complete description of the motion of the particle, which we shall call the *trajectory of the particle.* Alternatively, in Unit 7 the world-line of a particle was described in (x^0, x^1) space by two coordinate functions, $x^0(\tau)$ and $x^1(\tau)$, of the proper time, τ. So the solution of our basic problem of mechanics can be given as a trajectory in space as a function of time *or* as a world-line in spacetime.

Could it be that the solution to some problems in mechanics amounts to specifying the trajectory or giving some geometric prescription?

Galileo's law of horizontal motion is an example. In a uniform vertical force field, a particle moving across a horizontal, frictionless table moves in a straight line at constant velocity. The trajectory is given by a geometric concept. The idea that a straight line is the curve of shortest length between two points is geometric, and this gives us the path of the particle.

What we shall find in Unit 10 & 11 is the following: *there is a geometric solution, based on a concept akin to 'length', to every problem of motion of a test-body under the gravitational influence of other bodies* (such as the motion of the planets about the Sun). The remarkable thing about general relativity is that *everything* about the motion of bodies under gravity emerges from a geometric prescription. This includes a description of the changing speed of a planet in orbit around the Sun, going much further than simply a geometric description of the orbit.

The common sense definition of a straight line is 'the shortest distance between two points'; but what 'distance' means is usually assumed as obvious or is defined with a straight edge (i.e. a straight line). Unit 1, Section 6, sets out a way of dealing with the concepts of 'distance between points', 'length of a curve', and 'straight line' that keeps us from getting tangled up. Between any two points in three-dimensional space,

$$A = (x_A^1, x_A^2, x_A^3) \quad \text{and} \quad B = (x_B^1, x_B^2, x_B^3)$$

the distance $|AB|$ is defined by the function

$$|AB| \equiv [(x_B^1 - x_A^1)^2 + (x_B^2 - x_A^2)^2 + (x_B^3 - x_A^3)^2]^{1/2}$$

Using this distance function, we can eventually define

1 The straight line between A and B;

2 The length of this straight line;

3 The length of a curve between points A and B.

The major result (in Unit 1) of these definitions is that the straight line between A and B is the curve of minimum length between A and B; all other curves that connect A and B have greater lengths than the straight line between A and B. This is one aspect of geometry on which we shall concentrate: the construction of curves between points, the evaluation of their lengths and the identification of the curve of minimum length between points. This process of picking out the curve of shortest distance between two points from all the possible curves that connect these points is crucial: it is analogous to how general relativity solves the problem of motion under gravity.

geodesic

The curve of minimum length between two points is so important that we shall use its technical name: *geodesic*. The idea of a geodesic will still be useful in contexts in which the idea of a straight line has lost its relevance. To show how geometric statements made in terms of geodesics can solve mechanical problems in situations where straight lines do not help, we consider a second mechanical example. Figure 1(a) shows a bead sliding without friction on the interior surface of a hollow hemisphere in the absence of gravity. A close-up in Figure 1(b) shows the instantaneous velocity **v**, of the bead and the constraining force, **F**, exerted on the bead by the spherical shell. If we wish to find the trajectory of the bead along the shell, we may solve Newton's equations with the appropriate force. Newtonian theory predicts the *trajectory*, because it gives information about the *path* along which the bead moves *and* about how the position of the bead along this path will vary with *time*. But the first part of this prediction — the path — can be described very easily using the concept of a geodesic. For example, suppose we pick two points in the hemisphere, A and B say, and ask what is the form of the path of the bead that passes through those two points. The answer turns out to be that the path travelled by the bead is the shortest possible path along the hemisphere between the two points; that is, the geodesic between the points.

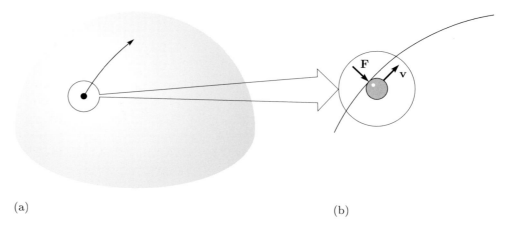

(a)   (b)

Figure 1   Bead sliding on the interior surface of a hemisphere.

In fact, the shortest path between any two points A and B on a hemisphere, as illustrated in Figure 2, is a segment of the great circle connecting them; that is, the curve made by intersecting the surface of the sphere, from which the hemisphere is formed, with the plane defined by

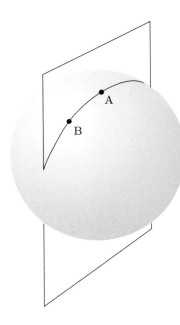

Figure 2 The intersection method of constructing a great circle through two points, A and B, on a sphere. Take the plane defined by A, B and the centre of the sphere. The curve produced by the intersection of this plane with the sphere is a great circle.

points A, B and the centre of the sphere. So we can find the geodesic connecting points A and B with a geometric construction; we shall use it in Sections 5 and 8. But regardless of how the geodesics are obtained, they are part of the geometric properties of the spherical surface. So in specifying that the bead travels along the geodesic connecting any two points on its path, we have given a geometric answer to the mechanical problem of describing the path of the bead that passes through points A and B. If we could derive mathematically the length of any curve on the surface of a sphere, we could find the curve of minimum length between points A and B and thus arrive analytically at the geometric solution to our mechanical problem rather than using the intersecting-plane method. But to find the curve of minimum length on the sphere we need a distance function for points on the sphere, rather like the function |AB| for points in three-dimensional space. We return to this problem in Section 6.

It is clear that the ordinary idea of a 'straight line' doesn't do us much good here; but the idea of a 'geodesic' is still relevant. Knowing that the bead follows a geodesic between two points on the hemisphere, we don't have to analyse forces or do any of the Newtonian calculations — it's purely a matter of geometry. The general theory of relativity is somewhat analogous since it explains motion under gravity — particles responding to the gravitational force — in terms of particles moving along some form of geodesic. But the attempt to pick out the paths of particles moving under gravity as geodesics in three-dimensional space will fail, as the following example shows:

Consider, in Figure 3, two points A and B on the surface of the Earth connected by various paths of artillery shells. Different elevations of the barrel and different muzzle velocities of the shells make them all possible. Clearly no description of the possible paths between A and B stated in terms of the minimum length of path is possible — because a continuous variety of paths longer than the path of minimum length, the straight line between A and B, is possible. However, although all possible paths go from the same points in space, A and B, they do *not* go through the same points in *spacetime* since the possible paths are of different durations.

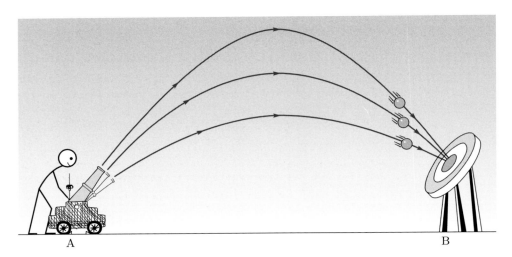

Figure 3 The paths of three artillery shells between the same two points A and B on the surface of the Earth.

In *general relativity* (as in the special relativity of Block 2) it is geodesics in four-dimensional *spacetime*, that solve the problem. To get a glimpse of the way in which the ideas of geodesics and spacetime provide a solution of the type 'pick the curve of minimum length. . .' to a problem of motion, consider the simplest case: free-particle motion (no gravity, no electromagnetic or nuclear forces). Then we can use Unit 7 to show that a geometric prescription of the type sketched above, but based in spacetime, can solve the problem of the motion of the free particle. But we must change three things:

(i)   We must examine world-lines in spacetime rather than paths in space.

(ii)   We must evaluate the *proper time* elapsed along a world-line rather than the length of a curve.

(iii)   We must select the world-line of *maximum* proper time rather than the curve of *minimum* length.

Below, we justify these claims using the arguments of Unit 7.

As in Unit 7, we consider the case of motion in one spatial dimension, but the conclusion is general. A free particle moves with constant velocity. Since any world-line in the (x^0, x^1) plane has a slope given by

$$\frac{\mathrm{d}x^0}{\mathrm{d}x^1} = \frac{\mathrm{d}(ct)}{\mathrm{d}x} = c\frac{\mathrm{d}t}{\mathrm{d}x} = c\Big/\frac{\mathrm{d}x}{\mathrm{d}t} = \frac{c}{v}$$

then constant velocity, v, means constant slope, $\mathrm{d}x^0/\mathrm{d}x^1$. *So the world-line of a free particle is a straight line in spacetime.* Its x^0 and x^1-coordinates are related by

$$x^0 = \frac{c}{v}x^1 + k$$

where k is some constant. The world-line is shown as $\mathscr{W}_1$ in Figure 4(a). The question is: can we pick out this world-line from all other world-lines of bodies moving between events $\mathscr{E}_a$ and $\mathscr{E}_b$ (see Figure 4(b)) using a geometric argument? *Yes*, by virtue of the following two statements:

1 The proper time elapsed along a given world-line between two events, as introduced in Unit 7, Sections 5.2 and 5.3, is a Lorentz invariant quantity; thus any statement made about proper time elapsed along a world-line will be agreed by all inertial observers.

2 The proper time elapsed between events $\mathscr{E}_a$ and $\mathscr{E}_b$ is greater along world-line $\mathscr{W}_1$ than it is along any other world-line of a material particle that connects $\mathscr{E}_a$ and $\mathscr{E}_b$, such as world-lines $\mathscr{W}_2$ or $\mathscr{W}_3$ in Figure 4(b).

We can prove statement 2 using statement 1 and Theorem II of Unit 7, Section 5.3. Since elapsed proper time is a Lorentz invariant quantity, let us compare the proper times elapsed along different world-lines in the inertial frame that is most convenient for us. The most convenient frame is the one moving in the positive x^1-direction at speed v with respect to the frame of Figure 4(a); this frame is the rest frame of the freely moving particle. The three world-lines $\mathscr{W}_1$, $\mathscr{W}_2$ and $\mathscr{W}_3$ of Figure 4(b) become the world-lines $\mathscr{W}'_1$, $\mathscr{W}'_2$ and $\mathscr{W}'_3$ in Figure 4(c). Comparing the proper times elapsed along three world-lines is easy because of the second sentence of Theorem II of Unit 7 (the key to the so-called twin paradox) which says:

> If a particle returns to its point of departure, then its elapsed proper time is strictly less than that for an inertial observer who has remained at that point in space.

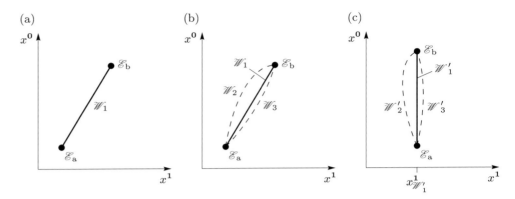

Figure 4 Spacetime diagrams of world-lines connecting two events $\mathscr{E}_a$ and $\mathscr{E}_b$.

The particle moving along world-line $\mathscr{W}'_1$ has stayed at one point in space, $x^1_{\mathscr{W}'_1}$, while particles moving along $\mathscr{W}'_2$ or $\mathscr{W}'_3$ have moved away from the point $x^1_{\mathscr{W}'_1}$, and then moved back. Thus the proper time elapsed along $\mathscr{W}'_2$ or $\mathscr{W}'_3$ will be strictly less than the proper time elapsed along $\mathscr{W}'_1$. Because of statement 1 above, the observer of Figure 4(b) will also say that the proper time elapsed along world-lines $\mathscr{W}_2$ or $\mathscr{W}_3$ is strictly less than the proper time elapsed along world-line $\mathscr{W}_1$, the world-line of the free particle.

This argument gives us our 'geometric' principle with which to solve a very simple mechanical problem. The principle is: *a free particle moving between two events in spacetime will move on that world-line along which the maximum proper time elapses between the events.* As you already know, Equation 22 of Unit 7, for events $\mathscr{E}_c$ and $\mathscr{E}_d$

$$\tau_{cd} = \text{ the sum from } t_c \text{ to } t_d \text{ of terms like } \Delta t\sqrt{1 - \left(\frac{u(t)}{c}\right)^2}$$

can be used to evaluate the proper time elapsed along any world-line. The terms of the equation are illustrated in Figure 5, with

$$u(t) = \frac{\Delta x^1}{\Delta t}.$$

Evaluating τ_{cd} for different world-lines between $\mathscr{E}_c$ and $\mathscr{E}_d$ allows us to identify the world-line of maximum proper time in the same sort of way that

$$|AB| = [(x^1_B - x^1_A)^2 + (x^2_B - x^2_A)^2]^{1/2}$$

allows us to pick out the curve of shortest length in the plane.

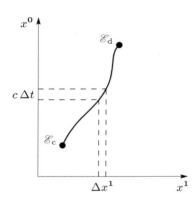

Figure 5 Illustration for the formula for elapsed proper time along a given world-line between two events $\mathscr{E}_c$ and $\mathscr{E}_d$.

In Section 6.2 we discuss in more detail the fact that the surface of a sphere is two-dimensional.

Let us pick out the key features of the examples we have discussed in this Section to show what we mean by saying that general relativity is a geometric theory of motion under gravity. The example of the bead on the hemispherical surface showed that we can sometimes encapsulate the Newtonian results in terms based on the idea of a curve of minimum length. But we had to take account of the 'space' in which the bead is moving. Instead of saying that the bead moves in three-dimensional space but forces keep it on the surface of the hemisphere, we say *that the bead is moving freely in a two-dimensional space* — the surface of a hemisphere. *The hemispherical surface becomes the whole 'space' in which the bead can move.* The path of a bead between any two points on the hemispherical surface will be the curve of minimum length *in the surface*. (The curve of minimum length between the points in three-dimensional space is completely useless in this problem.) By picking the hemispherical surface as our space and evaluating the lengths of curves in this space, force is no longer required to account for the path of a bead. The general theory of relativity similarly eliminates the Newtonian idea of gravity as a force. It replaces Newton's second law by an analysis based on selecting one curve between two points from all possible curves between those points. But general relativity cannot use ordinary three-dimensional space for this analysis, as the example of the artillery shell showed.

Now recall free-particle motion in special relativity. Just as *spacetime* and the concept of elapsed proper time gave us a geometric description of free-particle motion, so they will provide a similar description of motion under gravity.

In general relativity we shall be concerned with the movement of particles between events along world-lines in spacetime. We shall evaluate the proper time elapsed along different proposed world-lines connecting the same two events and we shall select the actual world-line followed by a test-body by finding the world-line of maximum proper time between the two events. We know that this prescription gives the correct world-line for a free particle. Our major hypothesis is that this same method of picking out the world-line also gives the motion of bodies under gravity.

What makes this procedure give different answers from those already obtained on p. 13 is that, as we stressed in Unit 9, spacetime in the presence of matter is not the same as the spacetime of special relativity. We have not yet said how matter modifies spacetime, and this is a major aim of this Unit. However, it *is* this difference that means that the world-lines of test-bodies in the presence of matter will not be of the form

$$x^0 = k_1 x^1 + k_2$$

as they were when no gravitational influence was present.

To give a quantitative description of the ideas sketched out in this section we have two major jobs:

1 We have to explain the mathematical concepts needed to calculate the proper time elapsed along a world-line and the method of selecting the curve of maximum elapsed proper time between two events.

2 We have to explain the difference between the spacetime of special relativity and spacetime in the presence of matter. This difference is usually stated by saying that spacetime in the presence of matter is 'curved' whereas the spacetime of special relativity is 'flat'. So this second job is to explain what 'curved spacetime' means.

We approach these two jobs from the standpoint of a simpler situation that provides an analogy of spacetime — we stay on two-dimensional surfaces namely, the plane and the surface of the sphere. We shall show how to calculate the length of a curve in the plane and on the surface of a sphere and how to select the curve of minimum length between any two points. We shall show how to distinguish a curved two-dimensional surface from a flat one. Once we have the mathematical apparatus to do these two jobs, the transitions

$$\text{space} \longrightarrow \text{spacetime}$$

$$\text{length} \longrightarrow \text{proper time}$$

$$\begin{array}{ccc}\text{selection of actual curve} & \longrightarrow & \text{selection of actual world-line on} \\ \text{on the basis of length} & & \text{the basis of elapsed proper time}\end{array}$$

will be easy to make. But we must begin at the beginning and that is with the idea of how to describe a curve in a two-dimensional space. We take this up in Section 3.

Objective: revision   **SAQ 1**   Explain the following statement: 'A crucial difference between an interval in *space* and an interval in *spacetime* is a minus sign.' What is the interpretation of an interval in spacetime of zero magnitude?

2.1   Summary of Section 2

1 A central problem of mechanics is to predict the trajectories or world-lines of particles.

2 The Newtonian solution to this problem is to find the forces acting on the particle and insert them into Newton's second law, a differential equation whose solution is the trajectory of the particle.

3 A 'geometric' solution to this problem, as we have used this term in Section 2, is a statement that the trajectory or world-line of a particle will be given by some geometric prescription based on the fundamental concept of length. Sometimes, even where Newtonian mechanics is valid, one can define 'geometric solutions' e.g. the straight line of Galileo.

4 There exist mechanical systems for which the path taken by a particle can be specified geometrically as a 'geodesic' (a curve of minimum length) between points. The path of a particle between any two points in these systems is the geodesic that connects these points. An example of such a system is a bead sliding on the interior surface of a hemisphere.

5 In special relativity, one can give a related geometric solution to the problem of free-particle motion. It is this: the world-line of a free particle moving between any two events is the world-line that maximizes the proper time elapsed between the two events. This follows from the solution of the twin 'paradox' in Unit 7.

3 The parametric description of curves in the plane

We saw in Section 2 that curves enter into both geometry and mechanics. In geometry we meet special curves such as the straight line, the ellipse or the parabola; in mechanics, it is the trajectory or the world-line of a particle that is required. From Block 1 you are familiar with the following description of a Newtonian trajectory. The idealized flight of a golf ball (in two dimensions for simplicity: height x^1, and horizontal travel x^2) is described in Unit 1 by the following pair of equations:

$$x^1(t) = \frac{4Ht}{T} - \frac{4Ht^2}{T^2} \tag{2a}$$

$$x^2(t) = \frac{Rt}{T} \tag{2b}$$

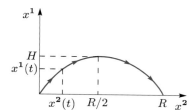

Figure 6   The path of a golf ball.

where H and R are defined in Figure 6 and T is the time at which the ball arrives at $(0, R)$. For any time t, between $t = 0$ and $t = T$, Equation 2a gives the height and Equation 2b the distance along the ground of the golf ball. Thus they allow us to plot the position of the ball on the (x^1, x^2) graph in Figure 6.

In Newtonian mechanics this is a natural way to specify a trajectory because time is a physical variable and it is reasonable to ask, at a given time, how high the ball is and how far along the ground it has gone. But Equations 2a and 2b also provide a prototype of a way of specifying any kind of curve. For example, the following pair of equations:

$$x^1(t) = \cos 2t \quad \text{and} \quad x^2(t) = \sin 2t$$

describe a circle of unit radius centred around the origin of the (x^1, x^2) axes. Any point on the circle is given by $(x^1(t_0), x^2(t_0))$ for some value, t_0, of the variable t. Now t could stand for time. In that case, the equations represent a particle that moves around the circle at constant speed and completes one revolution every π seconds. Or one could replace $2t$ by ϕ and write

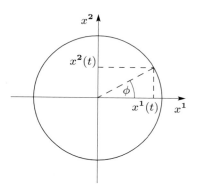

Figure 7   A circle of unit radius.

$$x^1(\phi) = \cos \phi \quad \text{and} \quad x^2(\phi) = \sin \phi$$

and that might seem natural since ϕ can be identified as the angle shown in Figure 7. But in order to describe a curve in the (x^1, x^2) plane we need not make any physical identification of the variable t or ϕ. It can simply be used as a convenient way of relating x^1 values to x^2 values and thus plotting points on the (x^1, x^2) plane. This method of describing curves will be extensively used in this Unit. Variables such as t or ϕ are referred to as *parameters*; the functions $x^1(t)$ and $x^2(t)$ of this parameter are called *coordinate functions*, and this method of specifying curves is called the *parametric definition of a curve*.

parameter
coordinate function
parametric definition of a curve

Objective 2

SAQ 2   Identify, by plotting a few points, the curves that have the following parametric definitions:

(a) $x^1(t) = t + 1; \quad x^2(t) = 2t + 3.$

(b) $x^1(t) = t; \quad x^2(t) = +[1 - t^2]^{1/2}; \quad -1 \leqslant t \leqslant 1.$

18

Objective 2   **SAQ 3**   In the two examples given in SAQ 2, eliminate the parameter t to obtain the usual equations between x^1 and x^2 for these curves.

Objective 2   **SAQ 4**   Consider the parametric equations

$$x^1(t) = at + b; \quad x^2(t) = ct + d.$$

(a) What is the slope dx^2/dx^1 of the straight line so described?

(b) What condition would have to be placed on the constants used to specify another line

$$x^1(t) = gt + h; \quad x^2(t) = jt + k$$

in order that it be parallel to (but not identical with) the first line?

---

parametric definition of a straight line

parallel lines in the plane

The answers to the above SAQs will be needed later in the following form:

1 A curve with the following parametrization

$$x^1(t) = at + b; \quad x^2(t) = ct + d$$

(where a, b, c and d are constants) is a straight line in the (x^1, x^2) plane.

2 Two straight lines

$$x^1(t) = at + b; \quad x^2(t) = ct + d$$
$$x^1(t) = gt + h; \quad x^2(t) = jt + k$$

are parallel if the constants c, a, j and g have values such that

$$\frac{c}{a} = \frac{j}{g}.$$

3 The technique used in SAQ 3(a) to eliminate the parameter t and thus obtain a formula of the form

$$x^2 = k_1 x^1 + k_2$$

for the straight line, can be used to show that the parametrization given in 1 above is not the only parametrization that describes a given straight line. For example, the coordinate functions

$$x^1(t) = t^2 + 1; \quad x^2(t) = 2t^2 + 3$$

describe the same straight line as that given in SAQ 2(a), because t^2 can be eliminated between the two equations to give

$$x^2 = 2x^1 + 1$$

exactly as t was eliminated in SAQ 2. Similarly

$$x^1(t) = t^3 + 1; \quad x^2(t) = 2t^3 + 3$$

describe the same straight line. Clearly there are infinitely many pairs of functions, $x^1(t)$ and $x^2(t)$, that describe the same straight line. This multiplicity of ways of describing a given curve by coordinate functions $x^1(t)$ and $x^2(t)$ will be of importance in Section 8.

4   The metric of the plane and the length of a curve in the plane

4.1   The metric of the plane in Cartesian coordinates

Before we can compare the lengths of different curves joining the same two points, we must be able to calculate the length of a curve. In this section we show how to calculate the length of a curve drawn in the plane, given the coordinate functions that describe it.

We begin by saying exactly what we mean by the terms 'distance' and 'length'. Our definitions are based on ideas introduced in Unit 1, but specialized in a way that may at first seem unnecessarily restricted. However, the new definitions allow us to generalize in a way that the definitions of Unit 1 do not. This generalization is important to general relativity, as we shall explain in Section 4.4.

Unit 1, Section 6, defines the distance $|PQ|$, between any two points

$$P = (x_P^1, x_P^2, x_P^3) \quad \text{and} \quad Q = (x_Q^1, x_Q^2, x_Q^3)$$

in three-dimensional space by the following function of their Cartesian coordinates

$$|PQ| \equiv [(x_Q^1 - x_P^1)^2 + (x_Q^2 - x_P^2)^2 + (x_Q^3 - x_P^3)^2]^{1/2}. \tag{3a}$$

We shall be dealing with points in the (x^1, x^2) plane; that is with points whose x^3-coordinates are zero. The distance formula then reduces to

$$|PQ| = [(x_Q^1 - x_P^1)^2 + (x_Q^2 - x_P^2)^2]^{1/2}. \tag{3b}$$

Equation 3a also defines the 'length' of the straight line connecting P and Q. So the length of a straight line in the (x^1, x^2) plane is given by Equation 3b.

If the points P and Q are restricted to be very close together then their coordinates differ by very small amounts:

$$x_Q^1 = x_P^1 + \Delta x^1 \quad \text{and} \quad x_Q^2 = x_P^2 + \Delta x^2$$

neighbouring points in the plane

where Δx^1 and Δx^2 are extremely small quantities. The 'distance' between these points, which we shall call *neighbouring points*, is then

$$|PQ| = [(\Delta x^1)^2 + (\Delta x^2)^2]^{1/2}.$$

We shall label this extremely small distance Δl, so the formula for the distance between neighbouring points is

$$\Delta l = [(\Delta x^1)^2 + (\Delta x^2)^2]^{1/2} \tag{4}$$

where Δx^1 and Δx^2 are the differences in the Cartesian coordinates of these points. For the rest of this Unit, we shall apply the term 'distance' only to neighbouring points, i.e. points whose separation is arbitrarily small. Further, we shall define Equation 4, which relates the distance Δl of any two neighbouring points to their Cartesian coordinate differences, as *the metric of the plane in Cartesian coordinates*. The reason for this specialization of Equation 3b to neighbouring points will become apparent in Section 4.4. Because of the relationship between the 'distance' between points and the 'length' of the infinitesimal straight line connecting them, the length also tells us the 'length' of the infinitesimal straight line

At a later stage we shall be able to give a meaning to the word 'distance' as applied to points with large coordinate separations.

This definition of 'metric' is not the standard definition given in other text-books. To enable you to refer easily to other texts, if you so desire, we shall correlate this definition with the more standard one in Section 7.

connecting neighbouring points. In Section 4.2 we show that once we know the metric of the plane, we can calculate the length of *any* curve in the plane.

4.2 The length of a curve in the plane

Having established the formula for the metric of the plane in Cartesian coordinates, we now derive from it an expression for the length of any curve in the plane that is described by given Cartesian coordinate functions $x^1(s)$ and $x^2(s)$, where s is a parameter.

Figure 8(a) shows a curve $\mathscr{C}$, drawn in the (x^1, x^2) plane between the points P and Q. A small segment C, of the curve is shown enlarged, as Figure 8(b). For any small segment such as C, the path of the curve segment is approximately that of the straight line, L, joining the end-points of the segment. We can then say that the length of the small curve segment C, will also be approximately that of the straight line L. Using Equation 4, this means that the length, Δl_{C}, of the small curve segment C is given approximately by the formula

$$\Delta l_{\mathrm{C}} \approx \Delta l = [(\Delta x^1)^2 + (\Delta x^2)^2]^{1/2}. \tag{5}$$

This approximation improves as the size of C is made smaller. So our metric, Equation 4, shows how to calculate approximately the length of a small segment of a curve in the plane. To go from small segments to complete curves, we make use of the parametric definition of curves introduced in Section 3.

If we say that our curve $\mathscr{C}$ is defined in terms of a parameter s, it means that we have two coordinate functions, $x^1(s)$ and $x^2(s)$, such that if we pick any particular value s_{A} of the parameter s and put it into the coordinate functions, the point

$$\mathrm{A} \;=\; (x^1(s_{\mathrm{A}}), x^2(s_{\mathrm{A}})) \tag{6a}$$

is a point on the curve. In particular, two values s_{P} and s_{Q} can pick out the end-points of the curve of Figure 8(a)

$$\mathrm{P} \;=\; (x^1(s_{\mathrm{P}}), x^2(s_{\mathrm{P}})) \quad \text{and} \quad \mathrm{Q} \;=\; (x^1(s_{\mathrm{Q}}), x^2(s_{\mathrm{Q}})). \tag{6b and c}$$

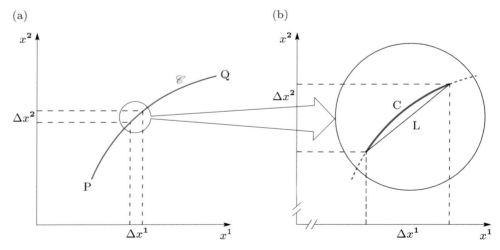

(a)   (b)

Figure 8 (a) A curve $\mathscr{C}$, drawn in the (x^1, x^2) plane. (b) A small segment, C of the curve $\mathscr{C}$.

The changes Δx^1 and Δx^2 in the coordinates shown in Figure 8 can be related to the change Δs in the parameter s along the segment C of the curve $\mathscr{C}$. For example, suppose that for the segment C the x^1-coordinate function varies with s, as shown in Figure 9. The increments Δs and Δx^1 are shown in black. But for small changes Δs, we can approximate Δx^1 as

$$\Delta x^1 \approx \left.\frac{\mathrm{d}x^1}{\mathrm{d}s}\right|_{s=s_A} \cdot \Delta s \tag{7a}$$

where the derivative $\dfrac{\mathrm{d}x^1}{\mathrm{d}s}$ is evaluated at some value s_A, in the interval Δs. (This is the tangent approximation to the $x^1(s)$ curve at the point A.) The right-hand side of Equation 7a is shown in blue in Figure 9; you can see that the interval marked $\left.\dfrac{\mathrm{d}x^1}{\mathrm{d}s}\right|_{s=s_A} \cdot \Delta s$ is approximately equal to that marked Δx^1.

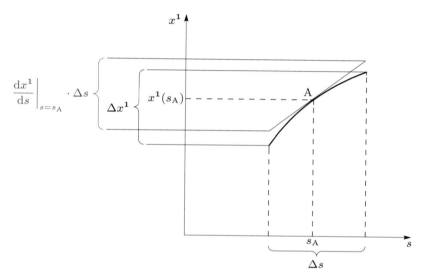

Figure 9 Showing a possible dependence of x^1 upon s near $s = s_A$; the approximation of Δx^1 by the product $\left.\dfrac{\mathrm{d}x^1}{\mathrm{d}s}\right|_{s=s_A} \cdot \Delta s$.

There is a corresponding expression relating the change Δx^2, in x^2 to the change Δs, in s:

$$\Delta x^2 \approx \left.\frac{\mathrm{d}x^2}{\mathrm{d}s}\right|_{s=s_A} \cdot \Delta s \tag{7b}$$

We put Equations 7a and 7b into Equation 5 to get

$$\begin{aligned}
\Delta l_C &\approx \left[\left(\left.\frac{\mathrm{d}x^1}{\mathrm{d}s}\right|_{s=s_A} \cdot \Delta s\right)^2 + \left(\left.\frac{\mathrm{d}x^2}{\mathrm{d}s}\right|_{s=s_A} \cdot \Delta s\right)^2\right]^{1/2} \\
&= \left[\left\{\left(\left.\frac{\mathrm{d}x^1}{\mathrm{d}s}\right|_{s=s_A}\right)^2 + \left(\left.\frac{\mathrm{d}x^2}{\mathrm{d}s}\right|_{s=s_A}\right)^2\right\}(\Delta s)^2\right]^{1/2} \\
&= \left[\left(\left.\frac{\mathrm{d}x^1}{\mathrm{d}s}\right|_{s=s_A}\right)^2 + \left(\left.\frac{\mathrm{d}x^2}{\mathrm{d}s}\right|_{s=s_A}\right)^2\right]^{1/2} \cdot \Delta s.
\end{aligned} \tag{8a}$$

This equation relates the length Δl_C of the small curve segment C to the change Δs in the parameter s along the curve segment.

Expressions similar in form to Equation 8a will appear frequently in this Unit, so we now introduce a special notation to make Equation 8a look neater. Although it is usual in mathematical physics to reserve the

S357 dot notation

notation $\dot{x}$ for differentiation with respect to time, i.e. $\dot{x} \equiv dx/dt$, we shall for the rest of Unit 10 & 11 use it to mean differentiation with respect to the parameter s, i.e. $\dot{x} \equiv dx/ds$. Equation 8a then becomes

$$\Delta l_{\mathrm{C}} \equiv [(\dot{x}^{1}(s_{\mathrm{A}}))^{2} + (\dot{x}^{2}(s_{\mathrm{A}}))^{2}]^{1/2}\Delta s. \tag{8b}$$

We make the further simplification that, unless we especially need it, we shall leave out the symbol s_{A}, that identifies the point at which the derivatives are evaluated. Equation 8b then takes its final simplified form

$$\Delta l_{\mathrm{C}} \approx [(\dot{x}^{1})^{2} + (\dot{x}^{2})^{2}]^{1/2}\Delta s \tag{8c}$$

which is a great improvement in notation over Equation 8a.

Equations 8 and 5 are two ways of saying the same thing. They both tell us the approximate length of the small segment C of a curve $\mathscr{C}$. We use Equation 5 if we know the differences in the coordinates of the two ends of the segment; we use Equations 8b and 8c if we know how much the parameter s changes in moving from one end of the segment to the other.

Objective 3

SAQ 5 Let a curve $\mathscr{C}$ be defined by the two coordinate functions

$$x^{1}(s) = 3s^{2}; \quad x^{2}(s) = 4s^{2}.$$

(a) Use Equation 8b to get an approximation to the length of $\mathscr{C}$ between the points labelled by $s = 1.00$ and $s = 1.50$ (let $s_{\mathrm{A}} = 1.00$).

(b) Repeat the above calculation with the end-points labelled by $s = 1.00$ and $s = 1.10$ (let $s_{\mathrm{A}} = 1.00$).

We now use Equation 8c to obtain the expression that allows us to calculate exactly the length of any smooth curve in the plane. For the curve $\mathscr{C}$, shown in Figure 10(a), we simply divide it into N small segments, as shown in Figure 10(b). Equation 8c is applied to each small segment and we add the results to get an approximate value for the length $\mathscr{L}_{\mathscr{C}}(\mathrm{P}, \mathrm{Q})$ of the curve $\mathscr{C}$ between the points P and Q.

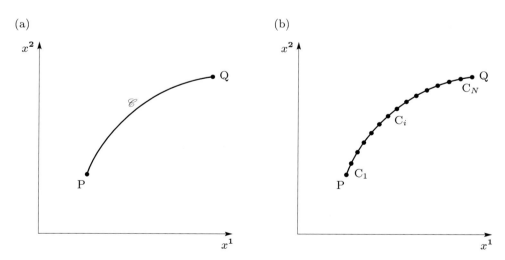

Figure 10 The division of a curve $\mathscr{C}$, into N pieces.

$$\mathcal{L}_{\mathscr{C}}(\mathrm{P},\mathrm{Q}) = \Delta l_{\mathrm{C}_1} + \Delta l_{\mathrm{C}_2} + \cdots + \Delta l_{\mathrm{C}_i} + \cdots + \Delta l_{\mathrm{C}_N}$$
$$\approx [(\dot{x}^1(s_1))^2 + (\dot{x}^2(s_1))^2]^{1/2}\Delta s_1 + \cdots + [(\dot{x}^1(s_i))^2 + (\dot{x}^2(s_i))^2]^{1/2}\Delta s_i$$
$$+ \cdots + [(\dot{x}^1(s_N))^2 + (\dot{x}^2(s_N))^2]^{1/2}\Delta s_N. \tag{9}$$

The symbols s_1, s_i and s_N in the expressions $\dot{x}^1(s_1)$, $\dot{x}^1(s_i)$ or $\dot{x}^1(s_N)$ mean that the derivatives are evaluated at points in the first, ith or Nth segments of the curve. The approximation gets better as we take a larger number N, of smaller segments.

The limiting value of the sum on the right-hand side of Equation 9 as N goes to infinity and Δs_i goes to zero is just the integral of

$$L(s) = [(\dot{x}^1(s))^2 + (\dot{x}^2(s))^2]^{1/2} \tag{10}$$

length of curve $\mathscr{C}$ between P and Q

between the values s_P and s_Q. That is, the length $\mathcal{L}_{\mathscr{C}}(\mathrm{P},\mathrm{Q})$ of the curve $\mathscr{C}$ between the points P and Q is given by

$$\mathcal{L}_{\mathscr{C}}(\mathrm{P},\mathrm{Q}) = \int_{s_\mathrm{P}}^{s_\mathrm{Q}} [(\dot{x}^1(s))^2 + (\dot{x}^2(s))^2]^{1/2}\,\mathrm{d}s. \tag{11}$$

As long as we know the coordinate functions $x^1(s)$ and $x^2(s)$ that define the curve $\mathscr{C}$, we can take their derivatives with respect to s to get $\dot{x}^1$ and $\dot{x}^2$; then putting these into Equation 11 gives the length of the curve.

Using Equation 11 to calculate the length of a specific curve will help to illustrate the ideas involved. In Section 3 the unit circle was written in terms of a parameter (in that case ϕ, but we replace ϕ by s)

$$x^1(s) = \cos s$$
$$x^2(s) = \sin s.$$

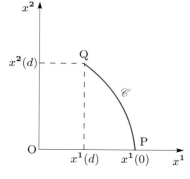

Suppose we wish to evaluate the length of this curve, as shown in Figure 11, between the points P and Q associated with the values $s = 0$ and $s = d$ of the parameter s. First, the derivatives of the coordinate functions x^1 and x^2 must be worked out:

$$\dot{x}^1(s) = -\sin s$$
$$\dot{x}^2(s) = \cos s.$$

Figure 11 A segment of the circle of unit radius.

Then the integrand of Equation 11 takes the form

$$[(\dot{x}^1(s))^2 + (\dot{x}^2(s))^2]^{1/2} = [(-\sin s)^2 + (\cos s)^2]^{1/2}$$
$$= [\sin^2 s + \cos^2 s]^{1/2} = 1$$

so that the length of the curve, $\mathscr{C}$, is

$$\mathcal{L}_{\mathscr{C}}(\mathrm{P},\mathrm{Q}) = \int_0^d 1 \cdot \mathrm{d}s = d.$$

Objective 4

SAQ 6 (a) Using the same coordinate functions as in SAQ 5
$$x^1(s) = 3s^2; \quad x^2(s) = 4s^2$$
determine the exact formula for the length of this curve between the points with values s_P and s_Q of the parameter s.

(b) By what percentage were the approximate lengths, calculated in SAQ 5, actually in error?

Finding the length of any given curve is obviously an important step towards finding the curve of minimum length. Hence the importance of the metric to the completion of the first major job outlined on p. 15. But the metric is even more central to our concerns than that. The second major job outlined on p. 15 involves explaining the difference between the words 'flat' and 'curved' as applied to spacetime. It turns out that this difference can be explained by geometric properties. We saw in Unit 1 that once the distance function |PQ| of three-dimensional space is known, all the geometric properties can be derived. We assert here that once the *metric* of *any* space is known, i.e. a distance function for neighbouring points in the space has been established, then all the geometric properties of that space can be derived. Thus, we must find the expression for Δl appropriate to the space, or, as we say, 'determine the metric'. The distinction between 'flat' and 'curved' can be found from the metric.

The ideas sketched out in the preceding paragraph are central to general relativity and will be developed in much more detail in later sections.

Objective 4

SAQ 7   Write down the generalization of Equation 4 to three-dimensional Euclidean space and hence write an integral expression for $\mathscr{L}_{\mathscr{C}}(P, Q)$ between points P and Q in three-dimensional Euclidean space.

4.3 Summary of Section 4.2

1 The basic formula from which we derive all calculations of length in the plane is Equation 4:

$$\Delta l = [(\Delta x^1)^2 + (\Delta x^2)^2]^{1/2}. \tag{4}$$

It is called 'the metric of the plane written in Cartesian coordinates' and it relates the distance Δl, between neighbouring points in the plane to the infinitesimal differences, Δx^1 and Δx^2, between their coordinate values. It also relates the length Δl, of a very small section of a straight line in the plane to the differences, Δx^1 and Δx^2, in the Cartesian coordinates of the end-points of the straight-line section.

2 For any smooth curve $\mathscr{C}$, a very small segment C, will have a length Δl_C, that is approximately the same as the length of the straight line drawn between its end-points. Thus

$$\Delta l_C \approx \Delta l = [(\Delta x^1)^2 + (\Delta x^2)^2]^{1/2}. \tag{5}$$

3 If the curve $\mathscr{C}$ is described by the coordinate functions $x^1(s)$ and $x^2(s)$ of a parameter s and if s varies by the small amount Δs over the small segment C of $\mathscr{C}$, then the length Δl_C of segment C can be written as

$$\Delta l_C \approx [(\dot{x}^1)^2 + (\dot{x}^2)^2]^{1/2}\, \Delta s \tag{8c}$$

where

$$\dot{x}^1 \equiv \frac{\mathrm{d}x^1}{\mathrm{d}s} \quad \text{and} \quad \dot{x}^2 \equiv \frac{\mathrm{d}x^2}{\mathrm{d}s}$$

and the derivatives are evaluated at some point, s_A, in the interval Δs. Both Equations 8c and 5 get better as the segment C, of $\mathscr{C}$ is made smaller.

4 For any smooth curve $\mathscr{C}$ determined by the coordinate functions $x^1(s)$ and $x^2(s)$ between the points P and Q, given by

$$\mathrm{P} = (x^1(s_{\mathrm{P}}), x^2(s_{\mathrm{P}})) \quad \text{and} \quad \mathrm{Q} = (x^1(s_{\mathrm{Q}}), x^2(s_{\mathrm{Q}}))$$

where s_{P} and s_{Q} are specific values of the parameter s, the length $\mathscr{L}_{\mathscr{C}}(\mathrm{P}, \mathrm{Q})$ of the curve $\mathscr{C}$ between the points P and Q is given by the integral of the function

$$L(s) = [(\dot{x}^1(s))^2 + (\dot{x}^2(s))^2]^{1/2} \tag{10}$$

between s_{P} and s_{Q}. That is

$$\mathscr{L}_{\mathscr{C}}(\mathrm{P}, \mathrm{Q}) = \int_{s_{\mathrm{P}}}^{s_{\mathrm{Q}}} [(\dot{x}^1(s))^2 + (\dot{x}^2(s))^2]^{1/2} \mathrm{d}s. \tag{11}$$

4.4 The metric of the plane in plane polar coordinates

In Section 4.2 we quoted the metric of the plane in Cartesian coordinates and we showed how it allows us to calculate the length of any curve in the plane. We pointed out in Unit 1 that once you can compute lengths in three-dimensional space, you can establish all the geometric properties of this space; angles were defined in terms of lengths, for example. This applies to the plane of ordinary two-dimensional Euclidean geometry; shortly we shall show how certain results of Euclidean plane geometry can be derived from the formula for calculating the length of a curve, i.e. from the metric. Can we then work backwards and associate a *unique* metric with a set of geometric properties for some space?

The answer is *no* — even in a Euclidean space we can have different coordinate systems which each require a different expression for the distance between points. In terms of the polar coordinates, for example, the distance relation no longer looks like Equation 4. In other words, for a given space, *the distance relation (metric) depends upon the coordinate system*. In describing the effects of gravitation, we shall make much use of metrics involving polar coordinates, and *plane polar coordinates* are the subject of the rest of this section.

plane polar coordinate system

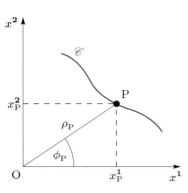

Figure 12 The Cartesian coordinate description and the plane polar coordinate description of the curve $\mathscr{C}$.

Figure 12 shows a curve $\mathscr{C}$, in the plane, and a particular point P on it. In Section 4.2 the point P would have been described in terms of its two Cartesian coordinates, x_{P}^1 and x_{P}^2. But P is also specified by the length of the radius ρ_{P}, to the point P from the origin and the angle ϕ_{P}, that the radius to P makes with the positive x^1-axis. To each set of values $(\rho_{\mathrm{P}}, \phi_{\mathrm{P}})$ there corresponds a unique point P, where ρ can vary from zero to plus infinity and ϕ can vary from zero to 2π radians. (The origin is a special point because it corresponds to $(0, \phi)$ for any value of ϕ.) So any curve in the plane can be as easily described by the plane polar coordinates (ρ, ϕ) of its points as by the Cartesian coordinates (x^1, x^2) of the same points.

In Section 3, we described how the points of a curve can be labelled by an arbitrary parameter, s. The Cartesian coordinates of any point P, on the curve are then given by the values, $x^1(s_{\mathrm{P}})$ and $x^2(s_{\mathrm{P}})$, of the two coordinate functions, $x^1(s)$ and $x^2(s)$. In the same way, we can use a parameter s, to describe a curve and obtain the plane polar coordinates, ρ_{P} and ϕ_{P}, of any point P on the curve as the values, $\rho(s_{\mathrm{P}})$ and $\phi(s_{\mathrm{P}})$, of the two functions $\rho(s)$ and $\phi(s)$ associated with the curve. So any curve in the plane can be described by plane polar coordinate functions, $\rho(s)$ and $\phi(s)$, just as it can be described by the Cartesian coordinate functions $x^1(s)$ and $x^2(s)$. For example, the circle of unit radius drawn in

Figure 13(a) can be described by the polar coordinate functions

$$\rho(s) = 1; \quad 0 \leqslant s < 2\pi$$
$$\phi(s) = s; \quad 0 \leqslant s < 2\pi$$

while the blue straight line of Figure 13(b) can be specified by the coordinate functions

$$\rho(s) = \frac{1}{\cos s}; \quad -\frac{\pi}{2} < s < \frac{\pi}{2}$$
$$\phi(s) = s; \quad -\frac{\pi}{2} < s < \frac{\pi}{2}.$$

Objective 4

SAQ 8   What point on the blue straight line of Figure 13(b) is labelled by the value $s = 0$?

(a)   (b)

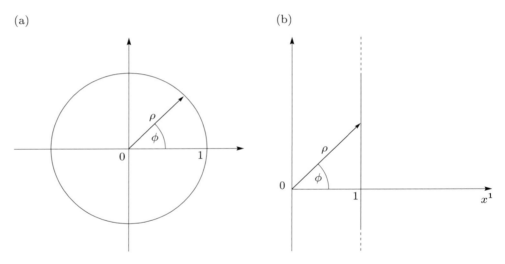

Figure 13   Plane polar coordinate description of curves in the plane: (a) the circle of unit radius, (b) the straight line perpendicular to the x^1-axis through the point $(\rho = 1, \phi = 0)$.

Having introduced plane polar coordinates as a way of describing points and curves in the plane, we write the four major concepts of Section 4.2 in terms of these coordinates. These four concepts are:

I Δl, the metric of the plane;

II Δl_{C}, the approximate length of a small curve segment, as a function of the differences of the coordinates of the end-points;

III Δl_{C}, the approximate length of a small curve segment, as a function of the difference Δs, of the parameter values of the end-points of the segment;

IV $\mathscr{L}_{\mathscr{C}}(\mathrm{P}, \mathrm{Q})$, the length of the curve $\mathscr{C}$ between the points P and Q.

We shall organize the calculation as a series of six steps so as to break it down into manageable pieces and set up a model for Section 6.

The plan is to take the third of the four concepts listed above and use it as a bridge to move from Cartesian coordinates to plane polar coordinates. From the plane polar form of Δl_{C}, we shall reconstruct the other three expressions in plane polar form.

We therefore begin with Equation 8c

$$\Delta l_C \approx [(\dot{x}^1)^2 + (\dot{x}^2)^2]^{1/2}\Delta s \tag{12}$$

for the length of a curve segment. Any curve can be described by its Cartesian coordinate functions, $x^1(s)$ and $x^2(s)$, or its plane polar coordinate functions, $\rho(s)$ and $\phi(s)$. As Figure 14 makes clear, there is a relationship between these two sets of coordinate functions:

$$x^1(s) = \rho(s)\cos\phi(s) \tag{13a}$$
$$x^2(s) = \rho(s)\sin\phi(s). \tag{13b}$$

1 As the first step, we use Equations 13a and 13b to relate the derivatives $\dot{x}^1$ and $\dot{x}^2$ that appear in Equation 12 to the derivatives of $\rho(s)$ and $\phi(s)$. We differentiate (13a) and (13b) to get

$$\dot{x}^1(s) = \dot{\rho}(s)\cos\phi(s) - \rho(s)\sin\phi(s)\,\dot{\phi}(s)$$
$$\dot{x}^2(s) = \dot{\rho}(s)\sin\phi(s) + \rho(s)\cos\phi(s)\,\dot{\phi}(s)$$

where $\dot{\rho} \equiv \mathrm{d}\rho/\mathrm{d}s$ and $\dot{\phi} \equiv \mathrm{d}\phi/\mathrm{d}s$.

2 Step two involves squaring the above two equations. We leave the s-dependence of ρ and ϕ as understood in order to make the equations neater. We obtain

$$(\dot{x}^1)^2 = (\dot{\rho})^2\cos^2\phi - 2\dot{\rho}\rho\dot{\phi}\cos\phi\sin\phi + \rho^2\sin^2\phi\,(\dot{\phi})^2$$
$$(\dot{x}^2)^2 = (\dot{\rho})^2\sin^2\phi + 2\dot{\rho}\rho\dot{\phi}\cos\phi\sin\phi + \rho^2\cos^2\phi\,(\dot{\phi})^2.$$

3 In the third step we add the above equations together, using the fact that $\sin^2 A + \cos^2 A = 1$ for any A: this gives

$$(\dot{x}^1)^2 + (\dot{x}^2)^2 = (\dot{\rho})^2 + \rho^2(\dot{\phi})^2. \tag{14}$$

Replacing the expression within the square root in Equation 12 with the right-hand side of Equation 14 gives

$$\Delta l_C \approx [(\dot{x}^1)^2 + (\dot{x}^2)^2]^{1/2}\Delta s = [(\dot{\rho})^2 + \rho^2(\dot{\phi})^2]^{1/2}\,\Delta s \tag{15}$$

where the quantities ρ, $\dot{\rho}$, $\dot{\phi}$ are evaluated at some point on the small curve segment C. Equation 15 does the same job for us as Equation 12, but for a curve specified by the functions $\rho(s)$ and $\phi(s)$, rather than $x^1(s)$ and $x^2(s)$.

Having obtained one of the four quantities (Δl_C) in plane polar coordinate form, we use it to find the plane polar representation of the other three.

4 The fourth step of the calculation is to convert Δl_C from the parametric form (Equation 15) into the coordinate difference form. To do this, we re-write the equations

$$\Delta\rho \approx \dot{\rho}\,\Delta s \quad\text{and}\quad \Delta\phi \approx \dot{\phi}\,\Delta s \tag{16a and b}$$

in the form

$$\dot{\rho} \approx \frac{\Delta\rho}{\Delta s} \quad\text{and}\quad \dot{\phi} \approx \frac{\Delta\phi}{\Delta s} \tag{17a and b}$$

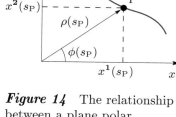

Figure 14 The relationship between a plane polar coordinate description and the Cartesian coordinate description of a point P, on a curve in the plane.

and substitute the right-hand sides of (17a) and (17b) for $\dot{\rho}$ and $\dot{\phi}$ in Equation 15 to get:

$$\Delta l_{\mathrm{C}} \approx \left[\left(\frac{\Delta\rho}{\Delta s}\right)^2 + \rho^2\left(\frac{\Delta\phi}{\Delta s}\right)^2\right]^{1/2}\Delta s$$

$$= \left[((\Delta\rho)^2 + \rho^2(\Delta\phi)^2)\frac{1}{(\Delta s)^2}\right]^{1/2}\Delta s$$

$$= [(\Delta\rho)^2 + \rho^2(\Delta\phi)^2]^{1/2}. \tag{18}$$

Equation 18 relates the length Δl_{C} of a small curve segment C to the differences $\Delta\rho$ and $\Delta\phi$ of the plane polar coordinates of its end-points *and* to the value of the ρ-coordinate of some point on the segment. This makes the plane polar form of Δl_{C} quite different from the Cartesian form, where neither x^1 nor x^2 itself appears within the square root, only Δx^1 and Δx^2. We shall take up this difference again after completing step five.

5 Step five, which is to obtain the plane polar form of the metric from Equation 18, is very simple. From Equations 4 and 5 we see that we get the form of the metric from the approximate formula for Δl_{C} by simply turning Δl_{C} into Δl and turning the approximate equality, $\approx$, into an equality $=$. Therefore the *metric of the plane in plane polar coordinates* is

$$\Delta l = [(\Delta\rho)^2 + \rho^2(\Delta\phi)^2]^{1/2}. \tag{19}$$

metric of the plane in plane polar coordinates

This equation defines the distance between two neighbouring points in terms of the differences, $\Delta\rho$ and $\Delta\phi$, of their coordinates and the ρ-coordinate of one of them.

With this plane polar form we can easily see why, in general, we must say that the metric defines the distance between two points whose coordinates differ by only *extremely small amounts*. This is forced on us because Equation 19 does not say which of the two points should be used to give the value of ρ in the second term within the square root. The two values of ρ differ by $\Delta\rho$, which means that we do not know which of the two values of Δl, given by Equation 19, to choose:

$$\Delta l = [(\Delta\rho)^2 + \rho^2(\Delta\phi)^2]^{1/2}$$

or

$$\Delta l = [(\Delta\rho)^2 + (\rho + \Delta\rho)^2(\Delta\phi)^2)]^{1/2}$$

$$= [(\Delta\rho)^2 + \rho^2(\Delta\phi)^2 + 2\rho\Delta\rho(\Delta\phi)^2 + (\Delta\rho)^2(\Delta\phi)^2]^{1/2}.$$

Only when $\Delta\rho$ and $\Delta\phi$ are vanishingly small do the third and fourth terms of the second expression become so much smaller than the first two that they may be ignored and the two expressions become the same. This problem does not arise in the Cartesian form of the metric, where only coordinate differences appear. So the Cartesian metric can be used to define distances on any scale but the plane polar form of the metric cannot. Since the metrics of general relativity resemble the plane polar form in this respect, we shall have to interpret them as we have interpreted Equation 19.

6 Finally, step six is to produce the plane polar form for the expression $\mathscr{L}_{\mathscr{C}}(\mathrm{P},\mathrm{Q})$. Equation 15 can be used to obtain an exact expression for the length of any curve in the plane in the same way that Equation 11 was developed from Equation 8c. For any curve $\mathscr{C}$ described by the coordinate functions $\rho(s)$ and $\phi(s)$ between the points P and Q given by

$$\mathrm{P} = (\rho(s_{\mathrm{P}}), \phi(s_{\mathrm{P}})) \quad \text{and} \quad \mathrm{Q} = (\rho(s_{\mathrm{Q}}), \phi(s_{\mathrm{Q}}))$$

we can break the curve into a large number of small segments. Equation 15 applied to each one gives its approximate length. Adding the approximate lengths of each segment gives an approximate length for the whole curve. Taking a large number of smaller segments leads to the integral of the function

$$L(s) = [(\dot{\rho}(s))^2 + \rho^2(s)(\dot{\phi}(s))^2]^{1/2} \tag{20}$$

so that

$$\mathscr{L}_{\mathscr{C}}(P, Q) = \int_{s_P}^{s_Q} [(\dot{\rho}(s))^2 + \rho^2(s)(\dot{\phi}(s))^2]^{1/2} \, ds. \tag{21}$$

Equation 20 is the counterpart of Equation 10 in plane polar coordinates and Equation 21 is the counterpart of Equation 11.

Objective 4

SAQ 9   Use the coordinate functions of the circle of unit radius, given on page 26, and Equation 21 to calculate the length of the circle from the point given by the value $s = 0$ to the point given by the value $s = d$.

If you compare the answer to SAQ 9 with the calculation on p. 23 you will find that the same problem has been done in two different ways and the same result obtained. The plane polar form of the metric does not represent a different set of geometric properties from those of the Cartesian form of the metric — applied to the same curve, they give the same length; their different appearances are deceptive. This is important because shortly we shall ask what is the simplest reliable way to determine when two metrics represent the same geometric properties.

4.5   Summary of Section 4.4

In Section 4.4 we have shown that the metric and the expressions for the length of a curve take forms that look quite different from those of Section 4.2 when they are expressed in plane polar coordinates. In particular these expressions now depend on the values of one of the coordinates ρ, as well as the coordinate differences, $\Delta\rho$ and $\Delta\phi$. Table 2 shows the forms that these expressions take in the two coordinate systems. Clearly, two metrics that are quite different in form may describe exactly the same geometric properties but in terms of different coordinates. So while it is true that once a metric has been given for a space it determines all the geometric properties of that space, different forms of metric *can* result in the same geometric properties.

TABLE 2   The metric and the length of a curve in the plane.

Concept	Representation in Cartesian coordinates	Representation in plane polar coordinates
1 Coordinate system of the plane		
2 Coordinate functions of a curve in the plane	$x^1(s), x^2(s)$	$\rho(s), \phi(s)$
3 Points on a curve in the plane	$\mathrm{P} \equiv (x^1(s_\mathrm{P}), x^2(s_\mathrm{P}))$	$\mathrm{P} \equiv (\rho(s_\mathrm{P}), \phi(s_\mathrm{P}))$
4 Metric Δl, of the plane	$\Delta l = [(\Delta x^1)^2 + (\Delta x^2)^2]^{1/2}$	$\Delta l = [(\Delta\rho)^2 + \rho^2(\Delta\phi)^2]^{1/2}$
5 Length of small curve segment, Δl_C, in terms of (i) coordinate differences (ii) parameter difference	$\Delta l_\mathrm{C} \approx [(\Delta x^1)^2 + (\Delta x^2)^2]^{1/2}$ $\Delta l_\mathrm{C} \approx [(\dot{x}^1)^2 + (\dot{x}^2)^2]^{1/2} \Delta s$	$\Delta l_\mathrm{C} \approx [(\Delta\rho)^2 + \rho^2(\Delta\phi)^2]^{1/2}$ $\Delta l_\mathrm{C} \approx [(\dot{\rho})^2 + \rho^2(\dot{\phi})^2]^{1/2} \Delta s$
6 Length, $\mathscr{L}_\mathscr{C}(\mathrm{P, Q})$, of curve, $\mathscr{C}$, between points P and Q in the plane	$\mathscr{L}_\mathscr{C}(\mathrm{P, Q}) =$ $\displaystyle\int_{s_\mathrm{P}}^{s_\mathrm{Q}} [(\dot{x}^1)^2 + (\dot{x}^2)^2]^{1/2} \, \mathrm{d}s$	$\mathscr{L}_\mathscr{C}(\mathrm{P, Q}) = \displaystyle\int_{s_\mathrm{P}}^{s_\mathrm{Q}} [(\dot{\rho})^2 + \rho^2(\dot{\phi})^2]^{1/2} \, \mathrm{d}s$

5 The study of geometry on a two-dimensional curved surface

We wish to know what is meant by 'curved spacetime'. A principal objective of Unit 10 & 11 is to give an understanding, at a level truthful to Einstein's work but stopping short of a full-blown mathematical exposition, of what it means to say that spacetime, in the presence of matter, is curved.

So what is *curved* spacetime and how is it different from *flat* spacetime? To answer these questions we begin by asking: how does a curved *two*-dimensional space differ from a flat one? The simplest answer is that a curved two-dimensional space exhibits geometric properties that differ from those that hold in a flat two-dimensional space. But what geometric properties?

Here are two examples of what we mean by geometric properties for the two-dimensional plane:

1 for *any* triangle drawn in the plane the three interior angles sum to 180 degrees or π radians;

2 *any* circle in the plane has the ratio of its circumference to its diameter equal to π.

The fact that these two properties of geometric figures hold independently of the size of the figures says something about the space (i.e. the two-dimensional plane) in which they are drawn. We can investigate the properties of other two-dimensional spaces as follows: take simple geometric figures like the triangle and the circle and examine their properties when drawn on curved surfaces to see how they differ from the properties of triangles and circles drawn in the plane. The surface of a sphere is a suitable surface; the points in the surface of a sphere constitute a two-dimensional space since every point can be specified by just two numbers which might be the latitude and longitude, or alternatively, the polar angles θ and ϕ.

It is easier to formulate the distinction between flat and curved in two dimensions than in four. We can put the pictures and the mathematics side by side in two dimensions; we cannot draw pictures of curved four-dimensional spacetime. So two-dimensional curved surfaces provide the simplest meaningful analogy to four-dimensional spacetime. It is not a perfect analogy, as we shall see, but it contains certain key features in simple form.

We have already made claims and used vocabulary that need explaining and justifying. For example, we have talked about drawing triangles on a sphere. But how does one draw a triangle on a surface where the usual idea of 'straight line' has lost its meaning? That is what this section is primarily about — how to do geometry on two-dimensional curved surfaces.

Consider for example the surface of a sphere (Figure 15). To do the simplest of geometric constructions we need two concepts to play the parts of 'points' and 'straight lines' (which we shall simply call 'lines' for short — lines which are not necessarily straight will be called 'curves'). These two concepts (points and lines) allow us to form triangles and define circles of given radius. Now the concept of a point raises no difficulty — one can pick a point on a sphere as easily as pick a point on a

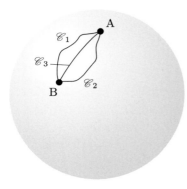

Figure 15 Examples of curves drawn on the surface of a sphere.

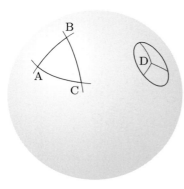

Figure 16 A triangle and a circle drawn on the surface of a sphere.

plane. But the concept of a line needs a bit more thought. One can draw a curve (or any number of curves) connecting two points on a sphere, for example the curves $\mathscr{C}_1$ and $\mathscr{C}_2$ connecting points A and B in Figure 15. But the idea of straightness, as implemented by a ruler or straight edge, cannot be used on a sphere. So we generalize the property that a straight line in the plane is the curve of shortest length between two points. Consider the sphere of Figure 15. We measure the lengths of all curves between A and B and pick the curve of minimum length to be what we call 'a line' on the sphere between points A and B. That is, the geodesic, introduced in Section 2 now becomes what we mean by a line on a curved surface. In this section we shall leave 'distance between points' and 'length of a curve' on a curved surface as intuitive concepts. You can imagine sticking pins into the sphere at points A and B and stretching an elastic band between them; the tension in the elastic will make it find the curve of minimum length $\mathscr{C}_3$, along the surface. The curve selected by the elastic band is, by our definition, a line between points A and B.

With this concept of line, we can now draw triangles on the sphere by connecting three points A, B and C with lines; we can also draw circles on the sphere by plotting out all the points that can be connected to the point D by lines of a fixed length, drawn with the aid of string (Figure 16).

Having defined circles and triangles in the surface of a sphere, we can compare their geometric properties with the properties of circles and triangles in a plane. Two simple relationships will demonstrate very quickly what is novel about the geometry of curved surfaces. Beginning with circles, we know that the ratio of the circumference to the diameter of any circle *in a plane* is a constant, π.

We shall write this as

$$C = \pi d = 2\pi r \quad \text{(PLANE)} \tag{22}$$

where C, d and r are circumference, diameter and radius respectively. Figure 17 shows two circles, labelled 1 and 2, drawn about the north pole N of a sphere. From this figure it can be seen that the circumference, C_1, of circle 1 is given by

$$C_1 = 2\pi k_1 = 2\pi R \sin\theta_1$$

but the radius, r_1, of the circle *as measured along the surface of the sphere* is given by

$$r_1 = R\theta_1.$$

This equation can be rewritten as

$$2\pi r_1 = 2\pi R\theta_1.$$

Then

$$\frac{C_1}{2\pi r_1} = \frac{2\pi R \sin\theta_1}{2\pi R \theta_1}$$

$$= \frac{\sin\theta_1}{\theta_1} < 1$$

so that

$$C_1 < 2\pi r_1 \quad \text{(SPHERE)}.$$

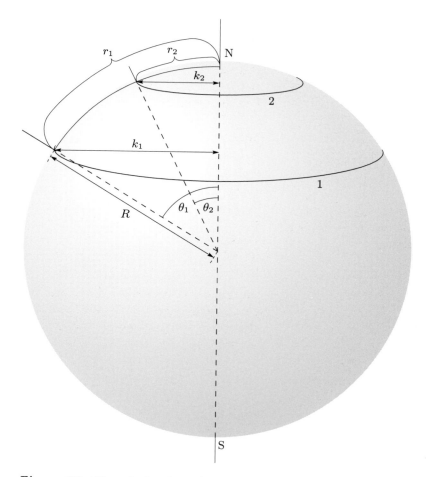

Figure 17 The relationship of circumference to radius of circles drawn on the surface of a sphere.

The traditional formula applying on the plane does NOT hold on the surface of a sphere. Even more novel is the result that the ratio C/r is not a constant for all circles on a given sphere. We see that the ratio

$$\frac{C}{r} = 2\pi \frac{\sin\theta}{\theta}$$

depends upon θ. However, since as $\theta \to 0$, the ratio $\sin\theta/\theta \to 1$ and hence $C/r \to 2\pi$. So as the radius r of a circle on a sphere becomes small, its geometric properties approach the properties of circles on a plane. But the similarity of all circles on a plane, expressed by the common constant value 2π of all ratios C/r, disappears on the sphere. As circles on the surface of a sphere get bigger they differ from one another in a way that circles on the plane do not.

This simple example gives a hint as to how we might detect whether the spacetime in which we live is flat or curved. Suppose we could make analogous geometric measurements in spacetime (don't worry about how at this stage) and suppose we found that ratios analogous to C/r seemed to vary with the size of the volume of spacetime over which they were measured. Then our experience with two-dimensional curved surfaces would suggest that the experiments show that spacetime is curved.

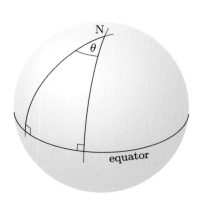

Figure 18 A triangle drawn on the surface of a sphere: the sum of the interior angles is greater than π radians.

Objective 5   **SAQ 10**   (a) What is the length of the radius (along the spherical surface) of the circle of maximum circumference on the sphere?

(b) What is C/r for this circle?

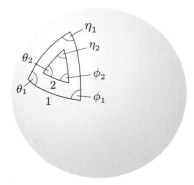

Figure 19   Two triangles drawn on the surface of a sphere.

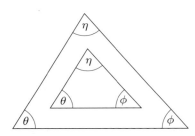

Figure 20   Similar triangles drawn in the plane.

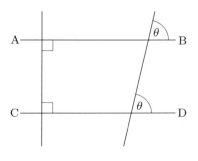

Figure 21   Illustration of two definitions of parallel lines.

The second geometric relationship that differentiates flat from curved two-dimensional surfaces is the property of plane triangles that the sum of the interior angles is 180° or π radians. Is this true of triangles drawn on a sphere? Figure 18 gives the answer. The curves of shortest length between two points in the same hemisphere of a sphere are segments of great circles. They can be formed (Section 2, Figure 2) by cutting the sphere with a plane which intersects the two points in question and the centre of the sphere. So the equator of Figure 18 is a great circle and so are the meridians of longitude, which are found by cutting the sphere with a plane that contains the north pole and the centre. Now consider the triangle in Figure 18 formed from a segment of the equator and the halves of two meridians connecting the equator to the north pole. The meridians both intersect the equator at right angles while the angle θ between the two meridians at the north pole can be anything from 0 to π. So the sum of the interior angles of this triangle is equal to $\pi + \theta$; it is always greater than π but becomes closer and closer to π the smaller the area enclosed by the triangle. This is true of any triangle drawn on a sphere, although it is less obvious to the eye. For the triangle 1 drawn in Figure 19, the sum of the interior angles

$$\theta_1 + \phi_1 + \eta_1 = k_1 > \pi$$

while, for the smaller triangle 2,

$$\theta_2 + \phi_2 + \eta_2 = k_2 > \pi$$

and

$$k_2 < k_1.$$

So just as was the case with circles on a sphere, triangles of different sizes are not similar in the way that the triangles drawn in Figure 20 are. The equality of each of the three pairs of angles, η, θ and ϕ, cannot be preserved for triangles on a sphere. So triangles of different size on a sphere must differ by more than a simple change of scale.

Our next feature of geometry on a curved surface concerns parallel lines. In the plane there are many ways of defining parallel lines; Figure 21 shows two of them. Two lines, AB and CD, are parallel if:

1 Any straight line perpendicular to one of them is perpendicular to the second;

2 The two angles marked θ made by any line intersecting them are equal.

Thirdly we have the definition that

3 Given one line, L, and a point P, not on it, a line through P is parallel to L if it does not intersect L no matter how far it is extended.

Suppose we try to implement this last definition on a sphere. We pick a line $\mathscr{C}_1$, and a point A, not on it (Figure 22a). But a line is a segment of a great circle defined by a plane, i.e. the plane PL_1 in Figure 22(b). Now we try to draw a line through A. But any such line must define a plane, PL_2, through the centre of the circle, as in Figure 22(c). The two planes meet at the centre, so the lines they define must intersect somewhere on the sphere. So there are *no* parallel lines on a sphere according to definition 3.

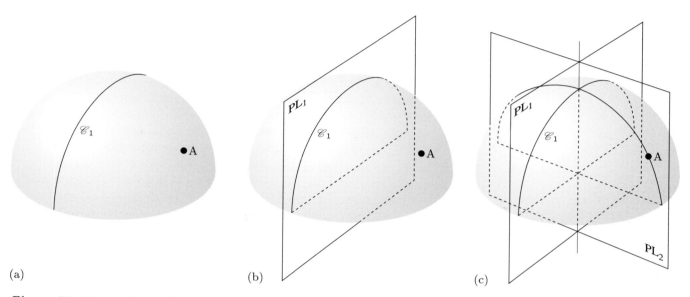

(a)   (b)   (c)

Figure 22   Illustration to demonstrate the impossibility of drawing parallel lines on the surface of a sphere.

Objective 5   **SAQ 11**   Try to implement definition 1 on a sphere. Are there any parallel lines under this definition?

There is another novel feature of that two-dimensional space which is the surface of a sphere. It is that if you continue to go in a straight line in this space, you return to your starting point. (This is definitely not a property of the plane.) We say it is a closed space. General relativity raises the possibility that our universe might indeed be closed. We address this possibility in Block 4.

In this section we have taken the surface of a sphere as an example of a two-dimensional space. Geometric figures have been drawn in this space by using definitions like those used in plane geometry (line, circle, radius, triangle). We find that the geometry is fundamentally different from Euclidean plane geometry. In particular, geometric properties are not invariant with respect to changes in size of the figure. As the figures become very small (compared to the radius R, of the sphere) they become Euclidean; that is, the ratio of circumference to radius of a circle approaches 2π, and the sum of the interior angles of a triangle approaches π radians. But the larger a geometric figure is, the more non–Euclidean its properties are.

We have deliberately kept the discussion intuitive. But there are two areas where we shall need to be more precise:

First, we have relied on an informal idea of what 'curved' means. From the discussion so far, you might guess that non-Euclidean properties of triangles would apply to figures drawn on the cylinder shown in Figure 23. But we shall find that the properties of figures (triangles and circles) on a

Figure 23   Triangles drawn on the surface of a cylinder.

cylinder are exactly the same as those of the same figures on a plane. In other words, it is one thing to 'look curved' and quite another to '*be curved' in the sense of having a geometry different from that of the plane.* We need a more mathematical distinction, because (i) for two-dimensional surfaces seen in three-dimensional space (the cylinder or the sphere) our visual impression of curvedness is misleading and, more importantly, (ii) in four-dimensional spacetime we have no visual impression of 'curvedness' at all. The mathematical definition of curvature is the subject of Section 12.

Second, our discussions of distance and length have been quite informal, allowing rubber bands to find the curves of minimum length along a curved surface between two points. Such informal methods don't work for four-dimensional spacetime. The methods that do work are analogous to more general methods for two-dimensional spaces. So, we first extend to the sphere the mathematical methods that we developed in the plane for calculating the lengths of curves. We then define 'lines' in the surface of a sphere as curves of minimum length, calculated using the metric appropriate to the surface of a sphere instead of using the pictorial definition of great circles (cutting the sphere with planes). The new method gives the familiar results on the surface of a sphere but will also extend to four-dimensional spacetime. Integrals along curves in four dimensions are really no more difficult than those in two dimensions (although they may look messier), but four-dimensional pictures are impossible. The mathematics can carry us where our pictorial intuition cannot.

5.1   Summary of Section 5

1 The geometric properties of a two-dimensional space are the properties of geometric figures drawn in that space.

2 Among the geometric properties of the plane, certain properties of geometric figures are independent of the size of the figure. These properties include the unique ratio of circumference to diameter of any circle in the plane and the fact that the sum of the interior angles of any triangle in the plane is π radians.

3 The concept of a geodesic between two points on a sphere allows the construction of geometric figures (triangles and circles) on a sphere.

4 The geometric properties of figures drawn on a sphere are *not* independent of their size. The properties change with size, approaching the properties of the figures in the plane in the limit of small size.

5 We describe this distinction between the properties of geometric figures on the sphere and on the plane, by saying that the plane is flat and the surface of the sphere is curved. A quantitative definition of 'flat' and 'curved' will be given in Section 12.

6 The metric of the surface of a sphere

6.1 Introduction

In Section 5, when we described the geometric properties of figures drawn on a sphere, we kept an intuitive concept of length. We now wish to find mathematical expressions representing the 'distance between neighbouring points' and the 'length of a curve' on the surface of the sphere, just as we did in Section 4 for the plane. The surface of the sphere is going to be our two-dimensional analogue of curved spacetime.

In Section 4.2 we argued that once we have an equation for the distance between neighbouring points in a plane (i.e. the metric), all the geometric properties of the plane follow from it. A simple calculation gives an example: in Section 5 we mentioned that for a circle of any radius centred at any point in the plane, the ratio C/r of the circumference and the radius is 2π. Here we shall show that this follows immediately from the formulae of Section 4.2.

Figure 24 shows a circle of radius R, centred at the point (a, b) in the plane. The parametric representation of this circle is given by the Cartesian coordinate functions

$$x^1(s) = a + R\cos s; \quad x^2(s) = b + R\sin s; \quad 0 \leqslant s < 2\pi.$$

For example, the point A in Figure 24 is associated with the value $s = 0$ since putting $s = 0$ into the two equations above gives

$$x^1(0) = a + R; \quad x^2(0) = b.$$

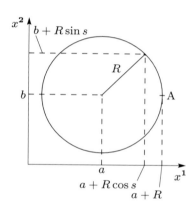

Figure 24 The Cartesian coordinate functions of the circle of radius R centred on the point (a, b) in the plane.

We use the formula for $\mathscr{L}_{\mathscr{C}}(\mathrm{P}, \mathrm{Q})$ of Equation 11 to calculate the length C, of this curve. The derivatives are

$$\dot{x}^1(s) = -R\sin s$$
$$\dot{x}^2(s) = R\cos s$$

so,

$$C = \int_{s=0}^{s=2\pi} [(\dot{x}^1)^2 + (\dot{x}^2)^2]^{1/2} \ \mathrm{d}s$$

$$= \int_{s=0}^{s=2\pi} R[\sin^2 s + \cos^2 s]^{1/2} \ \mathrm{d}s$$

$$= R \int_0^{2\pi} \ \mathrm{d}s = 2\pi R$$

and thus

$$\frac{C}{R} = 2\pi.$$

This is one example of the way that the geometric properties of a space follow from the form of the metric, since it was on the basis of the metric that we established the formula for $\mathscr{L}_{\mathscr{C}}(\mathrm{P}, \mathrm{Q})$ in Section 4.2.

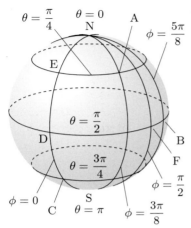

Figure 25   Spherical polar coordinate system.

The north and south poles are exceptional points in this coordinate system, as the origin was in the plane polar coordinate system. $N = (0, \phi)$ for any ϕ, and $S = (\pi, \phi)$ for any ϕ. The exceptional nature of these points will not affect our discussion.

The plan for this section is to take the same three steps in the case of the surface of the sphere that we have taken in the case of the plane. We thus:

1 Establish the metric of the surface of a sphere;

2 Establish a formula for the length of any curve drawn on the surface of the sphere between any two points;

3 Give an example of the fact that the geometric properties of the sphere can be derived from the metric. The properties we shall derive are those described in Section 5 concerning circles drawn on spheres.

6.2   A coordinate system for the surface of a sphere

As we showed in Section 4 in the case of the plane, the form of a metric of a surface depends on the coordinate system used to label points on the surface. The coordinate system that we use for the sphere is the spherical polar coordinate system introduced in Unit 1. We remind you of this system in Figure 25, which shows the relationship to the geographical system of latitude and longitude. The parallels of latitude are defined by cutting the sphere with planes perpendicular to the line joining the north and south poles, as is shown in Figure 26(a). The meridians of longitude are defined by cutting the sphere with planes that contain the line joining the north and south poles, as is shown in Figure 26(b). Referring again to Figure 25, although only a few parallels of latitude (lines of constant θ) and a few meridians of longitude (lines of constant ϕ) are shown, they are enough to illustrate that any point on the sphere can be labelled by two numbers, (θ, ϕ). For example,

$$A = \left(\frac{\pi}{4}, \frac{3\pi}{8}\right) \quad B = \left(\frac{\pi}{2}, \frac{5\pi}{8}\right) \quad C = \left(\frac{3\pi}{4}, 0\right).$$

The *surface* of the sphere is thus clearly *two*-dimensional.

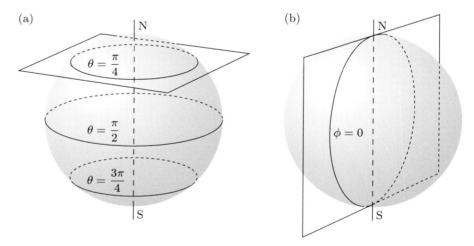

Figure 26   (a) The construction of parallels of latitude on the surface of a sphere by intersecting the sphere with a plane. (b) The construction of meridians of longitude on the surface of a sphere by intersecting the sphere with a plane.

In Figure 27 we remind you of the relationship between the full spherical polar coordinates for three-dimensional space and the Cartesian coordinates for three-dimensional space.

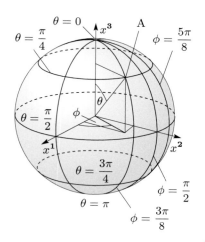

Figure 27 The relationship between the spherical polar coordinate system of the surface of a sphere and Cartesian coordinates in three-dimensional space.

6.3   The metric of the surface of a sphere in spherical polar coordinates

The Cartesian framework provides the starting point from which to work out the form of the metric of the surface of the sphere, in (θ, ϕ) coordinates. The essential details of this Cartesian framework are reproduced in Figure 28. From this figure we can work out how the Cartesian coordinates of any point on the sphere, such as the point A, are related to the (θ, ϕ) coordinates by the equations originally given in Section 3.3 of Unit 1:

$$x^1_A = R \sin \theta_A \cos \phi_A \tag{23a}$$
$$x^2_A = R \sin \theta_A \sin \phi_A \tag{23b}$$
$$x^3_A = R \cos \theta_A \tag{23c}$$

where R is the radius of the sphere, a constant.

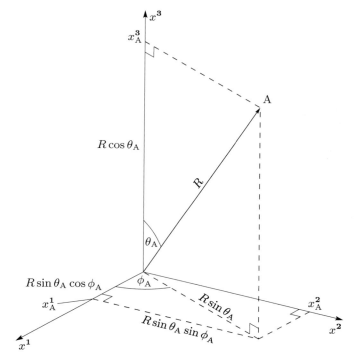

Figure 28 Expanded detail of Figure 27, showing the angles and lengths involved in the relationships expressed by Equations 23a–c.

The Cartesian coordinates of any point on a sphere of radius R, centred on the origin of coordinates, obey the equation

$$(x^1)^2 + (x^2)^2 + (x^3)^2 = R^2.$$

In SAQ 4 of Unit 1 you showed that Equations 23a–c satisfy this equation. Any curve drawn on the surface of a sphere will be a succession of points, each with its (θ, ϕ) coordinates. If we label each point on the curve by the value of some parameter s, as we did with points on a curve in the plane, then the coordinate functions $\theta(s)$ and $\phi(s)$ specify a curve on the sphere in the same way that $x^1(s)$ and $x^2(s)$ specify a curve in the plane.

Objective 6   **SAQ 12**   Identify on Figure 25 the curves given by the following coordinate functions:

(a) $\mathscr{C}_1$: $\theta(s) = \pi/2$
$\phi(s) = s$; for all s between 0 and $\pi/2$;

(b) $\mathscr{C}_2$: $\theta(s) = s$; for all s between 0 and $\pi/4$
$\phi(s) = 0$.

The (x^1, x^2, x^3) coordinates of any point on the sphere are related to the (θ, ϕ) coordinates of that point by Equations 23a–c, so we can write the three functions $x^1(s)$, $x^2(s)$ and $x^3(s)$ of a curve on the sphere as

$$x^1(s) = R \sin \theta(s) \cos \phi(s) \tag{24a}$$
$$x^2(s) = R \sin \theta(s) \sin \phi(s) \tag{24b}$$
$$x^3(s) = R \cos \theta(s). \tag{24c}$$

Objective 6   **SAQ 13**   What are the three Cartesian coordinate functions of s for the curve $\mathscr{C}_1$ of SAQ 12?

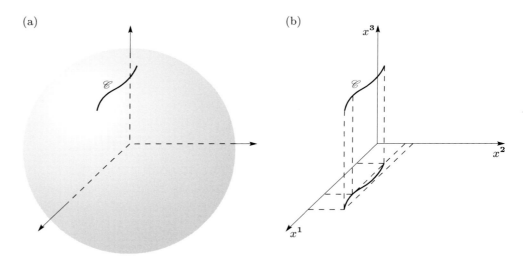

(a)   (b)

Figure 29   (a) A curve drawn on the surface of a sphere. (b) The curve of Figure 29(a) considered as a curve in three-dimensional space.

To find the metric of the surface of a sphere we first find an approximate formula for the length of a small segment of a curve drawn on the sphere. Such a curve, although drawn on the sphere, as shown in Figure 29(a), can be thought of as a curve in ordinary three-dimensional space, as in Figure 29(b). So we begin by looking for the length of a small segment of a curve in three-dimensional space, described in Cartesian coordinates. The formula is so similar to that for the length of a small curve segment in the plane and described in Cartesian coordinates, that we reproduce in Table 3 two-dimensional formulae from Table 2 and beside them we give their three-dimensional counterparts. The only difference in going to three dimensions is the third coordinate function in each expression.

TABLE 3   The metric and the length of a small curve segment in the plane and in three-dimensional space.

Concept	Two-dimensional version in Cartesian coordinates	Three-dimensional version in Cartesian coordinates
Metric	$\Delta l = [(\Delta x^1)^2 + (\Delta x^2)^2]^{1/2}$	$\Delta l = [(\Delta x^1)^2 + (\Delta x^2)^2 + (\Delta x^3)^2]^{1/2}$
Length of a small curve segment in terms of (i) coordinate differences	$\Delta l_C \approx [(\Delta x^1)^2 + (\Delta x^2)^2]^{1/2}$	$\Delta l_C \approx [(\Delta x^1)^2 + (\Delta x^2)^2 + (\Delta x^3)^2]^{1/2}$
(ii) parameter difference	$\Delta l_C \approx [(\dot{x}^1)^2 + (\dot{x}^2)^2]^{1/2}\Delta s$	$\Delta l_C \approx [(\dot{x}^1)^2 + (\dot{x}^2)^2 + (\dot{x}^3)^2]^{1/2}\Delta s$

Consider the expression in the bottom right-hand corner of Table 3:

$$\Delta l_C \approx [(\dot{x}^1)^2 + (\dot{x}^2)^2 + (\dot{x}^3)^2]^{1/2}\Delta s. \tag{25}$$

length of a small curve segment (of a curve) in three-dimensional space

It says how the *length*, Δl_C, *of a small curve segment* of a curve in three-dimensional space described by the three coordinate functions $x^1(s)$, $x^2(s)$ and $x^3(s)$ is related to the change, Δs, in the parameter s in moving from one end of the segment to the other.

Now for a curve in three-dimensional space that is also on a sphere, the Cartesian coordinate functions of the curve are related to the $\theta(s)$ and $\phi(s)$ functions of the same curve by Equations 24a–c. We can convert Equation 25 into an expression in terms of θ and ϕ by using Equations 24a–c as equations of transformation in exactly the same way that, in Section 4.4, we used Equations 13a and 13b to derive Equation 15 from Equation 12. This calculation is an exact parallel of steps 1, 2, and 3 of the calculation of p. 27.

We first quote the result and then derive it. The length Δl_C of a small segment of a curve on a sphere of radius R, described by the coordinate functions $\theta(s)$ and $\phi(s)$, is approximately

$$\Delta l_C \approx [R^2\{(\dot{\theta})^2 + \sin^2\theta(\dot{\phi})^2\}]^{1/2}\Delta s \tag{26}$$

length of a small curve segment on a sphere of radius R

where the derivatives $\dot{\theta}$, $\dot{\phi}$ and the function $\sin^2\theta$ are evaluated at some point on the curve segment.

Derivation of Equation 26

The derivation of Equation 26 from Equation 25 proceeds in exactly the same fashion as the derivation of Equation 15 from Equation 12.

1 Our first step is to compute the derivatives $\dot{x}^1$, $\dot{x}^2$ and $\dot{x}^3$ in terms of θ, ϕ, $\dot{\theta}$ and $\dot{\phi}$ using Equations 24a–c.

$$\dot{x}^1 = R\cos\theta\,\dot{\theta}\cos\phi - R\sin\theta\sin\phi\,\dot{\phi}$$
$$\dot{x}^2 = R\cos\theta\,\dot{\theta}\sin\phi + R\sin\theta\cos\phi\,\dot{\phi}$$
$$\dot{x}^3 = -R\sin\theta\,\dot{\theta}.$$

2 The second step is to square each of the above derivatives

$$(\dot{x}^1)^2 = R^2 \{\cos^2\theta \cos^2\phi(\dot\theta)^2 + \sin^2\theta \sin^2\phi(\dot\phi)^2$$
$$- 2\cos\theta\cos\phi\sin\theta\sin\phi\,\dot\theta\,\dot\phi\}$$
$$(\dot{x}^2)^2 = R^2 \{\cos^2\theta \sin^2\phi(\dot\theta)^2 + \sin^2\theta \cos^2\phi(\dot\phi)^2$$
$$+ 2\cos\theta\cos\phi\sin\theta\sin\phi\,\dot\theta\,\dot\phi\}$$
$$(\dot{x}^3)^2 = R^2 \sin^2\theta(\dot\theta)^2.$$

3 The third step is to add the above three expressions together. We do this in two stages: first we add $(\dot{x}^1)^2$ to $(\dot{x}^2)^2$, noticing that the third terms of these two expressions cancel each other

$$(\dot{x}^1)^2 + (\dot{x}^2)^2 = R^2 \{\cos^2\theta(\dot\theta)^2(\cos^2\phi + \sin^2\phi) + \sin^2\theta(\dot\phi)^2(\sin^2\phi + \cos^2\phi)\}$$
$$= R^2 \{\cos^2\theta(\dot\theta)^2 + \sin^2\theta(\dot\phi)^2\}.$$

To this expression we add $(\dot{x}^3)^2$ to obtain

$$(\dot{x}^1)^2 + (\dot{x}^2)^2 + (\dot{x}^3)^2 = R^2 \{(\dot\theta)^2(\sin^2\theta + \cos^2\theta) + \sin^2\theta(\dot\phi)^2\}$$
$$= R^2 \{(\dot\theta)^2 + \sin^2\theta(\dot\phi)^2\}.$$

Then

$$\Delta l_{\mathrm C} \approx [(\dot{x}^1)^2 + (\dot{x}^2)^2 + (\dot{x}^3)^2]^{1/2}\Delta s = [R^2\{(\dot\theta)^2 + \sin^2\theta(\dot\phi)^2\}]^{1/2}\Delta s$$

which is Equation 26.

End of derivation

With Equation 26 we can relate $\Delta l_{\mathrm C}$ to coordinate differences $\Delta\theta$ and $\Delta\phi$ in the same way as we did for plane polar coordinates in step 4 of Section 4.4.

4 We write the approximate equations

$$\Delta\theta \approx \dot\theta\,\Delta s \quad \text{and} \quad \Delta\phi \approx \dot\phi\,\Delta s$$

in the forms

$$\dot\theta \approx \frac{\Delta\theta}{\Delta s} \quad \text{and} \quad \dot\phi \approx \frac{\Delta\phi}{\Delta s}$$

and insert these two expressions into Equation 26 to get

$$\Delta l_{\mathrm C} \approx \left[R^2\left\{\left(\frac{\Delta\theta}{\Delta s}\right)^2 + \sin^2\theta\left(\frac{\Delta\phi}{\Delta s}\right)^2\right\}\right]^{1/2}\Delta s$$
$$= \left[R^2\{(\Delta\theta)^2 + \sin^2\theta(\Delta\phi)^2\}\frac{1}{(\Delta s)^2}\right]^{1/2}\Delta s$$
$$= [R^2\{(\Delta\theta)^2 + \sin^2\theta(\Delta\phi)^2\}]^{1/2}. \tag{27}$$

5 This approximate form for $\Delta l_{\mathrm C}$ gives us the metric for the surface of the sphere Δl, in spherical polar coordinates, as we discussed in step 5 of Section 4.4 for the plane:

$$\Delta l = [R^2\{(\Delta\theta)^2 + \sin^2\theta(\Delta\phi)^2\}]^{1/2}. \tag{28}$$

metric of the sphere of radius R in spherical polar coordinates

It tells us the distance between two neighbouring points on a sphere of radius R whose coordinates differ by very small amounts $\Delta\theta$ and $\Delta\phi$.

6 Finally, as in step 6 of Section 4.4, we can use Equation 26 to write the expression for $\mathscr{L}_{\mathscr{C}}(\mathrm{P}, \mathrm{Q})$, the length of the curve $\mathscr{C}$ between the points

$$\mathrm{P} = (\theta(s_{\mathrm P}), \phi(s_{\mathrm P})) \quad \text{and} \quad \mathrm{Q} = (\theta(s_{\mathrm Q}), \phi(s_{\mathrm Q}))$$

on the sphere. It is

$$\mathscr{L}_\mathscr{C}(P, Q) = \int_{s_P}^{s_Q} [R^2\{(\dot{\theta})^2 + \sin^2\theta(\dot{\phi})^2\}]^{1/2} \, ds. \tag{29}$$

length of a curve between points P and Q on a sphere of radius R

This completes the derivation of expressions for the three major concepts Δl, Δl_C, $\mathscr{L}_\mathscr{C}(P, Q)$ for the surface of a sphere of radius R described by spherical polar coordinates. Table 4 summarizes and compares these concepts for the plane and surface of the sphere.

TABLE 4 Comparison of metrics and lengths of curves.

Space	The plane	The plane	Surface of sphere of radius R
Coordinates	Cartesian	plane polar	spherical polar
Metric	$\Delta l = [(\Delta x^1)^2 + (\Delta x^2)^2]^{1/2}$	$\Delta l = [(\Delta\rho)^2 + \rho^2(\Delta\phi)^2]^{1/2}$	$\Delta l = [R^2\{(\Delta\theta)^2 + \sin^2\theta(\Delta\phi)^2\}]^{1/2}$
Length of a small curve segment in terms of (i) coordinate differences	$\Delta l_C \approx [(\Delta x^1)^2 + (\Delta x^2)^2]^{1/2}$	$\Delta l_C \approx [(\Delta\rho)^2 + \rho^2(\Delta\phi)^2]^{1/2}$	$\Delta l_C \approx [R^2\{(\Delta\theta)^2 + \sin^2\theta(\Delta\phi)^2\}]^{1/2}$
(ii) parameter difference	$\Delta l_C \approx [(\dot{x}^1)^2 + (\dot{x}^2)^2]^{1/2}\Delta s$	$\Delta l_C \approx [(\dot{\rho})^2 + \rho^2(\dot{\phi})^2]^{1/2}\Delta s$	$\Delta l_C \approx [R^2\{(\dot{\theta})^2 + \sin^2\theta(\dot{\phi})^2\}]^{1/2}\Delta s$
Length of a curve $\mathscr{C}$ between two points P and Q	$\mathscr{L}_\mathscr{C}(P, Q) = \int_{s_P}^{s_Q} [(\dot{x}^1)^2 + (\dot{x}^2)^2]^{1/2} \, ds$	$\mathscr{L}_\mathscr{C}(P, Q) = \int_{s_P}^{s_Q} [(\dot{\rho})^2 + \rho^2(\dot{\phi})^2]^{1/2} \, ds$	$\mathscr{L}_\mathscr{C}(P, Q) = \int_{s_P}^{s_Q} [R^2\{(\dot{\theta})^2 + \sin^2\theta(\dot{\phi})^2\}]^{1/2} \, ds$

Although we used the parametric form of Δl_C to construct the other expressions of the right-hand column of Table 4, the fundamental quantity is the metric. The expressions for the curve length Δl_C and $\mathscr{L}_\mathscr{C}(P, Q)$ follow from it as they did in Section 4.4 for the plane. As in the case of the plane in plane polar coordinates, the metric of the surface of the sphere in spherical polar coordinates depends not only on the coordinate differences but also on the value of one of the coordinates. Remember that the surface of a sphere is a two-dimensional space with two coordinates, θ and ϕ. R is simply a constant defining the underlying sphere and as we shall see, it determines the curvature of this two-dimensional space.

Objective 6

SAQ 14 Use Equation 29 to compute the length of the following curves on a sphere of radius R:

(a) $\mathscr{C}_1:$ $\theta(s) = \dfrac{\pi}{2}$

             $\phi(s) = s;$ $0 \leqslant s \leqslant \dfrac{\pi}{2}$

(b) $\mathscr{C}_2:$ $\theta(s) = s;$ $0 \leqslant s \leqslant \dfrac{\pi}{4};$

             $\phi(s) = 0.$

6.4 The metric controls geometric properties; an example in the surface of a sphere

We have completed two of the three steps of the plan set out in Section 6.1. We found the metric of the surface of the sphere of radius R:

$$\Delta l = [R^2\{(\Delta\theta)^2 + \sin^2\theta(\Delta\phi)^2\}]^{1/2} \tag{28}$$

and it gives the length $\mathscr{L}_{\mathscr{C}}(P, Q)$ of any curve $\mathscr{C}$, between two points, P and Q, specified by the coordinate functions $\theta(s)$ and $\phi(s)$:

$$\mathscr{L}_{\mathscr{C}}(P, Q) = \int_{s_P}^{s_Q} [R^2\{(\dot\theta)^2 + \sin^2\theta(\dot\phi)^2\}]^{1/2}\,\mathrm{d}s. \tag{29}$$

We now carry out step 3 and derive the ratio of the circumference of a circle in the surface of a sphere to its radius, see p. 33. To do this we consider a circle on the sphere, with centre N at $\phi = 0$, $\theta = 0$. This circle will be a curve $\mathscr{C}_C$ of constant θ as shown in Figure 30.

$$\mathscr{C}_C : \phi(s) = s$$
$$\theta(s) = \text{constant} = \theta_0$$

where $0 \leqslant s < 2\pi$. Any radius of this circle will be a curve $\mathscr{C}_r$, of constant ϕ.

$$\mathscr{C}_r : \phi(s) = \text{constant} = \phi_0$$
$$\theta(s) = s$$

where for this curve s takes values $0 \leqslant s \leqslant \theta_0$. We calculate the lengths of the circumference and the radius using Equation 29 and evaluate the ratio C/r of the circumference to the radius.

To calculate the length of the circumference, we work out $\dot\theta$ and $\dot\phi$ for the functions of $\mathscr{C}_C$:

$$\dot\phi(s) = 1; \quad 0 \leqslant s \leqslant 2\pi$$
$$\dot\theta(s) = 0; \quad \text{all } s.$$

Thus the integrand of Equation 29 becomes $[R^2(\sin^2\theta_0)]^{1/2}$ so that

$$C = \int_0^{2\pi} R\sin\theta_0\,\mathrm{d}s = 2\pi R\sin\theta_0. \tag{30}$$

To calculate the length of the radius we require $\dot\theta$ and $\dot\phi$ for $\mathscr{C}_r$:

$$\dot\phi(s) = 0; \quad \text{all } s$$
$$\dot\theta(s) = 1; \quad 0 \leqslant s \leqslant \theta_0.$$

From Equation 29, the length of the radius is then

$$r = \mathscr{L}_{\mathscr{C}_r}(N, P) = \int_0^{\theta_0} [R^2\{(\dot\theta)^2 + \sin^2\theta(\dot\phi)^2\}]^{1/2}\,\mathrm{d}s$$
$$= \int_0^{\theta_0} [R^2(1 + \sin^2 s \cdot 0)]^{1/2}\,\mathrm{d}s = \int_0^{\theta_0} R\,\mathrm{d}s = R\theta_0. \tag{31}$$

Thus the ratio C/r is given by the ratio of Equations 30 and 31:

$$\frac{C}{r} = \frac{2\pi R\sin\theta_0}{R\theta_0} = \frac{2\pi\sin\theta_0}{\theta_0}$$

which agrees with the expression given in Section 5. Thus all the properties of this ratio discussed in Section 5 follow from the metric of the sphere. This is an example of the fact that if one knows the metric of a space one can determine the geometric properties of that space.

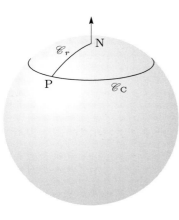

Figure 30   The radius and the circumference of a circle drawn on a sphere about the point N as centre.

6.5 *Summary of Section 6*

1 The surface of a sphere is a space in which any point can be labelled by two coordinates. We use spherical polar coordinates, introduced in Unit 1 and illustrated in Figure 25.

2 The metric of the surface of a sphere of radius R in spherical polar coordinates is:

$$\Delta l = [R^2 \{(\Delta\theta)^2 + \sin^2\theta(\Delta\phi)^2\}]^{1/2}. \tag{28}$$

It gives the distance Δl, between neighbouring points on the sphere in terms of the coordinate differences $\Delta\theta$ and $\Delta\phi$ of these points and the θ-coordinate of one of them.

3 The length $\mathscr{L}_{\mathscr{C}}(\text{P, Q})$ of a curve $\mathscr{C}$ specified by coordinate functions $\theta(s)$ and $\phi(s)$ between the points

$$\text{P} = (\theta(s_{\text{P}}), \phi(s_{\text{P}})) \quad \text{and} \quad \text{Q} = (\theta(s_{\text{Q}}), \phi(s_{\text{Q}}))$$

is

$$\mathscr{L}_{\mathscr{C}}(\text{P, Q}) = \int_{s_{\text{P}}}^{s_{\text{Q}}} [R^2 \{(\dot{\theta})^2 + \sin^2\theta(\dot{\phi})^2\}]^{1/2} \, ds. \tag{29}$$

4 The metric of the surface of a sphere determines the geometric properties of figures drawn in the surface.

7 A uniform notation

Our discussion of general relativity will involve metrics a great deal. We have seen some particular metrics, but we need a more general notation so that we can discuss metrics in a way which is not rooted in the use of particular coordinate systems (e.g. x^1 and x^2 or ρ and ϕ for the same space).

general metric of a two-dimensional space

We shall use the symbols q^1 and q^2 to represent *any* pair of coordinates. In terms of these two coordinates the most general form of metric of a two-dimensional space *that we shall use in this Unit* has the form

$$\Delta l = [g_1(\Delta q^1)^2 + g_2(\Delta q^2)^2]^{1/2} \tag{32}$$

Other books use a slightly different notation for g_1 and g_2. We compare our notation with more generally accepted notations in Section 7.1.

where g_1 and g_2 are called the *metric coefficients* and are restricted to be functions of q^1 only: $g_1(q^1)$, $g_2(q^1)$.

metric coefficients

> The fact that g_1 is a function of q^1 could be reflected in us writing $g_1(q^1)$ everywhere that g_1 occurs in equations. But this is found to make many equations hard to read, especially when we use parentheses () for other purposes such as clarifying the square of a component, as in $(x^2)^2$. For this reason, we shall tend to omit the arguments of functions, especially in complicated equations. You will have to bear in mind what is a function of what, but we think that on balance the clearer equations will be more helpful. Sometimes, we shall remind you in a marginal note that some quantity is a function of some other quantity. When we first write down functions, or where we think it would be particularly helpful to indicate what certain quantities depend on, we shall indicate the functionality, as we do in the expressions for g_1 and g_2 below this box.

metric coefficients of plane in Cartesian coordinates

As the first example, let $g_1(q^1) = g_2(q^1) = 1$ for all q^1. Then the metric of Equation 32 becomes

$$\Delta l = [(\Delta q^1)^2 + (\Delta q^2)^2]^{1/2}$$

which is identical with the metric of the plane in Cartesian components, with q^1 playing the part of x^1 and q^2 the part of x^2. However, if we take for g_1, the function

metric coefficients of the plane in plane polar coordinates

$$g_1(q^1) = 1, \quad \text{for all } q^1$$

and for g_2, the function

$$g_2(q^1) = (q^1)^2, \quad \text{for all } q^1$$

then the metric of Equation 32 becomes

$$\Delta l = [(\Delta q^1)^2 + (q^1)^2(\Delta q^2)^2]^{1/2}$$

which is identical with the metric of the plane in plane polar coordinates, with q^1 representing ρ and q^2 representing ϕ. So the essential difference between these two metrics clearly lies in the form of the function g_2. In Section 6 we have shown that the metric of the surface of a sphere of radius R (Equation 28) can be written in the form of the metric of Equation 32 with:

metric coefficients of surface of sphere of radius R in spherical polar coordinates

$$g_1(q^1) = R^2, \quad \text{for all } q^1$$
$$g_2(q^1) = R^2 \sin^2 q^1, \quad \text{for all } q^1$$

where q^1 plays the role of θ and q^2 the role of ϕ.

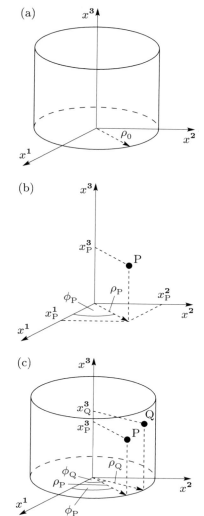

Figure 31 (a) A right-circular cylinder of radius ρ_0. (b) The cylindrical polar coordinates of a point P, in three-dimensional space. (c) The cylindrical polar coordinates of two points, P and Q, on the surface of a right-circular cylinder of radius ρ_0.

This uniform notation allows us to justify a remark made at the end of Section 5 to the effect that the geometric properties of the surface of a cylinder are the same as those of the plane even though the cylinder looks curved and the plane looks flat. Figure 31(a) shows a cylinder (more precisely a right-circular cylinder) whose central axis is the x^3-axis and whose intersection with the (x^1, x^2) plane is a circle of radius ρ_0. We wish to show that the geometric properties of the surface of the cylinder are identical with those of the plane. Since we have argued in Section 6 that the geometry on a surface is determined by the metric of that surface, we determine the metric of the cylindrical surface. Section 6 gives a model of the method to follow: we write the metric of three-dimensional Euclidean space (in which the two-dimensional surface is embedded) and then impose the constraint that points whose distance apart it evaluates are points on the surface. We begin in the same way that we did in Section 6, but the constraint will be easier to impose than on the sphere.

The metric of three-dimensional Euclidean space, written in Cartesian components, is

$$\Delta l = [(\Delta x^1)^2 + (\Delta x^2)^2 + (\Delta x^3)^2]^{1/2}.$$

From Section 4.4 we know that points in the (x^1, x^2) plane can be as easily labelled by their plane polar coordinates, ρ and ϕ, as they can by their Cartesian coordinates, x^1 and x^2. As Figure 31(b) shows, any point P in three-dimensional space can be identified by the coordinates (ρ_P, ϕ_P, x_P^3). Further, row 4 of Table 2 shows us that the quantity in plane polar coordinates that corresponds to

$$(\Delta x^1)^2 + (\Delta x^2)^2$$

in Cartesian coordinates is

$$(\Delta \rho)^2 + \rho^2 (\Delta \phi)^2.$$

So the metric of three-dimensional space, written in the coordinates ρ, ϕ and x^3 is

$$\Delta l = [(\Delta \rho)^2 + \rho^2 (\Delta \phi)^2 + (\Delta x^3)^2]^{1/2}.$$

Figure 31(c) shows that the condition which implies that two points P and Q are both on the cylinder is that they have a common value of the ρ-coordinate, ρ_0. Therefore $\Delta \rho$ is zero for two points on the cylinder, and the metric of the surface of the cylinder is

$$\Delta l = [\rho_0^2 (\Delta \phi)^2 + (\Delta x^3)^2]^{1/2}.$$

Since ρ_0 is constant, $\rho_0 \Delta \phi = \Delta(\rho_0 \phi)$ so the metric of the surface of the cylinder is just

$$\Delta l = [(\Delta(\rho_0 \phi))^2 + (\Delta x^3)^2]^{1/2}.$$

If we identify $\rho_0 \phi = q^1$ and $x^3 = q^2$ this metric becomes

$$\Delta l = [(\Delta q^1)^2 + (\Delta q^2)^2]^{1/2}$$

which is the metric of the plane written in Cartesian coordinates. Since the metrics are identical, geometry on the surface of the cylinder and on the plane must be identical as well, as we set out to prove.

Our uniform notation also shows us something essential that we have not yet come to grips with. It isn't obvious why, when one changes g_2 from $g_2(q^1) = 1$ to $g_2(q^1) = (q^1)^2$, no essential change in geometric properties should occur, whereas making the change from $g_2(q^1) = 1$ to $g_2(q^1) = R^2 \sin^2 q^1$ changes the geometry from that of a plane to that of the surface of a sphere of unit radius. More than one form of the functions g_1 and g_2 are related to the same geometric properties, but it is not obvious from looking at them which forms of g_1 and g_2 are associated with the same properties. The method with which we *can* identify the geometric properties from the forms of the metric coefficients g_1 and g_2 will be discussed in Section 12. We shall then be able to determine whether or not two metrics that look different represent the same geometric properties (i.e. the same space).

Objective 8   **SAQ 15**   Write the metric, for which the general form is Equation 32 with $g_1 = 1$, $g_2 = (q^1)^2$, in the more natural form in which you first saw it.

7.1   Notation for more general cases

It will make it possible for us to exhibit Einstein's famous field equations if we make one more extension of the notation. This will also allow you to compare this Unit with other texts. For most of our purposes the form of the metric presented in Equation 32 is sufficiently general. But if you consult other texts on general relativity or the geometry of surfaces you will see a more general expression for the metric of a two-dimensional surface:

$$\Delta l = [g_{11}(\Delta q^1)^2 + g_{12}\Delta q^1 \Delta q^2 + g_{21}\Delta q^2 \Delta q^1 + g_{22}(\Delta q^2)^2]^{1/2}$$

where g_{11}, g_{12}, g_{21} and g_{22} are, in general, functions of q^1 and q^2. The functions g_{12} and g_{21} can be taken to be identical, so this expression reduces to

$$\Delta l = [g_{11}(\Delta q^1)^2 + 2g_{12}\Delta q^1 \Delta q^2 + g_{22}(\Delta q^2)^2]^{1/2}.$$

A further difference between our notation and that used in other textbooks concerns what mathematical expression should be labelled by the term 'metric'. In many texts, the expression

$$(\mathrm{d}l)^2 = g_{11}(\mathrm{d}q^1)^2 + g_{12}\mathrm{d}q^1\mathrm{d}q^2 + g_{21}\mathrm{d}q^2\mathrm{d}q^1 + g_{22}(\mathrm{d}q^2)^2$$

is called the metric, where our finite coordinate differences Δq^1 and Δq^2 have been replaced by differentials $\mathrm{d}q^1$ and $\mathrm{d}q^2$. Others group the functions $g_{11}, \ldots g_{22}$ into a matrix

$$\begin{pmatrix} g_{11} & g_{12} \\ g_{21} & g_{22} \end{pmatrix}$$

and it is this expression that is called the metric. We mention this more general form here since it will be relevant much later when we introduce Einstein's field equations in Section 12.

8   Geometry and motion — the geodesic equations

8.1   The geodesic equations of a two-dimensional surface

The concept of the geodesic has now turned up twice. In Section 2 it was the path of the bead on the hemisphere. In Section 5 the geodesic in the surface of a sphere played the rôle that the straight line does in the plane, allowing us to draw triangles and the radii of circles. Since all the geometric properties of a surface are determined by the metric of that surface, the metric should tell us which curve between any two points in that surface is the geodesic between them. To find this geodesic from the metric we use the 'geodesic equations' of the title of this Section.

First recall why we want geodesics. As we explained in Section 2, once we know the geodesics on the sphere, we have the path of a bead moving on the hemisphere: the geodesic between any two points. Einstein's theory of motion under gravity involves geodesics in four-dimensional spacetime, but we must find the geodesics from the *metric*. By contrast, in the 'bead on the hemisphere' problem we could find the geodesics simply by having planes cut the sphere that contains the hemisphere, as in Figure 2. In four-dimensional spacetime we can do nothing like this. We must find the appropriate metric and extract the geodesics from this metric. So we begin with a two-dimensional surface where the mathematics is simpler and the pictorial method helps us check our answers.

We can solve more than one problem at the same time if we take advantage of the general notation just introduced. The most general two-dimensional metric that we need in Unit 10 & 11 can be written:

$$\Delta l = [g_1(\Delta q^1)^2 + g_2(q^1)(\Delta q^2)^2]^{1/2}. \tag{33}$$

This means that we always set $g_1(q^1)$ equal to a constant. This general form of metric represents the three cases listed in Table 4 with the following identifications of q^1, q^2, g_1 and $g_2(q^1)$:

Plane in Cartesian coordinates	*Plane in plane polar coordinates*	*Sphere in spherical polar coordinates*
$q^1 = x^1;\ q^2 = x^2$	$q^1 = \rho;\ q^2 = \phi$	$q^1 = \theta;\ q^2 = \phi$
$g_1 = 1;\ g_2(q^1) = 1$	$g_1 = 1;\ g_2(q^1) = (q^1)^2$	$g_1 = R^2;\ g_2(q^1) = R^2 \sin^2 q^1$

For the general metric, Equation 33, we can immediately write down the lengths of a curve segment and a curve:

In the following equations we omit arguments, i.e. we write g_2 instead of $g_2(q^1)$. You must keep in mind whatever dependence of g_1 and g_2 on the coordinates has been declared.

$$\Delta l_C \approx [g_1(\Delta q^1)^2 + g_2(\Delta q^2)^2]^{1/2} \tag{34a}$$

$$\approx [g_1(\dot{q}^1)^2 + g_2(\dot{q}^2)^2]^{1/2}\,\Delta s \tag{34b}$$

$$\mathscr{L}_\mathscr{C}(\text{P, Q}) = \int_{s_\text{P}}^{s_\text{Q}} [g_1(\dot{q}^1)^2 + g_2(\dot{q}^2)^2]^{1/2}\ \text{d}s \tag{35}$$

where in Equations 34b and 35 the curve $\mathscr{C}$ is specified by the two coordinate functions $q^1(s)$ and $q^2(s)$ in terms of a parameter s.

The function

$$[g_1(\dot{q}^1)^2 + g_2(\dot{q}^2)^2]^{1/2}$$

Remember, g_2 is $g_2(q^1)$.

In Equation 36, g_2 is $g_2(q^1(s))$. This is the last reminder for a while.

The key question

appears so frequently that we give it a special symbol (cf. Equation 20):

$$L(s) = [g_1(\dot{q}^1(s))^2 + g_2(\dot{q}^2(s))^2]^{1/2} \tag{36}$$

so that Equations 34b and 35 become

$$\Delta l_C \approx L(s)\Delta s \tag{37a}$$

$$\mathscr{L}_\mathscr{C}(P, Q) = \int_{s_P}^{s_Q} L(s)\mathrm{d}s. \tag{37b}$$

With Equation 37b we can pose the major question of this section. A two-dimensional space will be described by specific functions g_1 and g_2. Any curve in this space will be described by two specific coordinate functions, $q^1(s)$ and $q^2(s)$. For any two points P and Q in this space, the length of any curve between these two points will be given by Equation 37b with the specific functions g_1, $g_2(q^1(s))$, $q^1(s)$ and $q^2(s)$ put into the integrand L. The question is: how do we find the curve between P and Q of *minimum* length? That is, which particular pair of functions $\tilde{q}^1(s)$ and $\tilde{q}^2(s)$ that describe a curve between P and Q will, when put into the integrand of Equation 37b, produce an integral of lower value than that given by any other pair of functions $q^1(s)$ and $q^2(s)$ that describe a curve between P and Q? If we can determine these functions $\tilde{q}^1(s)$ and $\tilde{q}^2(s)$, they define the geodesic between P and Q.

The straightforward way to find a function is to first find and then solve a differential equation that the function must satisfy. This technique has been discussed in this Course (cf. Unit 2) in the process of determining the trajectory of a particle (i.e. the three functions $x^1(t)$, $x^2(t)$ and $x^3(t)$) by writing Newton's second law in the form of three differential equations

$$m\frac{\mathrm{d}^2x^i}{\mathrm{d}t^2} = F^i; \quad i = 1, 2 \text{ or } 3.$$

In the present case we must discover differential equations, written in terms of $\tilde{q}^1(s)$ and $\tilde{q}^2(s)$, that play the part that Newton's second law plays in the determination of the trajectories of particles. We must find these differential equations by applying some mathematical process to the integral of Equation 37b that forces it to take its lowest value for the functions $\tilde{q}^1(s)$ and $\tilde{q}^2(s)$, because that is all the information that we have about $\tilde{q}^1$ and $\tilde{q}^2$. (From now on we suppress the tilde, $\tilde{}$, on the particular functions q^1 and q^2 which solve the problem.)

We could now apply mathematical analysis to the integral of Equation 37b and generate the differential equations that we seek. But for the purposes of this Course it is much more important that you understand that the differential equations produce the geodesics than it is for you to work through the derivation of these differential equations. We therefore proceed as follows:

1 We quote the differential equations, a solution of which minimizes the integral (37b). These equations are the 'geodesic equations' of the title of this section.

2 We apply these equations to the surface of the sphere and to the plane to show that they give the results that we would expect.

3 We give a *completely optional* derivation of these equations. Only the material of points 1 and 2 is needed to understand subsequent text.

To perform step 1 we write down the geodesic equations for the general metric of Equation 33. The equations are:

geodesic equations for our most general metric in two dimensions

$$\frac{\mathrm{d}}{\mathrm{d}s}\left(\frac{g_1 \dot{q}^1}{L}\right) - \frac{1}{2L}\frac{\mathrm{d}g_2}{\mathrm{d}q^1}(\dot{q}^2)^2 = 0 \tag{38a}$$

$$\frac{\mathrm{d}}{\mathrm{d}s}\left(\frac{g_2 \dot{q}^2}{L}\right) = 0 \tag{38b}$$

where $L(s)$ is given by Equation 36, but repeated for easy reference:

$$L(s) = [g_1(\dot{q}^1)^2 + g_2(\dot{q}^2)^2]^{1/2}. \tag{38c}$$

To repeat: solutions to Equations 38a and 38b are a pair of functions $q^1(s)$ and $q^2(s)$ which define the shortest path between two points in the space.

Study comment

You will not be expected to recall the above boxed equations from memory, but you should be able to apply them and interpret them.

In their most general form, these equations are quite complex. However, we can apply them in special cases where they become simpler to use. Although these cases *are* special, they still illustrate the use that is made of these equations.

Let us begin step 2 by applying these equations to the plane. We know already that the curve of minimum length between two points in the plane is a straight line. We should therefore be able to show that the geodesic equations with g_1 and g_2 appropriate to the plane yield $q^1(s)$ and $q^2(s)$ describing a straight line. For the plane described in Cartesian coordinates the functions g_1 and g_2 take the form

$$g_1 = 1 \tag{39a}$$

$$g_2(q^1) = 1, \quad \text{for all } q^1. \tag{39b}$$

This means that

$$\frac{\mathrm{d}g_2}{\mathrm{d}q^1} = 0, \quad \text{for all } q^1 \tag{40}$$

so that the geodesic equations of the plane in Cartesian coordinates are

$$\frac{\mathrm{d}}{\mathrm{d}s}\left(\frac{\dot{q}^1}{L}\right) = 0 \tag{41a}$$

$$\frac{\mathrm{d}}{\mathrm{d}s}\left(\frac{\dot{q}^2}{L}\right) = 0. \tag{41b}$$

These follow by applying Equations 39 and 40 to Equations 38a and 38b. Equation 40 makes the second term of Equation 38a zero.

Equation 41a says that the derivative of the function $\dot{q}^1/L$ is zero. That means that $\dot{q}^1/L$ must be a constant:

$$\frac{\dot{q}^1}{L} = k_1$$

which can be rewritten as

$$\frac{\dot{q}^1}{k_1} = L. \tag{42a}$$

The same applies to Equation 41b; the function $\dot{q}^2/L$ is also constant:

$$\frac{\dot{q}^2}{L} = k_2$$

which can be rewritten as

$$\frac{\dot{q}^2}{k_2} = L. \tag{42b}$$

Equations 42a and 42b can be used to eliminate the complicated function L:

$$\frac{\dot{q}^1}{k_1} = \frac{\dot{q}^2}{k_2}$$

or

$$\dot{q}^2 - \frac{k_2}{k_1}\dot{q}^1 = 0.$$

If we write d/ds for the dots in the above equation we get

$$\frac{dq^2}{ds} - \frac{k_2}{k_1}\frac{dq^1}{ds} = 0$$

or

$$\frac{d}{ds}\left(q^2 - \frac{k_2}{k_1}q^1\right) = 0. \tag{43}$$

Equation 43 means that the function inside the brackets is a constant:

$$q^2 - \frac{k_2}{k_1}q^1 = k_3$$

or $\quad q^2 = kq^1 + k_3 \qquad (k = k_2/k_1)$ \hfill (44)

which is the equation of a straight line in Cartesian coordinates (cf. Section 1). If we imposed the condition that the line actually passes through the points P and Q, this would force the constants k and k_3 to take specific values. So there is only one curve between two points that minimizes the integral of Equation 37b and that curve is a straight line.

In terms of the parameter s, the solution to Equation 44 does not identify a unique pair of functions $q^1(s)$ and $q^2(s)$ that define a straight line. This is because, as was explained in Section 3, there exist infinitely many pairs of functions $q^1(s)$ and $q^2(s)$ that can be used to describe a given straight line in the plane. But what Equation 44 does tell us is that once you have picked one of the two functions, say $q^1(s)$, then the other is determined for you. For example, if you choose

$$q^1(s) = s^3 \tag{45a}$$

then

$$q^2(s) = ks^3 + k_3 \tag{45b}$$

and these functions describe a straight line in the plane. So Equation 44 does allow us to find pairs of functions $q^1(s)$ and $q^2(s)$ that are solutions to the geodesic equations of the plane, Equations 41a and 41b.

Since this calculation of the geodesics of the plane is a typical, albeit simple, example of the way we get the geodesics of a given space from the geodesic equations, we recapitulate the steps. We pick a coordinate system and identify the metric coefficients (in our case the constant g_1 and the function $g_2(q^1)$) of the space in that coordinate system. The metric coefficients are put into the general geodesic equations, (38a) and (38b), to produce the form of the geodesic equations appropriate to that space and coordinate system. For the plane in the Cartesian coordinate system, this led to Equations 41a and 41b. We then solve these equations to produce coordinate functions $q^1(s)$ and $q^2(s)$, such as Equations 45a and 45b, which describe the geodesics of the plane. Picking appropriate values of the constants k and k_3 in Equation 45b identifies the geodesic connecting two specific points P and Q in the plane.

To complete step 2 we carry out the programme described in the preceding paragraph for the surface of the sphere of radius R. We begin by finding the appropriate forms of Equations 38a and 38b. On p. 49 we gave the forms of the functions g_1 and g_2 appropriate to this sphere, described in the coordinates θ and ϕ:

$$g_1 = R^2 \quad \text{and} \quad g_2(q^1) = R^2 \sin^2 q^1.$$

This means that

$$\frac{\mathrm{d}g_2}{\mathrm{d}q^1} = 2R^2 \sin q^1 \cos q^1$$

and the geodesic equations (38a) and (38b) become:

$$\frac{\mathrm{d}}{\mathrm{d}s}\left(\frac{R^2 \dot{q}^1}{L}\right) - \frac{R^2}{L}\sin q^1 \cos q^1 (\dot{q}^2)^2 = 0 \tag{46a}$$

$$\frac{\mathrm{d}}{\mathrm{d}s}\left(R^2 \sin^2 q^1 \frac{\dot{q}^2}{L}\right) = 0 \tag{46b}$$

where

$$L = [R^2(\dot{q}^1)^2 + R^2 \sin^2 q^1 (\dot{q}^2)^2]^{1/2}. \tag{46c}$$

Equations 46a and 46b are much too complicated for us to solve from scratch as we did with the geodesic equations of the plane. Earlier we found geodesics in the surface of a sphere by intersecting the sphere with planes containing the centre of the sphere. What we can do is take examples of curves that are geodesics according to this previous method and show that they satisfy the geodesic equations (46a–c). We also take an example of a curve that is not a geodesic according to the intersecting-plane method and show that it fails to satisfy these geodesic equations.

Figure 32 shows three curves on a sphere of radius R. Curve A is a part of a meridian and curve B is a portion of the equator. Both these curves are geodesics according to the intersecting-plane definition. Let us show that curve B satisfies the geodesic equations (46a and 46b). Curve B can be specified by the coordinate functions:

$$\theta(s) = \frac{\pi}{2}$$

$$\phi(s) = s; \quad 0 \leqslant s \leqslant s_0.$$

By the equations on p. 49 ($q^1 = \theta, q^2 = \phi$) this gives the following expressions for q^1 and q^2:

$$q^1(s) = \frac{\pi}{2} \tag{47a}$$

$$q^2(s) = s; \quad 0 \leqslant s \leqslant s_0. \tag{47b}$$

We begin the calculation by obtaining the expression for L for the curve B. From Equations 47a and 47b we get

$$\dot{q}^1(s) = 0 \quad \text{and} \quad \dot{q}^2(s) = 1 \tag{47c and d}$$

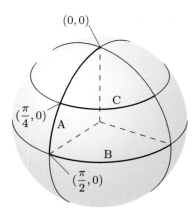

(0,0)

C

$(\frac{\pi}{4},0)$

A

B

$(\frac{\pi}{2},0)$

Figure 32 Three curves on the surface of a sphere. Certain points have coordinates (θ, ϕ) as indicated.

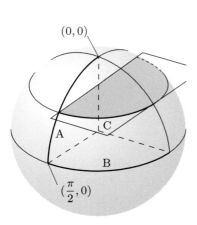

Figure 33 Demonstration that curve C of Figure 32 is not a geodesic of the sphere. Coordinates (θ, ϕ) of some points are indicated.

so

$$L = [R^2(\dot{q}^1)^2 + R^2 \sin^2 q^1 (\dot{q}^2)^2]^{1/2}$$

$$= \left[0 + R^2 \sin^2 \frac{\pi}{2}\right]^{1/2}$$

$$= R. \tag{48}$$

We put Equations 47a, 47d and 48 into the left-hand side of Equation 46b to get

$$\frac{\mathrm{d}}{\mathrm{d}s}\left(R^2 \sin^2 q^1 \frac{\dot{q}^2}{L}\right) = \frac{\mathrm{d}}{\mathrm{d}s}\left(R^2 \sin^2 \frac{\pi}{2} \cdot \frac{1}{R}\right) = \frac{\mathrm{d}}{\mathrm{d}s}(R) = 0.$$

So Equation 46b is satisfied by curve B. Similarly we put Equations 47a, 47c, 47d and 48 into Equation 46a to get

$$\frac{\mathrm{d}}{\mathrm{d}s}\left(\frac{R^2 \dot{q}^1}{L}\right) - \frac{R^2}{L} \sin q^1 \cos q^1 (\dot{q}^2)^2$$

$$= \frac{\mathrm{d}}{\mathrm{d}s}(R \cdot 0) - \frac{R^2}{R} \sin \frac{\pi}{2} \cdot \cos \frac{\pi}{2}(1)^2$$

$$= 0 - R \cdot 1 \cdot 0 \cdot 1 = 0$$

so Equation 46a is also satisfied by curve B. Thus curve B is a geodesic according to the geodesic equations because the coordinate functions that describe curve B are solutions to these questions.

Objective 9   **SAQ 16**   Curve A in Figure 32 can be described by the coordinate functions

$$\theta(s) = s; \qquad 0 \leqslant s \leqslant \frac{\pi}{2}$$

$$\phi(s) = 0.$$

Show that curve A satisfies the geodesic equations.

Finally, let us show that a particular curve that is *not* a geodesic under the intersecting-plane definition also *fails* to satisfy the geodesic equations. Curve C is one quarter of the line of latitude of 45° N. The plane that contains this curve does *not* contain the centre of the sphere, as is shown in Figure 33, and so curve C is not a geodesic according to the intersecting-plane definition. This curve can be described by the coordinate functions

$$\theta = \frac{\pi}{4}$$

$$\phi(s) = s; \quad 0 \leqslant s \leqslant \frac{\pi}{2}.$$

Thus

$$q^1 = \frac{\pi}{4}; \quad q^2(s) = s \tag{49a and b}$$

$$\dot{q}^1 = 0; \quad \dot{q}^2 = 1. \tag{49c and d}$$

Therefore

$$L = \left[R^2 \cdot 0 + R^2 \sin^2 \frac{\pi}{4}\right]^{1/2} = R \sin \frac{\pi}{4}. \tag{50}$$

We use the Equations 49a, 49c, 49d and 50 to check Equation 46a:

$$\frac{\mathrm{d}}{\mathrm{d}s}\left(\frac{R^2 \dot{q}^1}{L}\right) - \frac{R^2}{L}\sin q^1 \cos q^1 (\dot{q}^2)^2$$

$$= \frac{\mathrm{d}}{\mathrm{d}s}\left(\frac{R^2 \cdot 0}{R\sin(\pi/4)}\right) - \frac{R^2}{R \cdot \sin(\pi/4)}\cdot \sin\frac{\pi}{4}\cos\frac{\pi}{4}(1)^2$$

$$= 0 - R\cos\frac{\pi}{4}$$

$$\equiv -\frac{R}{\sqrt{2}} \neq 0.$$

Curve C fails to satisfy Equation 46a and so is not a geodesic according to the geodesic equations. (You may wish to verify that Equation 46b *is* satisfied; but *both* (46a) and (46b) must be simultaneously satisfied by a geodesic.)

This calculation completes step 2 of our programme. The geodesic equations allow us to find the geodesics of a space once we know the metric of that space.

Study comment

Step 3 which follows is *completely optional*. Neither subsequent main text nor any assessment depends on it. But if you have the desire and the time to read through a derivation of the geodesic equations, we provide it below.

Non-assessable ▼
optional text

Equations in the optional text generally retain arguments in g_2 etc. In some places, square brackets [ ] are used to clarify squared quantities.

Derivation of Equation 38b

We wish to make plausible the claim that the coordinate functions $q^1(s)$ and $q^2(s)$ of the curve of minimum length between any two points in a surface described by the metric

$$\Delta l = [g_1[\Delta q^1]^2 + g_2(q^1)[\Delta q^2]^2]^{1/2} \tag{51}$$

(where g_1 is always taken to be a constant) must satisfy Equations 38a and 38b.

We begin by reminding you that, for a small enough piece of any curve on this surface, its length Δl_C, is approximately related to the differences Δq^1 and Δq^2 between the q^1 and q^2-coordinates of its end-points by the formula

$$\Delta l_C \approx [g_1[\Delta q^1]^2 + g_2(q_R^1)[\Delta q^2]^2]^{1/2} \tag{52}$$

where q_R^1 is the q^1-coordinate of any intermediate point R on the curve segment. As the coordinates q^1 and q^2 can depend on some parameter s, we can relate Δl_C to the change Δs, in this parameter for the small segment of the curve by

$$\Delta l_C \approx [g_1[\dot{q}^1]^2 + g_2(q^1)[\dot{q}^2]^2]^{1/2}|_{s=s_R}\,\Delta s \tag{53}$$

where the terms in brackets must be evaluated at some point

$$\mathrm{R} = (q^1(s_R), q^2(s_R))$$

on the curve segment. In this optional passage we derive Equation 38b because it is simpler than Equation 38a. Equation 38a is derived in (optional) Appendix 2 from Equations 38b and 38c.

We begin the derivation of Equation 38b by considering a small segment of an arbitrary line $\mathscr{C}$, in the surface and we pick five points, A–E, on this segment (Figure 34(a)). By the term 'line', we mean the curve of shortest length between A and E. So if we connect the two points A and E by any other curve, such as the dashed curve in Figure 34(b), it will be longer than the continuous line. (If you think that $\mathscr{C}$ should be drawn as a 'straight line' in Figure 34a, that is because

Optional text   ▽ you are assuming that the metric used to calculate the length of $\mathscr{C}$ is that of the plane. For other forms of metric the curve of shortest length may not have coordinates related by the equation $q^2 = k_1 q^1 + k_2$ as the 'straight line' does.)

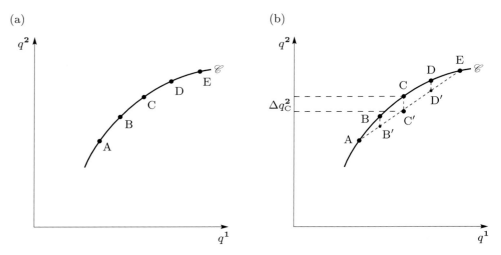

(a)   (b)

Figure 34   Illustration for derivation of Equation 38b.

Let us write down the length of the continuous line ABCDE as the sum of the lengths of the pieces ABC and CDE. We apply Equation 52 to each piece; the point B is taken to be the intermediate point between A and C, and D is taken as intermediate between C and E. Equation 52 then gives

$$\mathscr{L}_{\mathscr{C}}(A,\ C) \approx [g_1[q_C^1 - q_A^1]^2 + g_2(q_B^1)[q_C^2 - q_A^2]^2]^{1/2} \tag{54a}$$

$$\mathscr{L}_{\mathscr{C}}(C,\ E) \approx [g_1[q_E^1 - q_C^1]^2 + g_2(q_D^1)[q_E^2 - q_C^2]^2]^{1/2} \tag{54b}$$

and

$$\mathscr{L}_{\mathscr{C}}(A,\ E) \approx \mathscr{L}_{\mathscr{C}}(A,\ C) + \mathscr{L}_{\mathscr{C}}(C,\ E). \tag{54c}$$

Equations 54a–c will be used in the next step of the argument.

Suppose we generate a neighbouring curve by letting the q^2-coordinates of the points B, C and D vary, as shown in Figure 34(b). If you imagine the segment of $\mathscr{C}$ between points A and E as an elastic band that is pinned at A and E, then the dashed curve is produced by pulling the elastic along the q^2-direction at point C. Each point on the elastic maintains the same q^1 value. Since $\mathscr{C}$ is the curve of minimum length between A and E, any curve produced in this way should be longer than $\mathscr{C}$. This also means that $\mathscr{L}_{\mathscr{C}}(A,\ E)$ should be at a minimum with respect to changes in q_C^2. We know how $\mathscr{L}_{\mathscr{C}}(A,\ E)$ depends on the value of q_C^2 through Equations 54a–c. The mathematical expression of this minimum condition is

$$\frac{\mathrm{d}}{\mathrm{d}q_C^2}\mathscr{L}_{\mathscr{C}}(A,\ E) = 0 \tag{55}$$

or

$$\frac{\mathrm{d}}{\mathrm{d}q_C^2}(\mathscr{L}_{\mathscr{C}}(A,\ C) + \mathscr{L}_{\mathscr{C}}(C,\ E)) = \frac{\mathrm{d}}{\mathrm{d}q_C^2}\mathscr{L}_{\mathscr{C}}(A,\ C) + \frac{\mathrm{d}}{\mathrm{d}q_C^2}\mathscr{L}_{\mathscr{C}}(C,\ E) = 0. \tag{56}$$

Now evaluate these derivatives separately. From Equation 54a we get

$$\frac{\mathrm{d}}{\mathrm{d}q_C^2}\mathscr{L}_{\mathscr{C}}(A,\ C) = \frac{\mathrm{d}}{\mathrm{d}q_C^2}[g_1[q_C^1 - q_A^1]^2 + g_2(q_B^1)[q_C^2 - q_A^2]^2]^{1/2}$$

$$= \frac{g_2(q_B^1)[q_C^2 - q_A^2]}{\mathscr{L}_{\mathscr{C}}(A,\ C)}.$$

The point C is picked to be approximately halfway between points A and E. Points B and D are picked to satisfy the following conditions on their q^1-coordinates:

$$q_B^1 = \frac{q_C^1 + q_A^1}{2}$$

$$q_D^1 = \frac{q_E^1 + q_C^1}{2}.$$

The need for this condition on points B and D will not be obvious in the derivation of Equation 38b because it is the simpler of the two geodesic equations. But if, to derive Equation 38a, you tried to apply the technique that we are about to demonstrate with Equation 38b, you would need to use the above condition on points B and D.

Optional text   ▽   Similarly

$$\frac{d}{dq_C^2}\mathscr{L}_\mathscr{C}(C, E) = \frac{d}{dq_C^2}[g_1[q_E^1 - q_C^1]^2 + g_2(q_D^1)[q_E^2 - q_C^2]^2]^{1/2}$$

$$= \frac{-g_2(q_D^1)[q_E^2 - q_C^2]}{\mathscr{L}_\mathscr{C}(C, E)}.$$

(Remember that, in these differentiations, we are not letting the q^1-coordinate vary, so that $g_2(q_B^1)$ and $g_2(q_D^1)$ are constants.) So the minimum condition of Equation 56 may be written

$$\frac{g_2(q_B^1)[q_C^2 - q_A^2]}{\mathscr{L}_\mathscr{C}(A, C)} - \frac{g_2(q_D^1)[q_E^2 - q_C^2]}{\mathscr{L}_\mathscr{C}(C, E)} = 0. \tag{57}$$

At this point we invoke the idea that changes in the q^1- or q^2-coordinate can be related to changes in a parameter s. According to Equation 53,

$$\mathscr{L}_\mathscr{C}(A, C) \approx [g_1(\dot{q}^1(s_B))^2 + g_2(q^1(s_B))[\dot{q}^2(s_B)]^2]^{1/2}(s_C - s_A)$$

$$= L(s_B)(s_C - s_A) \tag{58a}$$

where the point R, in the interval AC has been chosen to be B.

Similarly

$$\mathscr{L}_\mathscr{C}(C, E) \approx [g_1(\dot{q}^1(s_D))^2 + g_2(q^1(s_D))[\dot{q}^2(s_D)]^2]^{1/2}(s_E - s_C)$$

$$= L(s_D)(s_E - s_C). \tag{58b}$$

Putting Equations 58a and 58b into Equation 57 gives

$$\frac{g_2(q^1(s_B))[q_C^2 - q_A^2]}{L(s_B)(s_C - s_A)} - \frac{g_2(q^1(s_D))[q_E^2 - q_C^2]}{L(s_D)(s_E - s_C)} = 0. \tag{59}$$

We now impose the conditions that

$$\frac{q_C^2 - q_A^2}{s_C - s_A} \approx \dot{q}^2(s_B)$$

and

$$\frac{q_E^2 - q_C^2}{s_E - s_C} \approx \dot{q}^2(s_D).$$

(Equations 7 and 17 have made similar statements if you wish to refer to them.) Then Equation 59 becomes

$$g_2(q^1(s_B))\frac{\dot{q}^2(s_B)}{L(s_B)} - g_2(q^1(s_D))\frac{\dot{q}^2(s_D)}{L(s_D)} = 0$$

or $$\left\{ \frac{\dfrac{g_2(q^1(s_B))\dot{q}^2(s_B)}{L(s_B)} - \dfrac{g_2(q^1(s_D))\dot{q}^2(s_D)}{L(s_D)}}{(s_D - s_B)} \right\}(s_D - s_B) = 0. \tag{60}$$

The term in the curly brackets we can recognize as being of the form

$$-\left\{ \frac{\mathscr{F}(s_D) - \mathscr{F}(s_B)}{s_D - s_B} \right\} \tag{61}$$

where

$$\mathscr{F}(s_D) = \frac{g_2(q^1(s_D))\dot{q}^2(s_D)}{L(s_D)}$$

and similarly for $\mathscr{F}(s_B)$. We can approximate the term in brackets of expression (61) by the derivative of the function $\mathscr{F}$ evaluated at a point intermediate between points B and D, which we choose to be point C. That is,

$$\frac{\mathscr{F}(s_D) - \mathscr{F}(s_B)}{s_D - s_B} \approx \frac{d}{ds}\mathscr{F}\Big|_{s=s_C} = \frac{d}{ds}\left(\frac{g_2\dot{q}^2}{L} \right)\Big|_{s=s_C}$$

Optional text   ▽ where g_2 is understood to be $g_2(q^1(s))$, and $\dot{q}^2$ and L are functions of s. Equation 60 then becomes

$$-\frac{\mathrm{d}}{\mathrm{d}s}\left(\frac{g_2\dot{q}^2}{L}\right)\bigg|_{s=s_C}(s_D - s_B) = 0.$$

Now we are at liberty to choose the segment from B to D so that $(s_D - s_B)$ is very small, but it can never be zero because s_D and s_B represents different points on the curve. Therefore it must be that

$$\frac{\mathrm{d}}{\mathrm{d}s}\left(\frac{g_2\dot{q}^2}{L}\right)\bigg|_{s=s_C} = 0. \tag{62a}$$

The final step in our argument is to note that the point C has not been specially chosen. It could be any point on $\mathscr{C}$. Thus the equation

$$\frac{\mathrm{d}}{\mathrm{d}s}\left(\frac{g_2\dot{q}^2}{L}\right) = 0 \tag{62b}$$

(which is the geodesic equation (38b)) must hold at every point of the curve $\mathscr{C}$.

We have proved that the coordinate functions of a curve of minimum length satisfy Equation 38b, and *asserted* that they satisfy Equation 38a. What we haven't proved is that any curve described by coordinate functions that are solutions to the geodesic equations is the curve of minimum length between any two points on it. That part of the relationship between the solutions of the geodesic equations and the lengths of paths between points is somewhat more complicated.

End of optional text   ▲

8.2   What is a metric theory of motion?

General relativity is a metric theory of motion under gravity. The fundamental postulate of a metric theory of motion is that *particles travel along the geodesics of the metric* of the space in which the motion takes place. There are three circumstances which we must now face:

1. Metric theory requires four-dimensional spacetime.

The first concerns the fact that general relativity is formulated in four-dimensional spacetime and not two-dimensional space. We have seen a two-dimensional space (the plane) with a Euclidean metric and another (the surface of a sphere) with a non-Euclidean metric. In fact we cannot formulate a metric theory of motion in either of these or in three dimensional Euclidean space. But we can find a metric theory of motion under gravity if we consider world-lines in *spacetime* rather than paths in three-dimensional space. We do this starting in Section 9 following a familiar pattern: we find the appropriate metric; geodesic equations pick out special world-lines between events; and particles move along the geodesics of the spacetime metric. Thus the full metric theory of gravity is four-dimensional since spacetime has four dimensions.

2. Geodesic is *maximum* in proper time.

The second point concerns a fact highlighted in Section 2; we proved there that a free particle moving between two given events in the (x^0, x^1) plane follows a world-line of *maximum proper time* with respect to any other world-line connecting these events. Now in the two-dimensional spaces that we have analysed in Sections 4, 6 and 8.1, we have been talking about curves of *minimum length* between points, not maximum. How does this change things? Well, it doesn't change them mathematically, because the geodesic equations have the property of picking out a minimum length if it exists, a maximum length if it exists, or both if they both exist. This is just like finding maxima and minima in ordinary calculus. Both maxima and minima of a function are points where the first derivative of the function is zero. The full method of deriving the geodesic equations from the integral of Equation 37b effectively takes a derivative and sets the result to zero (we did just that in the preceding optional section). It is therefore not surprising, though very useful, that the same equations do both jobs.

3. Key problem is getting the metric.

The third point is the most fundamental and will take quite a few pages to explain. Baldly stated, the problem is to get the metric in the first place. Indeed, finding the metric is central to general relativity; after all, we have already indicated that the very presence of matter modifies the properties of spacetime — and therefore the metric itself.

8.3   Summary of Section 8

1 The most general form of metric that we need to describe the two-dimensional surfaces, or spaces, discussed in this Unit is

$$\Delta l = [g_1(\Delta q^1)^2 + g_2(\Delta q^2)^2]^{1/2} \tag{33}$$

where g_1 is a constant and g_2 is a function of the q^1-coordinate only (for clarity we have not written the functional dependence $g_2(q^1)$). We avoid surfaces requiring a more complicated metric.

2 For any surface, or space, described by the above metric, the geodesics of this space are the curves whose coordinate functions $q^1(s)$ and $q^2(s)$ are solutions of the geodesic equations:

$$\frac{d}{ds}\left(\frac{g_1\dot{q}^1}{L}\right) - \frac{1}{2L}\frac{dg_2}{dq^1}(\dot{q}^2)^2 = 0 \tag{38a}$$

$$\frac{d}{ds}\left(\frac{g_2\dot{q}^2}{L}\right) = 0 \tag{38b}$$

where

$$L(s) = [g_1[\dot{q}^1(s)]^2 + g_2[\dot{q}^2(s)]^2]^{1/2} \tag{38c}$$

where, if we wrote all arguments of functions, we would have $g_2(q^1(s))$ for g_2 in Equation 38c.

3 For the plane, described in Cartesian coordinates, the geodesic equations become

$$\frac{d}{ds}\left(\frac{\dot{q}^1}{L}\right) = 0 \tag{41a}$$

$$\frac{d}{ds}\left(\frac{\dot{q}^2}{L}\right) = 0. \tag{41b}$$

The solutions of these equations are curves that obey the relationship

$$q^2 = kq^1 + k_3 \qquad \text{(where } k \text{ and } k_3 \text{ are constants)}$$

that is, they are straight lines.

4 For the surface of a sphere of radius R, the geodesic equations become

$$\frac{d}{ds}\left(\frac{R^2\dot{q}^1}{L}\right) - \frac{R^2}{L}\sin q^1 \cos q^1 (\dot{q}^2)^2 = 0 \tag{46a}$$

$$\frac{d}{ds}\left(R^2 \sin^2 q^1 \frac{\dot{q}^2}{L}\right) = 0 \tag{46b}$$

where

$$L = [R^2(\dot{q}^1)^2 + R^2 \sin^2 q^1 (\dot{q}^2)^2]^{1/2}. \tag{46c}$$

Curves that are geodesics by the intersecting-plane method of Section 2 have coordinate functions q^1 and q^2 that satisfy these equations. A curve that is not a geodesic by the intersecting-plane method has coordinate functions that fail to satisfy these equations.

5 The geodesic equations in the surface of a sphere give a way of describing the path of a bead on the surface of a hemisphere in the absence of gravity. Since the path of the bead is a geodesic of the space in which the bead moves we have, in effect, a metric theory of motion. General relativity is a metric theory of motion under gravity.

6 To find a metric theory of gravity we must change three things in the way we have obtained 'metric theory' solutions to mechanical problems.

(i) We must formulate our solutions in four-dimensional spacetime, not three-dimensional space.

(ii) The world-lines of test-bodies will be solutions of the geodesic equations for the appropriate spacetime metric. Such solutions will be world-lines of *maximum* elapsed proper time between two given events. This is described more fully in Sections 9 and 10.

(iii) We must establish a way to determine the metric of spacetime in the presence of matter. This is presented in Section 12.

9 Special relativity as a metric theory of motion

9.1 Free-particle motion in two-dimensional spacetime

The simplest application of a metric theory of motion is free-particle motion. To study this, we move from our two-dimensional surfaces to the spacetime of Unit 7 in which special relativity is cast. Since so much of Block 2 is written in terms of the (ct, x) plane (i.e. (x^0, x^1) plane), and since our two-dimensional mathematics can be adapted so easily to the (x^0, x^1) plane, we shall make this move into special relativity in two steps. First, we shall move from two-dimensional surfaces to two-dimensional spacetime. Then we shall generalize from two-dimensional spacetime to four-dimensional spacetime.

Now listen to AC3, Band 4, and look at Table 5; have Unit 7 handy.

The correspondences between our geometric discussion of the plane and the special relativity of two-dimensional spacetime are so close that we have displayed them in Table 5, and we have made an explanatory tape that you can listen to while you look at the table.

There is one correspondence between the plane and two-dimensional spacetime that is incomplete. In the plane, the metric, Δl, gives the distance between a chosen point and *any* neighbouring point in the plane, no matter what its direction from the initial point. The expression for $\Delta \tau$ contained in box 2B of Table 5 gives only the proper time difference between neighbouring events that can be connected by a light signal or the world-line of a test-body. That is, $\Delta \tau$, as written, applies only if $(\Delta x^0)^2 \geqslant (\Delta x^1)^2$. Such events are called 'time-like' (or 'connected by a light pulse') (see Figure 11 in Unit 7). For neighbouring events such that $(\Delta x^0)^2 < (\Delta x^1)^2$, called 'space-like' events, $\Delta \tau$, as presently defined, is an imaginary quantity.

There are two problems. First, can we extend our definition of $\Delta \tau$ so that we can assign a real number to any pair of neighbouring events, even if they are space-like separated? Second, what is the operational procedure for measuring the quantity $\Delta \tau$, for space-like separated events, that corresponds to having a clock move along the free-particle world-line to measure $\Delta \tau$ for neighbouring time-like separated events?

The solution to the first problem is that the 'distance' to be associated with two neighbouring events that are space-like separated is the quantity

$$\Delta \tau \equiv \frac{1}{c}[(\Delta x^1)^2 - (\Delta x^0)^2]^{1/2}$$
$$= \frac{1}{c}[-(\Delta S)^2]^{1/2}.$$

TABLE 5   The geometric concepts of two-dimensional spacetime.

Concept	Representation in plane with Cartesian coordinates	Representation in two-dimensional spacetime in an inertial frame
Curve or world-line	1A $\mathscr{C}: x^{\mathbf{1}}(s), x^{\mathbf{2}}(s)$	1B $\mathscr{W}: x^{\mathbf{0}}(s), x^{\mathbf{1}}(s)$
Metric	2A $\Delta l = [(\Delta x^{\mathbf{1}})^2 + (\Delta x^{\mathbf{2}})^2]^{1/2}$	2B $\Delta \tau = \dfrac{1}{c}[(\Delta x^{\mathbf{0}})^2 - (\Delta x^{\mathbf{1}})^2]^{1/2}$
Length of small 'curve' segment	3A $\Delta l_{\mathrm{C}} \approx [(\Delta x^{\mathbf{1}})^2 + (\Delta x^{\mathbf{2}})^2]^{1/2}$	3B $\Delta \tau_{\mathscr{W}} \approx \dfrac{1}{c}[(\Delta x^{\mathbf{0}})^2 - (\Delta x^{\mathbf{1}})^2]^{1/2}$
Parametric representation	4A $\Delta x^i \approx \dot{x}^i \Delta s;\ i = \mathbf{1} \text{ or } \mathbf{2}$ $\Delta l_{\mathrm{C}} \approx [(\dot{x}^{\mathbf{1}})^2 + (\dot{x}^{\mathbf{2}})^2]^{1/2} \Delta s$	4B $\Delta x^\mu \approx \dot{x}^\mu \Delta s;\ \mu = \mathbf{0} \text{ or } \mathbf{1}$ $\Delta \tau_{\mathscr{W}} \approx \dfrac{1}{c}[(\dot{x}^{\mathbf{0}})^2 - (\dot{x}^{\mathbf{1}})^2]^{1/2} \Delta s$
'Length' of 'curve'	5A $\mathscr{L}_{\mathscr{C}}(\mathrm{P}, \mathrm{Q}) = \displaystyle\int_{s_\mathrm{P}}^{s_\mathrm{Q}} [(\dot{x}^{\mathbf{1}})^2 + (\dot{x}^{\mathbf{2}})^2]^{1/2}\, \mathrm{d}s$	5B $\mathscr{P}_{\mathscr{W}}(\mathscr{E}_\mathrm{P}, \mathscr{E}_\mathrm{Q}) = \displaystyle\int_{s_\mathrm{P}}^{s_\mathrm{Q}} \dfrac{1}{c}[(\dot{x}^{\mathbf{0}})^2 - (\dot{x}^{\mathbf{1}})^2]^{1/2}\, \mathrm{d}s$
General notation of metric	6A $\Delta l = [g_1(\Delta q^{\mathbf{1}})^2 + g_2(\Delta q^{\mathbf{2}})^2]^{1/2}$ where $g_1 = 1,\ g_2 = 1$ $q^{\mathbf{1}} = x^{\mathbf{1}},\ q^{\mathbf{2}} = x^{\mathbf{2}}$	6B $\Delta \tau = [g_0(\Delta q^{\mathbf{0}})^2 + g_1(\Delta q^{\mathbf{1}})^2]^{1/2}$ where $g_0 = 1/c^2,\ g_1 = -1/c^2$ $q^{\mathbf{0}} = x^{\mathbf{0}},\ q^{\mathbf{1}} = x^{\mathbf{1}}$
Geodesic	7A A geodesic is the curve $\mathscr{C}$ between points P and Q such that $\mathscr{L}_{\mathscr{C}}(\mathrm{P}, \mathrm{Q})$ is a minimum.	7B A geodesic is the world-line $\mathscr{W}$ between events $\mathscr{E}_\mathrm{P}$ and $\mathscr{E}_\mathrm{Q}$ such that $\mathscr{P}_{\mathscr{W}}(\mathscr{E}_\mathrm{P}, \mathscr{E}_\mathrm{Q})$ is a maximum.
Geodesic equations	8A $\dfrac{\mathrm{d}}{\mathrm{d}s}\left(\dfrac{\dot{q}^{\mathbf{1}}}{L}\right) = 0$ $\dfrac{\mathrm{d}}{\mathrm{d}s}\left(\dfrac{\dot{q}^{\mathbf{2}}}{L}\right) = 0$ $L = [(\dot{q}^{\mathbf{1}})^2 + (\dot{q}^{\mathbf{2}})^2]^{1/2}$	8B $\dfrac{1}{c^2}\dfrac{\mathrm{d}}{\mathrm{d}s}\left(\dfrac{\dot{q}^{\mathbf{0}}}{L}\right) = 0$ $\dfrac{1}{c^2}\dfrac{\mathrm{d}}{\mathrm{d}s}\left(\dfrac{\dot{q}^{\mathbf{1}}}{L}\right) = 0$ $L = \left[\dfrac{1}{c^2}(\dot{q}^{\mathbf{0}})^2 - \dfrac{1}{c^2}(\dot{q}^{\mathbf{1}})^2\right]^{1/2}$

Combining this formula with that of box 2B of Table 5 for time-like separated events allows us to associate a 'distance' with any pair of neighbouring events. The procedure, given two neighbouring events whose coordinates differ by $\Delta x^{\mathbf{0}}$ and $\Delta x^{\mathbf{1}}$, is:

(a) If $(\Delta x^{\mathbf{0}})^2 \geqslant (\Delta x^{\mathbf{1}})^2$, then the 'distance' between them is just

$$\Delta \tau = \frac{1}{c}[(\Delta x^{\mathbf{0}})^2 - (\Delta x^{\mathbf{1}})^2]^{1/2}.$$

(b) If $(\Delta x^{\mathbf{0}})^2 < (\Delta x^{\mathbf{1}})^2$, then the 'distance' between them is just

$$\Delta \tau = \frac{1}{c}[(\Delta x^{\mathbf{1}})^2 - (\Delta x^{\mathbf{0}})^2]^{1/2}.$$

In the latter case, the physically significant quantity is $\Delta \lambda$, defined to be

$$\Delta \lambda \equiv c \Delta \tau = [(\Delta x^{\mathbf{1}})^2 - (\Delta x^{\mathbf{0}})^2]^{1/2}.$$

proper distance or proper length

The quantity $\Delta \lambda$ is called the *proper length* or *proper distance* between the space-like separated neighbouring events.

We can determine $\Delta \lambda$ operationally in much the same way that we determine $\Delta \tau$. The quantity $\Delta \tau$ for time-like separated events is given operationally by the readings on a clock that follows the short segment of straight world-line connecting the two events. This procedure amounts to saying that one goes to the rest frame of a free particle that encounters the two events, so that it encounters them at the same spatial position in its rest frame (i.e. $\Delta x^1 = 0$). One reads off the elapsed time, $\Delta t = \Delta x^0/c$, between the two events on a clock at rest in this frame. Then the quantity $\Delta x^0/c$ is $\Delta \tau$ by the formula for $\Delta \tau$ given in point (a) above.

The procedure for measuring the proper length $\Delta \lambda$, between neighbouring, space-like separated events, is to move to the inertial frame in which the two events are simultaneous; that is, $\Delta x^0 = 0$. Then $\Delta \lambda = \Delta x^1$ (the spatial separation of the two events in this frame) by the formula for $\Delta \lambda$ given in point (b).

In the first case, suppressing Δx^1 by moving to the rest frame allows one to measure $\Delta \tau$ by measuring Δx^0; in the second case, suppressing Δx^0 by changing one's frame of reference allows one to measure $\Delta \lambda$ by measuring Δx^1. And since $\Delta \lambda$ and $\Delta \tau$ are both Lorentz invariant quantities, the values of $\Delta \lambda$ or $\Delta \tau$ will be the same for all inertial observers.

The first of the following SAQs reinforces a point which will prove to be important in later units.

Objectives 11 & 12   **SAQ 17**   What does the equation $\mathscr{P}_{\mathscr{W}}(\mathscr{E}_\mathrm{P}, \mathscr{E}_\mathrm{Q}) = 0$ tell you about the world-line $\mathscr{W}$?

Objectives 8, 11, 12   **SAQ 18**   Show that the geodesic equations of box 8B in Table 5 follow from the general geodesic equations (38a) and (38b) when the functions g_1 and g_2 of Equations 38a and 38b are replaced by the functions g_0 and g_1, respectively, of box 6B.

Let us stay with box 8B of Table 5, where the geodesic equations of two-dimensional spacetime are introduced. We can write them down so easily because they follow from the general geodesic equations (38a) and (38b) of Section 8. The only difference between the plane and two-dimensional spacetime, as far as these equations are concerned, is that the functions represented by g_1 and g_2 in Equations 38a and 38b are equal to the constants $+1/c^2$ and $-1/c^2$ in spacetime, rather than the constants $+1$ and $+1$ in the plane. Since the derivative of $(-1/c^2)$ is zero, the second term of Equation 38a drops out for the spacetime geodesic equation. Putting $g_2 = -1/c^2$ in the second equation just means that

$$\frac{\mathrm{d}}{\mathrm{d}s}\left(-\frac{1}{c^2}\frac{\dot{q}^2}{L}\right) = 0$$

which is the same as

$$\frac{1}{c^2}\frac{\mathrm{d}}{\mathrm{d}s}\left(\frac{\dot{q}^2}{L}\right) = 0.$$

So the geodesic equations of the two-dimensional spacetime of special relativity written in terms of inertial coordinates are formally identical with the geodesic equations of the plane written in terms of Cartesian coordinates.

geodesic postulate in two-dimensional relativistic spacetime   To cast the theory of free-particle motion in special relativity into the form of a metric theory of motion we *make the fundamental postulate that a free particle moves on a geodesic in spacetime, that is the world-line of* maximum proper time between its end-events, the metric being that of special relativity. The geodesic equations in box 8B of Table 5 lead to these geodesics. Further, we have already solved these geodesic equations on p. 51 so we know what the world-lines of maximum proper time are: they are given by Equation 44, reproduced below (with q^0 and q^1 replacing q^1 and q^2, respectively).

$$q^1 = kq^0 + k_3.$$

Rewritten in terms of x and t, this gives

$$x = kct + k_3.$$

These equations (with specific values of k and k_3) describe world-lines of constant velocity in the (ct, x) plane; these are indeed the world-lines of free particles. So the metric of box 2B and the geodesic equations of box 8B of Table 5 do give a 'metric theory of motion' in spacetime that solves the mechanical problem: 'what are the world-lines of free particles in two-dimensional spacetime?'

We must be clear about the relationship of what we have just done to what we did in Section 2. In Section 2 we started from the assumption that a free particle moves on a world-line of constant velocity (relative to an inertial frame), which is a straight line in the (x^0, x^1) plane. We then proved, with the aid of Theorem II of Unit 7 and the Lorentz invariance of proper time, that a straight world-line is the world-line of maximum elapsed proper time between any two events on it. Here we have done the reverse. We first *postulated* that a free particle moves along a geodesic in the spacetime of special relativity, a geodesic in this spacetime being a world-line of maximum elapsed proper time between any two events on it. Elapsed proper time is given by the integral of box 5B of Table 5, which is derived from the metric of special relativistic spacetime of box 2B. The geodesic equations determine the geodesics and show that these are the world-lines of constant velocity. So this time we *start* from a geometric statement and *derive* the constant velocity of free particles. The geodesic principle is the basis of Einstein's theory of motion under gravity.

9.2   From two dimensions to four

In some ways, our next step is simple. Moving from two-dimensional spacetime to four-dimensional spacetime in special relativity just means including two more spatial variables in the equations of Table 5. But with this step we leave pictorial representations and graphs behind. The mathematical formulae stand on their own since we cannot draw four-dimensional pictures to illustrate them. But the similarity of the mathematics of two and four dimensions allows two-dimensional pictures to give us a feeling for the four-dimensional equations.

Before going to four dimensions, we choose the parameter s in a way that simplifies our equations. Up to now, parameter s has been arbitrary. For instance, we could describe a straight line in Cartesian coordinates with the functions

$$x^1(s) = s \quad \text{and} \quad x^2(s) = as + b$$

or with the functions

$$x^1(s) = s^2 \quad \text{and} \quad x^2(s) = as^2 + b.$$

No physical meaning has been associated with s which is just a mathematical way of saying which pairs of values of x^1 and x^2 go together at a point (x^1, x^2) on a curve. But now we choose a particular variable to be the parameter s. In Unit 7, Section 5.3, we said that the proper time τ, can itself be used as a parameter with which to label unambiguously every event on a given world-line of a material particle, and we described there how the coordinates x^0 and x^1 can be written as functions $x^0(\tau)$ and $x^1(\tau)$ of the proper time. Using τ as the parameter s in the equations of boxes 1B, 4B, 5B and 8B of Table 5, we get (in the limit $\Delta x \to \mathrm{d}x$):

$$\dot{x}^0 \equiv \frac{\mathrm{d}x^0}{\mathrm{d}s} = \frac{\mathrm{d}x^0}{\mathrm{d}\tau}, \quad \dot{x}^1 \equiv \frac{\mathrm{d}x^1}{\mathrm{d}s} = \frac{\mathrm{d}x^1}{\mathrm{d}\tau}$$

so

$$L = \frac{1}{c}\left[\left(\frac{\mathrm{d}x^0}{\mathrm{d}\tau}\right)^2 - \left(\frac{\mathrm{d}x^1}{\mathrm{d}\tau}\right)^2\right]^{1/2} = \frac{1}{c\,\Delta\tau}\left[(\Delta x^0)^2 - (\Delta x^1)^2\right]^{1/2} = \frac{c\,\Delta\tau}{c\,\Delta\tau} = 1.$$

The geodesic equations of box 8B become much simpler when $L = 1$. We get

$$\frac{\mathrm{d}}{\mathrm{d}\tau}\left(\frac{1}{c^2}\frac{\mathrm{d}q^0}{\mathrm{d}\tau}\right) = \frac{1}{c^2}\frac{\mathrm{d}^2 q^0}{\mathrm{d}\tau^2} = 0$$

and

$$\frac{\mathrm{d}}{\mathrm{d}\tau}\left(\frac{1}{c^2}\frac{\mathrm{d}q^1}{\mathrm{d}\tau}\right) = \frac{1}{c^2}\frac{\mathrm{d}^2 q^1}{\mathrm{d}\tau^2} = 0.$$

Finally the formula of box 5B for the elapsed proper time $\mathscr{P}_{\mathscr{W}}(\mathscr{E}_\mathrm{P}, \mathscr{E}_\mathrm{Q})$ becomes an identity:

$$\mathscr{P}_{\mathscr{W}}(\mathscr{E}_\mathrm{P}, \mathscr{E}_\mathrm{Q}) = \int_{s_\mathrm{P}}^{s_\mathrm{Q}} \frac{1}{c}\left[\left(\frac{\mathrm{d}x^0}{\mathrm{d}\tau}\right)^2 - \left(\frac{\mathrm{d}x^1}{\mathrm{d}\tau}\right)^2\right]^{1/2}\mathrm{d}\tau = \int_{s_\mathrm{P}}^{s_\mathrm{Q}} \mathrm{d}\tau,$$

since the integrand is unity. Thus the total change in proper time along the world-line $\mathscr{W}$, between the two events $\mathscr{E}_\mathrm{P}$ and $\mathscr{E}_\mathrm{Q}$ is the integral of the proper time along this world-line — a truism.

Because of the simplification that this choice of parameter brings to the geodesic equations, we shall use τ as our parameter s and consider x^0 and x^1 to be functions of the proper time, τ. All the quantities in column B of Table 5 are rewritten in terms of this parameter in column B of Table 6; the equivalent quantities in four-dimensional spacetime are written in column C. The generalization to four-dimensional spacetime is clear in boxes 2B and 2C of Table 6. The metric in box 2B can be written as

$$c\,\Delta\tau = [(\Delta x^0)^2 - (\Delta x^1)^2]^{1/2}$$
$$= [c^2(\Delta t)^2 - (\Delta x)^2]^{1/2}$$
$$= \Delta S.$$

Capital S in this equation is quite unrelated to parameter s. ΔS is the invariant interval of Equation 14 of Unit 7. Now the invariant interval of four-dimensional spacetime is given by the square root of Equation 6 of Unit 7,

$$S_{\mathrm{ab}} = [c^2(t_\mathrm{b} - t_\mathrm{a})^2 - (x_\mathrm{b}^1 - x_\mathrm{a}^1)^2 - (x_\mathrm{b}^2 - x_\mathrm{a}^2)^2 - (x_\mathrm{b}^3 - x_\mathrm{a}^3)^2]^{1/2}.$$

When the coordinate differences of the events $\mathscr{E}_\mathrm{a}$ and $\mathscr{E}_\mathrm{b}$ are very small we may write this equation as

$$\Delta S = [c^2(\Delta t)^2 - (\Delta x^1)^2 - (\Delta x^2)^2 - (\Delta x^3)^2]^{1/2}$$
$$= [(\Delta x^0)^2 - (\Delta x^1)^2 - (\Delta x^2)^2 - (\Delta x^3)^2]^{1/2}$$
$$= c\,\Delta\tau$$

so the sum of the squares of the three spatial coordinate differences Δx^1, Δx^2 and Δx^3 plays the part in the metric of four-dimensional spacetime that $(\Delta x^1)^2$ by itself did in two-dimensional spacetime.

TABLE 6   The geometric concepts of the four-dimensional spacetime of special relativity.

Concept	Representation in two-dimensional spacetime in an inertial frame	Representation in four-dimensional spacetime in an inertial frame
World-line	1B $\qquad \mathscr{W}: \quad x^0(\tau), x^1(\tau)$	1C $\qquad \mathscr{W}: \quad x^0(\tau), x^1(\tau), x^2(\tau), x^3(\tau)$
Metric	2B $\qquad \Delta\tau = \frac{1}{c}[(\Delta x^0)^2 - (\Delta x^1)^2]^{1/2}$	2C $\qquad \Delta\tau = \frac{1}{c}[(\Delta x^0)^2 - (\Delta x^1)^2 - (\Delta x^2)^2 - (\Delta x^3)^2]^{1/2}$
Length of small world-line segment	3B $\qquad \Delta\tau_{\mathscr{W}} \approx \frac{1}{c}[(\Delta x^0)^2 - (\Delta x^1)^2]^{1/2}$	3C $\qquad \Delta\tau_{\mathscr{W}} \approx \frac{1}{c}[(\Delta x^0)^2 - (\Delta x^1)^2 - (\Delta x^2)^2 - (\Delta x^3)^2]^{1/2}$
Parametric representation	4B $\qquad \Delta x^\mu \approx \frac{dx^\mu}{d\tau}\Delta\tau; \quad \mu = \mathbf{0} \text{ or } \mathbf{1}$ $$\Delta\tau_{\mathscr{W}} \approx \frac{1}{c}\left[\left(\frac{dx^0}{d\tau}\right)^2 - \left(\frac{dx^1}{d\tau}\right)^2\right]^{1/2}\Delta\tau$$	4C $\qquad \Delta x^\mu \approx \frac{dx^\mu}{d\tau}\Delta\tau; \quad \mu = \mathbf{0}, \mathbf{1}, \mathbf{2} \text{ or } \mathbf{3}$ $$\Delta\tau_{\mathscr{W}} \approx \frac{1}{c}\left[\left(\frac{dx^0}{d\tau}\right)^2 - \left(\frac{dx^1}{d\tau}\right)^2 - \left(\frac{dx^2}{d\tau}\right)^2 - \left(\frac{dx^3}{d\tau}\right)^2\right]^{1/2}\Delta\tau$$
Elapsed proper time along world-line	5B $$\mathscr{P}_{\mathscr{W}}(\mathscr{E}_P, \mathscr{E}_Q) = \int_{s_P}^{s_Q} \frac{1}{c}\left[\left(\frac{dx^0}{d\tau}\right)^2 - \left(\frac{dx^1}{d\tau}\right)^2\right]^{1/2} d\tau$$	5C $$\mathscr{P}_{\mathscr{W}}(\mathscr{E}_P, \mathscr{E}_Q) = $$ $$\int_{s_P}^{s_Q} \frac{1}{c}\left[\left(\frac{dx^0}{d\tau}\right)^2 - \left(\frac{dx^1}{d\tau}\right)^2 - \left(\frac{dx^2}{d\tau}\right)^2 - \left(\frac{dx^3}{d\tau}\right)^2\right]^{1/2} d\tau$$
General notation of metric	6B $\qquad \Delta\tau = [g_0(\Delta q^0)^2 + g_1(\Delta q^1)^2]^{1/2}$ where $$g_0 = \frac{1}{c^2}, \; g_1 = -\frac{1}{c^2}$$ $$q^0 = x^0, \; q^1 = x^1$$	6C $\qquad \Delta\tau = [g_0(\Delta q^0)^2 + g_1(\Delta q^1)^2 + g_2(\Delta q^2)^2 + g_3(\Delta q^3)^2]^{1/2}$ where $$g_0 = \frac{1}{c^2}, \; g_1 = g_2 = g_3 = -\frac{1}{c^2}$$ $$q^0 = x^0, \; q^1 = x^1, \; q^2 = x^2, \; q^3 = x^3$$
Geodesic	7B A geodesic between events $\mathscr{E}_P$ and $\mathscr{E}_Q$ is the world-line $\mathscr{W}$ between $\mathscr{E}_P$ and $\mathscr{E}_Q$ such that $\mathscr{P}_{\mathscr{W}}(\mathscr{E}_P, \mathscr{E}_Q)$ is a maximum.	7C A geodesic between events $\mathscr{E}_P$ and $\mathscr{E}_Q$ is the world-line $\mathscr{W}$ between $\mathscr{E}_P$ and $\mathscr{E}_Q$ such that $\mathscr{P}_{\mathscr{W}}(\mathscr{E}_P, \mathscr{E}_Q)$ is a maximum.
Geodesic equations	8B $$\frac{1}{c^2}\frac{d^2x^0}{d\tau^2} = 0$$ $$\frac{1}{c^2}\frac{d^2x^1}{d\tau^2} = 0$$	8C $$\frac{1}{c^2}\frac{d^2x^0}{d\tau^2} = 0; \; \frac{1}{c^2}\frac{d^2x^1}{d\tau^2} = 0$$ $$\frac{1}{c^2}\frac{d^2x^2}{d\tau^2} = 0; \; \frac{1}{c^2}\frac{d^2x^3}{d\tau^2} = 0$$

Once we have the metric of four-dimensional spacetime, we can fill in all the boxes from 3C to 7C by treating the three spatial coordinates in the same way that the single spatial coordinate is treated in the corresponding box from 3B to 7B. For example,

$$-\left(\frac{\mathrm{d}x^1}{\mathrm{d}\tau}\right)^2 \quad \text{in box 5B}$$

becomes

$$-\left(\frac{\mathrm{d}x^1}{\mathrm{d}\tau}\right)^2 - \left(\frac{\mathrm{d}x^2}{\mathrm{d}\tau}\right)^2 - \left(\frac{\mathrm{d}x^3}{\mathrm{d}\tau}\right)^2 \quad \text{in box 5C}$$

and so on. When it comes to the geodesic equations of box 8C we ask you to accept that, since all four functions g_μ are constants, they play the same role that g_0 and g_1 do in the two-dimensional case. Since g_0 and g_1 produce two identical geodesic equations in box 8B, g_0, g_1, g_2 and g_3 will produce four identical geodesic equations in box 8C. So the right-hand column of Table 6 gives us all the geometric concepts of the four-dimensional spacetime and special relativity. With them we can make a 'metric theory' of the motion of free particles in four-dimensional spacetime in exact analogy with the discussion of free-particle motion in two-dimensional spacetime in Section 9.1. We do this, briefly, in Section 9.3.

9.3   A metric theory of free-particle motion in four-dimensional spacetime

geodesic postulate in four-dimensional spacetime in the absence of matter

The metric theory of motion is based on the following postulate: 'the *world-line of a free particle is a geodesic of the four-dimensional spacetime of special relativity*.' Now, we know that the geodesics are given in a particular coordinate system by the solutions of the geodesic equations for the metric concerned. So the world-line of a particle, described by the coordinate functions x^0, x^1, x^2, x^3 of box 1C, is given by a solution of the geodesic equations of box 8C. These solutions are

$$x^0(\tau) = a^0\tau + b^0 \quad \text{and} \quad x^1(\tau) = a^1\tau + b^1 \qquad \text{(63a and b)}$$
$$x^2(\tau) = a^2\tau + b^2 \quad \text{and} \quad x^3(\tau) = a^3\tau + b^3 \qquad \text{(63c and d)}$$

where the a^μ and b^μ are all constants. The quickest way to see that these equations describe world-lines of constant velocity (i.e. world-lines of free particles) is to take the case in which all four constants b^μ are set equal to zero (which can easily be arranged by an appropriate choice of the origin of the inertial coordinate system). Then from Equation 63a we get

$$\tau = \frac{x^0}{a^0} = \frac{ct}{a^0}.$$

Putting this expression for τ into Equations 63b–d gives

$$x^1 = \frac{a^1 c}{a^0}t \qquad x^2 = \frac{a^2 c}{a^0}t \qquad x^3 = \frac{a^3 c}{a^0}t.$$

So each component of velocity is constant

$$\frac{\mathrm{d}x^i}{\mathrm{d}t} = \frac{a^i c}{a^0}, \quad i = 1, 2 \text{ or } 3$$

and the velocity is constant.

To recapitulate: in the example above, we have shown that the fundamental postulate of a metric theory of motion, *that a free particle moves on a geodesic in spacetime* (i.e. on a world-line of maximum proper time), replaces the statement *that free particles move with constant velocity* as the basic law of free-particle motion. It is by establishing a *metric* of a spacetime that we solve the problem of motion. A metric gives a measure of 'length' along a world-line. The 'length' that we use is the proper time, that is, the time measured on a clock on this world-line; this definition of proper time gives the metric theory of motion a firm physical meaning independent of any coordinate system. With the metric to specify the proper time elapsed on a given world-line between two events, we can select a world-line of maximum elapsed proper time between the two events. This is the world-line taken by a free particle moving between the events ('straight line' in spacetime). The geodesic equations of the metric determine world-lines of maximum proper time and so solve the problem of free-particle motion.

If there were no forces acting on particles, we would have solved the problem of mechanics. What Einstein achieved in general relativity was to solve the problem of motion for all particles influenced by the gravitational effects of other bodies. Since the geodesics of the metric of box 2C of Table 6 do not describe the world-lines of particles moving under gravitational influences (for a start, because such particles do not maintain constant velocity), *what general relativity does is to change the metric.* A **general relativity retains the geodesic postulate but changes the metric** new metric is found whose geodesic equations do correctly predict the world-lines of particles moving under the gravitational influence of other bodies. It is through the change in the metric that the effect of matter on spacetime, which we noted in Unit 9, is expressed mathematically. Naturally, the new metrics lead to geometric properties different from those of the metric of box 2C. We shall see that the difference is analogous to the way in which the metric

$$\Delta l = [R^2\{(\Delta q^1)^2 + \sin^2 q^1 (\Delta q^2)^2\}]^{1/2} \quad \text{(surface of sphere)}$$

results in geometric properties that differ from those of the metric

$$\Delta l = [(\Delta q^1)^2 + (\Delta q^2)^2]^{1/2} \quad \text{(plane)}.$$

But with this new type of metric the problem of motion under gravity is solved by applying the fundamental postulate of a metric theory. *Particles move along geodesics in the spacetime described by the new metric.* We no longer require gravitational forces.

General relativity is much more than just a geometric reinterpretation of Newton's theory of gravity (Newton's second law plus Newton's law of universal gravitation). As well as producing a new way of seeing the motion of bodies under the influence of other bodies, it predicted new facets of that motion not predicted by Newtonian mechanics. These have now been observed. Section 14 describes some of these tests of general relativity. They show that it is the most accurate theory of motion under gravity that we presently possess.

9.4   Summary of Section 9

1 There are seven major concepts developed in the discussion of curves in the plane that have direct analogues in the spacetime of special relativity with one spatial dimension. These concepts are listed in Table 7. The corresponding mathematical formulae are in Table 5.

TABLE 7   Analogies between the plane and the two-dimensional spacetime of special relativity.

Concept applied to the plane	Concept applied to two-dimensional spacetime of special relativity
curve in the plane	*world-line* in two-dimensional spacetime
metric in the plane	*metric* of the two-dimensional spacetime of special relativity
length of small curve segment	*proper time elapsed* along a small world-line segment
parametric representation of a curve	*parametric* representation of a world-line
length, $\mathscr{L}_{\mathscr{C}}(\mathrm{P}, \mathrm{Q})$, of curve $\mathscr{C}$ between points P and Q	*elapsed proper time*, $\mathscr{P}_{\mathscr{W}}(\mathscr{E}_{\mathrm{P}}, \mathscr{E}_{\mathrm{Q}})$, along world-line $\mathscr{W}$ between events $\mathscr{E}_{\mathrm{P}}$ and $\mathscr{E}_{\mathrm{Q}}$
geodesic in the plane (curve of minimum length)	*geodesic* in spacetime (world-line of maximum proper time)
geodesic equations (to find the geodesics in the plane)	*geodesic equations* (to find the geodesics in spacetime)

2 A metric theory of free-particle motion can be formulated in two-dimensional spacetime by postulating that the world-line of a free particle is a geodesic in the two-dimensional spacetime of special relativity, that is, a world-line of maximum elapsed proper time between any two events on it. The elapsed proper time along a world-line is computed with the formula of box 5B of Table 5, which is derived from the metric of special relativity, box 2B of that table. The world-line of a free particle is therefore a world-line of constant velocity relative to an inertial frame.

3 The formalism simplifies if the arbitrary parameter s, used in the parametric representation of world-lines, is chosen to be the elapsed proper time itself. We label events on a world-line by the proper time elapsed from some initial event on that world-line. The function

$$L(s) = \frac{1}{c}[(\dot{x}^0)^2 - (\dot{x}^1)^2]^{1/2}$$

then becomes

$$L(\tau) = \frac{1}{c}\left[\left(\frac{dx^0}{d\tau}\right)^2 - \left(\frac{dx^1}{d\tau}\right)^2\right]^{1/2}$$

and $L(\tau)$ is identically equal to unity for all τ. Restricting s to be τ simplifies the geodesic equations. The equations

$$\frac{1}{c^2}\frac{d}{ds}\left(\frac{\dot{q}^0}{L}\right) = 0 \quad \text{and} \quad \frac{1}{c^2}\frac{d}{ds}\left(\frac{\dot{q}^1}{L}\right) = 0$$

become

$$\frac{1}{c^2}\frac{d^2q^0}{d\tau^2} = 0 \quad \text{and} \quad \frac{1}{c^2}\frac{d^2q^1}{d\tau^2} = 0.$$

4 All the concepts in point 1 above, which have been explained with reference to two-dimensional spacetime, can be written in terms of four-dimensional spacetime. This generalization was given in Table 6.

5 A metric theory of free-particle motion can be formulated in four-dimensional spacetime by postulating that the world-line of a free particle is a geodesic in the four-dimensional spacetime of special relativity, that is, a world-line of maximum elapsed proper time between any two events on it. The elapsed proper time along a world-line is given by the formula of box 5C of Table 6, which is derived from the metric of special relativity, box 2C of that table. We *deduce* from this metric theory that the world-line of a free particle is a world-line of constant velocity in an inertial frame.

6 The metric theory of free-particle motion in spacetime, with elapsed proper time playing the role of 'length', is what is generalized to become a metric theory of the motion of bodies under gravity in general relativity.

10 What is a metric theory of gravity?

Let us sum up what we know about the metric theory of free-particle motion in spacetime; this will give us a starting point for introducing gravity. A metric theory of free-particle motion in spacetime can be described by the following two postulates:

1 *The geometric properties of empty spacetime* (i.e. spacetime devoid of aggregates of matter or concentrations of energy) *are described by the metric of special relativity.* That is, the proper time difference $\Delta\tau$, between neighbouring events described in an inertial frame of reference (with Cartesian coordinates q^1, q^2, q^3) is given by

$$\Delta\tau = [g_0(\Delta q^0)^2 + g_1(\Delta q^1)^2 + g_2(\Delta q^2)^2 + g_3(\Delta q^3)^2]^{1/2}$$

where

$$g_0 = \frac{1}{c^2}; \quad g_1 = g_2 = g_3 = -\frac{1}{c^2}.$$

2 *The world-lines of free test-bodies are geodesics of this metric.* That is, they are solutions of the geodesic equations (of box 8C of Table 6) when the metric coefficients g_0, g_1, g_2, g_3 are given the above form. Furthermore the elapsed proper time, $\mathscr{P}_\mathscr{W}(\mathscr{E}_P, \mathscr{E}_Q)$, between any two events $\mathscr{E}_P$ and $\mathscr{E}_Q$ on such a world-line $\mathscr{W}$, is a positive quantity. (This follows directly from the definition of proper time as the time recorded on a clock moving with the test-body.)

redefinition of the term 'geodesic'

We can view geodesics in two equivalent ways: as world-lines of maximum elapsed proper time or as solutions of geodesic equations. From here on we shall use the second viewpoint only: we now take the term *geodesic* to mean a solution of the appropriate geodesic equations.

There is one more important facet of motion in empty spacetime. We know that in empty space, light travels in straight lines at constant speed relative to an inertial frame of reference. This means that the world-lines are straight lines in empty spacetime, relative to an inertial frame of reference. Since any straight line in spacetime is a solution of the geodesic equations of special relativity, the world-line of a light signal in empty space is a geodesic of the spacetime of special relativity.

We now have a metric theory of the motion of *test-bodies and light* in empty space. It is given by the following three postulates.

1 The geometric properties of empty space are described by the metric of special relativity.

2 The world-line of any free test-body is a geodesic of this metric. Further, the proper time elapsed along any segment of such a geodesic will be a positive quantity.

3 The world-line of any light signal is a geodesic of this metric. Further, *the proper time elapsed along any segment of such a world-line is zero.*

null geodesic

This last property of the world-lines of light signals is often described by saying that the world-line of a light signal is a *null geodesic*. The adjective *null* refers to the zero elapsed proper time along any portion of the world-line. Null geodesics will be important when we discuss black holes and in cosmology.

10.1   Postulates of a metric theory of gravity

Generalizing from the case of empty space, we can now specify a metric theory of gravity in three statements:

1 *The geometric properties of spacetime are described by a metric, $\Delta\tau$.* For our purposes this metric is specified by four functions, g_0, g_1, g_2, g_3, of the four spacetime coordinates q^0, q^1, q^2, q^3, and the form of the metric is

$$\Delta\tau = [g_0(\Delta q^0)^2 + g_1(\Delta q^1)^2 + g_2(\Delta q^2)^2 + g_3(\Delta q^3)^2]^{1/2}.$$

2 *The world-line of a test-body subject only to gravitational influences* (i.e. not subject to electromagnetic or nuclear forces) *is a geodesic of this metric.* The proper time elapsed along any segment of such a geodesic will be a positive quantity.

3 *The world-line of a light ray (or other electromagnetic signal) travelling in vacuum is also a geodesic of this metric.* The proper time elapsed along any segment of such a geodesic is zero (i.e. it is a null geodesic).

We have used the word 'geodesic' in its new definition in these postulates.

At the heart of general relativity is the statement that the above three postulates hold in the presence of matter: general relativity is a metric theory of gravity. Now, test-particles obviously move differently when gravity is acting than in the absence of gravity and the theory must reflect this. Unit 9 provides a clue how: matter distorts spacetime and so what changes in the presence of matter is the form of the four functions g_0, g_1, g_2, g_3, the metric coefficients which define the structure of spacetime.

If we can find the four functions g_0, g_1, g_2, g_3, which apply when there is gravity, then postulates 1, 2 and 3 tell us how matter and light behave in the presence of gravity. The Newtonian concept of gravitational force is then replaced by a geometric way of solving the problem of motion in the presence of matter.

The central question addressed over the next two sections is: *what are the metric coefficients g_μ for a given distribution of matter;* i.e. *how much* and *in what way* does matter distort spacetime?

10.2   Concerning our notation for the metric coefficients

We explained in Section 7 that the expression of Equation 32, for the metric in general coordinates (q^1, q^2) used in this Block, is not the most general that can be written but is adequate to our needs. Similarly, we have just quoted a general form for the metric of spacetime with four functions g_0, g_1, g_2, g_3. This is as general an expression as we need for all the metrics we shall present explicitly. But there is a more general expression of the spacetime metric containing ten terms, which are

$$\begin{aligned}
\Delta\tau = [&g_{00}(\Delta q^0)^2 + 2g_{01}\Delta q^0 \Delta q^1 + 2g_{02}\Delta q^0 \Delta q^2 + 2g_{03}\Delta q^0 \Delta q^3 \\
&+ g_{11}(\Delta q^1)^2 + 2g_{12}\Delta q^1 \Delta q^2 + 2g_{13}\Delta q^1 \Delta q^3 \\
&+ g_{22}(\Delta q^2)^2 + 2g_{23}\Delta q^2 \Delta q^3 \\
&+ g_{33}(\Delta q^3)^2]^{1/2}.
\end{aligned}$$

It is usually written as

$$(\Delta\tau)^2 = \sum_{\substack{\mu=0-3 \\ \nu=0-3}} g_{\mu\nu} \Delta q^\mu \Delta q^\nu \quad \text{with} \quad g_{\nu\mu} = g_{\mu\nu}$$

or perhaps in the even briefer form

$$(\Delta\tau)^2 = g_{\mu\nu}\,\Delta q^\mu\,\Delta q^\nu$$

in which the summation is taken as understood.

You will *not* be expected to manipulate the ten metric coefficients $g_{00},\ \cdots\ g_{33}$, which we write collectively as $g_{\mu\nu}$. But we have presented them here since it will make our presentation of Einstein's field equations in Section 12 more meaningful. The essential points there will simply be the recognition of the symbol $g_{\mu\nu}$ as the metric coefficients of four-dimensional spacetime and the knowledge that in general there are ten of them.

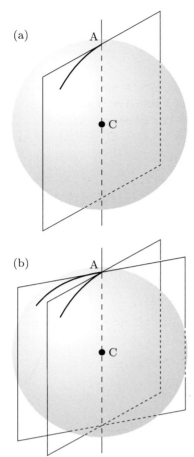

(a)

(b)

(c)

initial direction
of movement

Figure 35   (a) A geodesic of
the sphere leaving point A in
a given direction. (b) Two
geodesics of the sphere
leaving point A in different
directions. (c) Geodesic of a
sphere leaving the point A in
a prescribed initial direction.

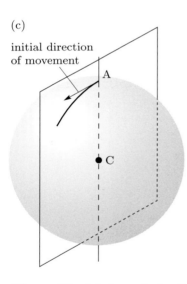

11   Spacetime is curved

We now show that a metric theory of gravity is plausible, starting from the
equivalence principle and the universality of free fall. The metric of
spacetime is modified by the presence of matter, and this means that
spacetime is made to *curve* by the presence of matter.

We start with the universality of free fall, a very well tested principle, as
discussed in Unit 9. According to this principle, the inertial mass m and
the gravitational mass μ are equal, i.e. $m = \mu$.

Consider a given distribution of matter, such as a star in isolation out in
empty space. If we pick a point in space at a given distance from the star,
place a test-body there and give this test-body an initial velocity, then
Newton's equations (with $m = \mu$ inserted) completely determine the
subsequent trajectory. The world-line of the test-body, acted on by only
the gravitational influences of some large body, is completely determined
by its velocity at some initial event in spacetime. But this statement is
true *only* if the trajectory does not depend on the composition of the
test-body, that is, if the universality of free fall is true.

This combination of the universality of free fall and Newton's theory of
gravity suggests a metric theory of gravity. To see this, look again at the
geodesics on the surface of a sphere. If we pick any point A on a sphere
and choose a particular direction in which to leave this point on a geodesic,
then we move along a unique geodesic. This can be seen by thinking of the
intersecting-plane method of defining a geodesic on a sphere. Once the
point A has been picked, then it and the centre, C, of the sphere must
both be in the intersecting plane (see Figure 35a). The only freedom of
movement left to the plane is to rotate about the line joining C to A
(Figure 35b). Determining the direction in which the geodesic leaves point
A fixes the intersecting plane in one orientation (Figure 35c), and the
geodesic is unique.

Given that

1 the world-line of a test-body originating at a given event with a specified
velocity, and moving under the influence of gravity only, is unique, and
2 the geodesic equations for either a space (curved or flat) or a spacetime
(special relativistic or otherwise) uniquely specify a geodesic in terms of
initial position and velocity,

then perhaps the world-lines of test-bodies moving under gravity *are* the
geodesics of some suitably chosen spacetime. *The universality of free fall
makes this plausible because it says the world-line of a test body is
independent of its chemical composition.* The only variables that remain
free are those that fit naturally into a metric description, namely initial
position and initial velocity.

In Unit 9 we found that the universality of free fall implied a key aspect of
the equivalence principle (EP) (actually, the *weak equivalence principle*):
that a freely falling frame of reference is a locally inertial frame of
reference. The statement that 'a freely falling frame is a locally inertial
frame' says that in any local region of spacetime we can erect a spacetime
frame of reference, the freely falling one, with respect to which physical
phenomena will be described by theories based on special relativity. This
means that within a freely falling frame the metric in Cartesian

coordinates is

$$\Delta\tau = \frac{1}{c}[(\Delta x^0)^2 - (\Delta x^1)^2 - (\Delta x^2)^2 - (\Delta x^3)^2]^{1/2}$$

and test-particles subject to no electromagnetic or nuclear forces move in straight lines at constant speed (or remain at rest). In other words, the world-lines of test-bodies within any *local* region, when described in the freely falling frame of reference, are described by the geodesics of the metric of special relativity, which we know from Section 9.3 are the curves of constant velocity.

Recalling from Unit 9 that the equivalence principle applied to *local* (not too large in spacetime) regions, the metric appropriate to a spacetime with massive bodies in it must have the following features:

1 The four functions g_μ that describe the geometry of spacetime must be such that in any local region of spacetime described in freely falling coordinates, they correspond to a metric of the form

$$g_0 = \frac{1}{c^2}; \quad g_1 = g_2 = g_3 = -\frac{1}{c^2}.$$

2 The g_μ do not retain this constant form when the x^μ vary over a large range.

3 The geodesics of this metric do not retain the form

$$x^\mu(\tau) = a^\mu\tau + b^\mu$$

over large spacetime regions.

It is helpful to look at the analogues to these statements in two dimensions. Consider again the surface of the sphere described in θ- and ϕ-coordinates (Figure 25). The metric for this space is

$$\Delta l = [R^2\{(\Delta\theta)^2 + \sin^2\theta(\Delta\phi)^2\}]^{1/2}.$$

Now consider this metric as it applies to a small region containing the equator, that is, the parallel of latitude $\theta = \pi/2$ (Figure 36). Since θ is going to be very close to $\pi/2$ for all points in this region, let us write

$$\theta = \frac{\pi}{2} + \eta$$

where η is very small. Then in terms of η and ϕ, the metric becomes

$$\Delta l = \left[R^2(\Delta\eta)^2 + R^2\sin^2\left(\frac{\pi}{2} + \eta\right)(\Delta\phi)^2\right]^{1/2}$$

$$= [R^2(\Delta\eta)^2 + R^2\cos^2\eta(\Delta\phi)^2]^{1/2}$$

since

$$\sin\left(\frac{\pi}{2} + \eta\right) = \cos\eta.$$

For small η, $\cos\eta$ is very well represented by the Taylor approximation

$$\cos\eta \approx 1 - \frac{\eta^2}{2}$$

so that

$$\cos^2\eta \approx \left(1 - \frac{\eta^2}{2}\right)^2 \approx 1 - \eta^2.$$

For η very close to zero, $\eta^2 \ll \eta \ll 1$, so to first order in η, only the first term of the approximate formula will contribute; that is

$$\cos^2\eta \approx 1; \quad |\eta| \ll 1.$$

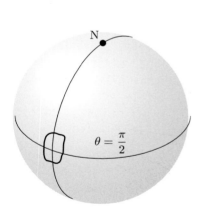

Figure 36   A small region of a sphere containing part of the equator.

In this approximation, the metric then becomes

$$\Delta l = [R^2(\Delta \eta)^2 + R^2(\Delta \phi)^2]^{1/2} = [\Delta(R\eta)^2 + \Delta(R\phi)^2]^{1/2}.$$

If we write $R\eta = q^1$ and $R\phi = q^2$, the metric becomes

$$\Delta l = [(\Delta q^1)^2 + (\Delta q^2)^2]^{1/2}$$

which is exactly the form of the metric of the two-dimensional plane in Cartesian coordinates. Since the small region that we have chosen is not special (any small piece of a sphere is just like any other), the geometry of *any* small region of a sphere is approximately that of a plane, an approximation that gets better the smaller the region. But, the geometry is never exactly that of a plane; it is always a question of how accurate one wishes to be. Thus the sum of the interior angles of a triangle on a surface tends to 180° as the triangle becomes very small.

It follows that the geodesics in any small region of the sphere are curves of (approximately) the form

$$q^2 = k_1 q^1 + k_2 \quad \text{where } k_1 \text{ and } k_2 \text{ are constants} \tag{64}$$

(cf. Equation 44) and two geodesics with the same value of k_1 and different values of k_2 maintain the same separation. But on the large scale, equations of the form of Equation 64 do not describe geodesics on a sphere. For example, the curve defined by

$$\phi = \theta \tag{65}$$

which is of the form of Equation 64 with $k_1 = 1$ and $k_2 = 0$, goes through the points $(0, 0)$ and $(\pi/2, \pi/2)$ on the sphere. The geodesic between these two points is shown in Figure 37. It is described by the equation

$$\phi = \frac{\pi}{2}.$$

This curve goes nowhere near such points as

$$\theta = \frac{\pi}{4} = \phi$$

which are on the curve of Equation 65. So the curve of Equation 65 is certainly not a geodesic between the points $(0,0)$ and $(\pi/2, \pi/2)$. We also know from Section 5 that, on a large scale, two geodesics G_1 and G_2, do not maintain constant separation since any two geodesics on a sphere intersect at two points. So the metric of the surface of the sphere is analogous to the metric of spacetime in the presence of matter, with the plane playing the role of the spacetime of special relativity. That is:

1 The two functions g_1 and g_2 that describe the geometry of the surface of the sphere are such that in any *small* region of the surface they correspond to a metric that describes a plane.

2 The functions g_1 and g_2 for the sphere do not maintain the form appropriate to the plane over a large region of the sphere.

3 The geodesics of any local region of the sphere are of the form

$$q^2 = k_1 q^1 + k_2$$

but do not maintain this form for large regions of the sphere. In particular two distinct geodesics cannot maintain constant separation over a large region of the sphere.

The central point of our analogy between the surface of the sphere and four-dimensional spacetime containing large aggregates of matter is the following. The property of the surface of the sphere that makes the metric,

Geometry of *small region* of surface of sphere is like geometry of a plane.

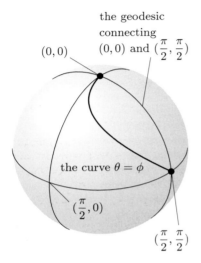

Figure 37 Illustration of the curve $\theta = \phi$ drawn on a sphere and the geodesic connecting the point $(0,0)$ and $(\pi/2, \pi/2)$.

and hence geometric properties, different on the large scale (i.e. 'globally') from those of the plane while behaving like the plane within a local region, is that it is *curved*. Can we say that four-dimensional spacetime in the presence of matter is in some way '*curved*' so that in any (freely falling) local region its properties are like those of special relativity but systematic differences show up as the size of the spacetime region is increased? If so, the analogous concepts and statements in two and four dimensions would be as shown in Table 8.

TABLE 8   Analogies between two-dimensional curved surfaces and four-dimensional spacetime in the presence of matter.

Two-dimensional surface	Four-dimensional spacetime
curved surface of sphere	curved spacetime
local region of sphere	local region of spacetime
Cartesian coordinate system in local region	freely falling frame in local region
metric of surface of sphere	metric of curved spacetime
metric of surface of sphere $\approx$ metric of plane in local region	metric of curved spacetime $\approx$ metric of special relativity in local region
geometric properties of the surface of sphere, on a large scale, differ from the geometric properties of the two-dimensional plane	geometric properties of spacetime in the presence of matter, on a large scale, differ from the geometric properties of the spacetime of special relativity

The principle of equivalence, in the form 'a freely falling frame is a locally inertial frame' shows that local regions of spacetime are small pieces of the whole of spacetime where special relativity holds locally *in the same way* that a small region of the surface of a sphere is effectively a plane. The local freely falling frame provides us with a particularly simple description of the local region in the same way that the Cartesian coordinate system provides a simple description of the plane.

But what can it possibly mean to say that 'spacetime is curved'? Because we can see the curved shape of a two-dimensional surface, it might seem obvious when it is curved (although we have noted that looking curved and being curved are not identical — the cylinder is an example to which we return shortly). The fact that the surface is two-dimensional but we see it in three dimensions allows us to perceive the curvature. But if spacetime is curved how can we see it? We have no extra dimensions left from which to observe the curvature.

We first show that we *can* detect curvature in two dimensions *without* the perspective provided by the third dimension. We could be ants crawling on the surface of a sphere (special ants with only two-dimensional vision) and we could still discover that the surface we are on is curved. When we have done that, we can ask how, as *we* crawl through spacetime, we could tell that it is curved.

Objective 13	SAQ 19	Suppose that, by means of some amazing chemical procedure, we produced a compound that accelerated in the gravitational field of ordinary matter at half the usual rate. Why would this discovery make impossible the geometric formulation of motion under gravity in which world-lines of free fall are geodesics?
Objective 13	SAQ 20	(a) What is an essential difference between the geometric properties of a plane and those of a curved surface that is revealed by taking larger and larger regions of the surface on which to draw geometric figures?

SAQ 20 (continued):

(b) What is the essential difference between free-fall motion of two test-bodies in the vicinity of a large mass and free-fall motion of the same test-bodies in empty space that is revealed by taking larger and larger regions of spacetime within which the motion of the test-bodies may be observed?

(c) If we wished to use two-dimensional surfaces as an analogy for a geometric description of free-fall motion, how would you group the following four terms into two pairs to express that analogy:

(i) free fall in outer space

(ii) free fall near a large mass

(iii) the Euclidean plane with its geodesics

(iv) a curved surface (such as a sphere) with its geodesics?

11.1   Summary of Section 11

1 The principle of equivalence, expressed in the form 'a freely falling frame is a locally inertial frame' or, as the universality of free fall, is very well supported by experiment (Unit 9). It is therefore plausible to interpret motion under gravity in terms of a metric theory based on a curved spacetime.

2 The universality of free fall implies that the world-line of a test-body moving under gravity is uniquely determined by its velocity at the initial event of the world-line. The path of a geodesic (e.g. on the surface of a sphere) is uniquely set by picking the initial point from which the geodesic is to be drawn and the initial direction in which it is to leave that point. Therefore it is plausible to associate the world-lines of test-bodies in free fall with the geodesics of the metric of some suitable spacetime.

3 Since a freely falling frame is a locally inertial frame, it follows that the metric of spacetime containing matter reduces to that of special relativity in a local region around any freely falling object. Note that any *event* (point in spacetime) has the possible world-line of a freely falling object passing through it. Thus a *local* region around any *event* can be, albeit instantaneously, flat, i.e. have the metric of special relativity. But on a larger (global) scale, spacetime is curved, rather as the surface of a sphere is curved.

12   The concept of curvature and Einstein's field equations

12.1   Introduction

We shall cover a lot of ground in this section, arriving at the idea that spacetime in the presence of matter is curved. To explain what the curvature of spacetime is and to illustrate how it is a central concept of the general theory of relativity, we must first explain what the curvature of a two-dimensional surface is. Then we can explain spacetime curvature by analogy without getting into messy mathematical details.

In previous sections we have already used the word 'curved' in two different ways in connection with two-dimensional surfaces.

Objective 14   **SAQ 21**   With what two meanings has the word 'curved' been applied to two-dimensional surfaces?

curved$_1$

The first meaning of curved, which we label *curved$_1$*, is the everyday meaning: a surface is curved$_1$ if it 'looks curved'. This meaning does not help us to explain the concept of 'curved spacetime' for two reasons. First, we cannot look at spacetime from the outside in the way that, as three-dimensional creatures, we can look at a two-dimensional surface to see if is curved$_1$ or not. Second, the notion curved$_1$ is too vague to lead to a way of distinguishing spacetime which is flat (in the absence of matter) from spacetime which is curved (in the presence of matter).

curved$_2$, curvature$_2$

We say a surface is 'curved' in a second sense (hereafter called *curved$_2$*) if its geometric properties vary with the size of the figures drawn on it and these properties smoothly become the properties of the plane as the size of the figures is reduced to zero. This use of the adjective curved$_2$ (or the noun *curvature$_2$*) leads to the analogy with curved spacetime, as explained in Section 11 in connection with the principle of equivalence.

Curvature$_2$ is still too qualitative, and in Sections 12.2–12.4 we introduce two more ways of saying that a two-dimensional surface is curved. The concept 'curved$_3$' (or 'curvature$_3$') gives a *quantitative* measure of curvature related to the ideas expressed by curved$_1$ and curved$_2$. Curvature$_3$ is thus a pivotal concept, allocating numbers to our pictorial ideas of 'curved' surfaces. Finally, 'curved$_4$' (or 'curvature$_4$') allows us to extract the quantitative measure, curvature$_3$, *from the metric* of a two-dimensional surface. It is curvature$_4$ that allows us to discuss curved spacetime in general relativity.

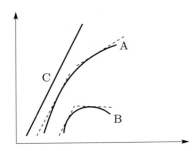

Figure 38 Curved lines in the plane with their tangents.

12.2   The curvature of a curve in the plane

We begin by introducing the simpler idea of the curvature of a curved line drawn in a plane.

Looking at the curves shown in Figure 38 commonsense suggests that curve B is more strongly curved than curve A and that C is not curved at all. After all, for the same length of travel along each of A, B and C, the tangent line to B (drawn as a dashed line) swings through a greater angle (from almost vertical to horizontal) than does the tangent to A. C is not curved because the tangent doesn't change at all. This idea of how fast the tangent swings is the basis of a mathematical definition of the curvature of a curved line. Consider the curve ABCDEFGH in Figure 39 and examine a small portion BCD of this curve, with C as its midpoint, and of length l. This small portion can be approximated by a circle of radius R_C, as shown in Figure 39. The angle through which the tangent swings in moving from point D to point B, marked as θ_C, is approximately the angle $\tilde{\theta}_C$ between the radii to points D and B. The quantities l, R_C and θ_C are related by the formula

$$l \approx R_C \tilde{\theta}_C \approx R_C \theta_C.$$

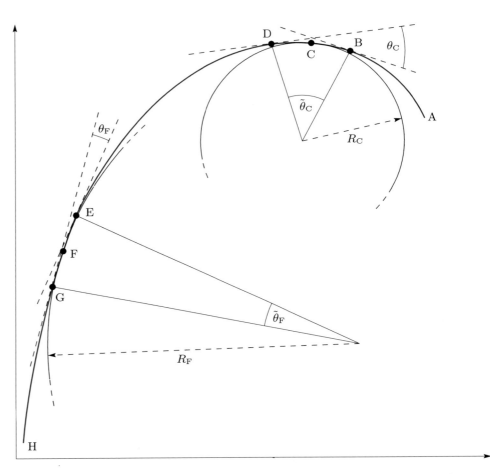

Figure 39   A curve ABCDEFGH drawn in the plane, and the approximating circles for the sections BCD and EFG.

The circle does not exactly replace the curve BCD so the length l is only approximately equal to $R_C \theta_C$. But the discrepancy gets smaller as the length l gets smaller.*

Another piece of curve ABCDEFGH, with midpoint F and of length l, can be approximated in the same way, as shown in Figure 39. For curve segment EFG, the angle θ_F is much smaller and the radius R_F of the approximating circle is much larger than θ_C and R_C respectively. The quantities l, θ_F and R_F obey the formula

$$l \approx \theta_F R_F.$$

Using the angle through which the tangent turns in a given length of travel along the curve as a measure of the curvature, the curvature of curve ABCDEFGH is greater at C than it is at F because θ_C is greater than θ_F. That is,

curvature at C > curvature at F

because

$$\theta_C > \theta_F.$$

But

$$\theta_C \approx \frac{l}{R_C} \quad \text{and} \quad \theta_F \approx \frac{l}{R_F}.$$

Thus

$$\frac{l}{R_C} > \frac{l}{R_F}$$

or

$$\frac{1}{R_C} > \frac{1}{R_F}.$$

So the quantity $1/R_X$ is a measure of the curvature at any point X, of a curve in the plane, where R_X is the radius of the circle that best approximates the curve in the region surrounding X. This measure associates to each point X of any curve $\mathscr{C}$ drawn in the plane a number,†

$$k_X = \frac{1}{R_X} \tag{66}$$

curvature, k_X, of a curve in the plane, at the point X on the curve

which we call the '*curvature* of $\mathscr{C}$ at X'. (We shall often write this as $k = 1/R$, with the point X left as understood.)

---

*In terms of Taylor approximations, we are approximating the curve BCD, given by some function f, by the curve $\tilde{f}(x)$

$$f(x) \approx \tilde{f}(x) = f(x_C) + \frac{\mathrm{d}f}{\mathrm{d}x}\bigg|_{x=x_C} \cdot (x - x_C) + \frac{1}{2}\frac{\mathrm{d}^2 f}{\mathrm{d}x^2}\bigg|_{x=x_C} \cdot (x - x_C)^2.$$

†It can be shown that, for a curve given by a function $f(x)$, the quantity k that we have defined may be computed from $f(x)$ through:

$$k_{x_0} = \left[\frac{\pm \dfrac{\mathrm{d}^2 f}{\mathrm{d}x^2}}{\left[1 + \left(\dfrac{\mathrm{d}f}{\mathrm{d}x} \right)^2 \right]^{3/2}} \right]_{x=x_0}.$$

Objective 14   **SAQ 22**   If you were told to draw a curve of constant curvature $k = 0.2 \, \text{cm}^{-1}$, what curve would you draw?

Objective 14   **SAQ 23**   Using $k = 1/R$ as the definition of curvature, argue that a straight line is a curve of constant curvature $k = 0$.

definition of a straight line and a curved line in the plane using k_X

The concept of curvature of a line, expressed as $k_X = 1/R_X$ for all points X on any curve, specifies the difference between a curved line and a straight line in the plane. The answer to SAQ 23 shows that a straight line in the plane is a line for which $k_X = 0$ for every point X on the line. A curve containing a point X for which $k_X \neq 0$ is not straight but is 'curved'.

12.3   The curvature₃ of a two-dimensional surface

curvature₃

The definition of curvature $k_X \equiv 1/R_X$ of any point X on a curved line (which has only one dimension, length) is the basis of a quantitative measure of curvature at any point of a two-dimensional surface. We call this measure *curvature₃*. As we shall soon see it has the property that a plane and a cylinder have zero curvature₃ everywhere but a sphere has a constant positive value of curvature₃.

Consider the surface drawn in Figure 40(a) and a given point A of the surface. Through this point, we can cut the surface with a plane, PL_1. This plane contains the vector **N** perpendicular to the surface at point A, and the plane is oriented in a given direction along the surface. A small section of PL_1 is shown.

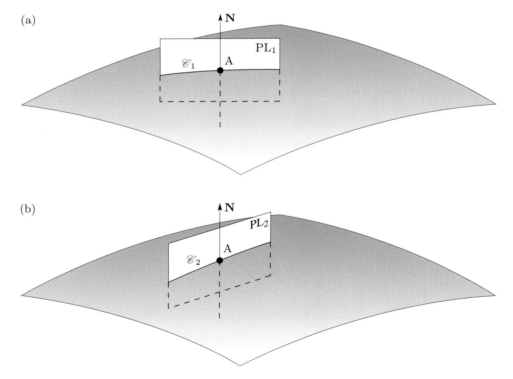

Figure 40   Illustration of curves generated by intersecting a surface with planes' containing the perpendicular vector **N**.

The intersection of the plane PL_1 and the surface defines a curve $\mathscr{C}_1$, in the plane PL_1. To this curve at point A we can associate a curvature k_A^1. It is $1/R_A^1$, where R_A^1 is the radius of the circle that best approximates $\mathscr{C}_1$ at A. We can pick another plane, PL_2, containing $\mathbf{N}$ but oriented at a different angle (see Figure 40(b)), and cut the surface with it. The intersection will define a curve, $\mathscr{C}_2$, in the plane PL_2, to which we can associate another curvature k_A^2, which can, in general, be quite different from k_A^1. This procedure can be continued indefinitely; in each new orientation, a plane PL_i will produce a new curve $\mathscr{C}_i$ with a new curvature k_A^i at the point A. Amongst all the curvatures k_A^i we can look for a largest, $k_A^{\max}$, and a smallest, $k_A^{\min}$.

An important distinction is illustrated in Figures 41(a) and 41(b). For the surface of Figure 41(a), the centres of the approximating circles to different curves at point A lie on different sides of the surface. Segments of two such circles are shown in Figure 42(a). This is not the case for point B of the surface of Figure 41(b), as is shown in Figure 42(b). All the approximating circles have centres on the same side of the surface. To differentiate these

definition of the sign of curvature k_A^i

two situations we *define* the curvature k_A^i to be *positive* if the centre of the approximating circle is on the opposite side of the surface from the arrowhead of the perpendicular vector $\mathbf{N}$ (the direction of the vector $\mathbf{N}$ being arbitrarily chosen). k_A^i is *defined to be negative* if the centre is on the same side of the surface as the arrowhead of $\mathbf{N}$. Negative curvatures are always taken to be smaller than positive curvatures in finding $k_A^{\max}$ or $k_A^{\min}$.

(a)

(b)

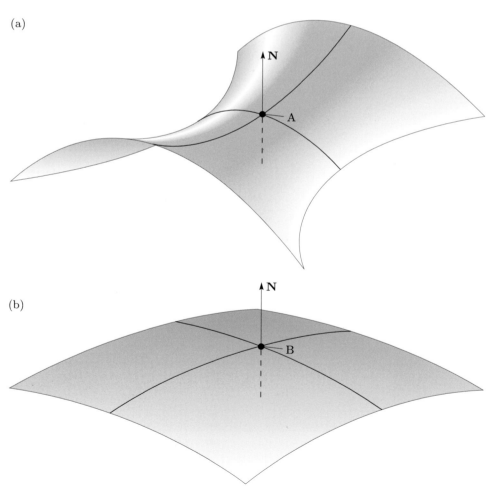

Figure 41   (a) A surface containing curves with curvature of opposite signs. (b) A surface containing curves with curvature of the same sign.

(a)

(b)

Figure 42 Curves of maximum and minimum curvature at a given point of the surfaces of Figure 41.

(a)

(b)

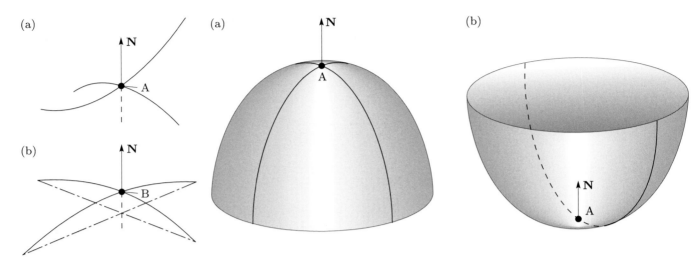

(c)

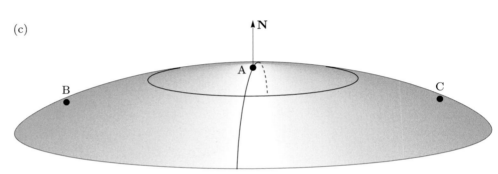

Figure 43 Surfaces of positive curvature.

We now combine the ideas of k_A^{max}, k_A^{min}, positive curvature and negative curvature to define a quantitative measure, curvature$_3$, of the curvature of a two-dimensional surface. At any point A of a two-dimensional surface, the *curvature$_3$* is defined to be

$$\mathscr{K}_A \equiv k_A^{max} \cdot k_A^{min}. \tag{67}$$

definition of the curvature$_3$ of a two-dimensional surface

$\mathscr{K}_A$ will be a positive or negative number depending on the signs of k_A^{max} and k_A^{min}. The curvature$_3$ of the whole surface is now the collection of numbers $\mathscr{K}_A$ for each point A of the surface.

To see that $\mathscr{K}_A$ is consistent with curvature$_1$ we compare values $\mathscr{K}_A$ to visual appearances. Figures 43(a) and 43(b) show surfaces of strong positive curvature at point A. It does not matter which way **N** points because the approximating circles all bend either away from or towards the arrowhead of **N** and k^{max} and k^{min} will either both be positive, (Figure 43(a)), or both be negative, (Figure 43(b)), making $\mathscr{K}_A$ positive. The surface of Figure 43(c) will be of smaller positive curvature$_3$ at point A than that of Figure 43(a). Although k_A^{max} is about the same for both surfaces, k_A^{min} will be smaller for Figure 43(c) because it slopes away more gently in the direction BAC. This shows that $\mathscr{K}_A$ gives a measure of the way the surface falls away from the point A averaged (*loosely* speaking) over all directions away from A. A large value of $\mathscr{K}_A$ means that the surface rapidly falls away from A in almost any direction — agreeing with our visual impression of a 'strongly curved surface'. Figures 44(a–c) show the same situation as it applies to surfaces of negative curvature. The value of $\mathscr{K}_A$ is more negative (further from zero) for the surfaces of Figures 44(a) and 44(b) than is the value of $\mathscr{K}_S$ for Figure 44(c). So the more $\mathscr{K}_A$ differs from zero, positively or negatively, the more curved$_1$ the surface is at A.

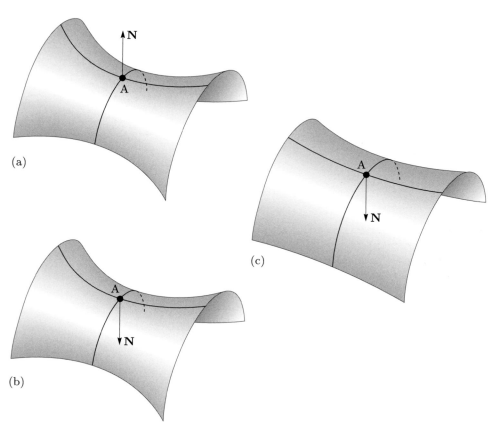

Figure 44   Surfaces of negative curvature.

We now relate curvature$_3$, expressed by $\mathscr{K}$, to curvature$_2$ (the extent that the geometric properties of a curved surface differ from those of the plane.) We first show that for every point P in the plane, $\mathscr{K}_P = 0$. For any point P on the plane S of Figure 45 and any orientation of the cutting plane, PL, the curve produced is a straight line. Since the curvature k, of a straight line is zero, for any point P, in the plane,

$$\mathscr{K}_P = k_P^{\max} \cdot k_P^{\min} = 0 \cdot 0 = 0.$$

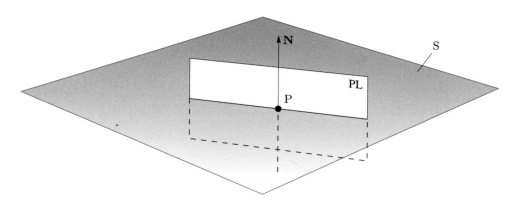

Figure 45   The plane as a surface of zero curvature.

We showed in Section 7 that the geometric properties of the surface of the circular cylinder are those of the plane since the metric is the same. Curvature$_3$ reflects this by assigning the same curvature function $\mathscr{K}$ to the cylinder and the plane: looking at Figure 46(a) we see that for a point P, the cutting plane in an arbitrary orientation produces a curve with positive curvature, k. But (see Figure 46(b)) for any point P, there is one orientation of the cutting plane that produces a straight line when it intersects the cylinder. So that $k^{\max} > 0$, $k^{\min} = 0$ and hence

$$\mathcal{K}_P = k^{\max} \cdot 0 = 0.$$

Point P is arbitrary so $\mathcal{K}_P = 0$ everywhere on the cylinder: the curvature$_3$ of the cylinder is everywhere zero. Whereas the cylinder may look curved, both curvature$_2$ and curvature$_3$ classify it with the plane, which is flat. After all, at any point on a cylinder there is one direction for which k is zero so the cylinder may be unfolded and straightened out into a plane without squeezing or stretching the surface, as shown in Figures 47(a–c). We can now use $\mathcal{K}$ to define 'flatness': a 'flat' surface is one for which $\mathcal{K}_P$ is zero for every point P in the surface. This definition makes yet another apparently curved surface 'flat': the cone.

Objective 14	**SAQ 24**	Argue intuitively that the cone should have the geometric properties of the plane. (Make a cone with a piece of paper.)
Objective 14	**SAQ 25**	Show by drawing a diagram and using the equation $\mathcal{K} = k^{\max} \cdot k^{\min}$, that the cone (excluding the vertex) is flat.
Objective 14	**SAQ 26**	Using the function $\mathcal{K} = k^{\max} \cdot k^{\min}$, prove that the sphere of radius R has constant curvature$_3$, $\mathcal{K} = 1/R^2$.

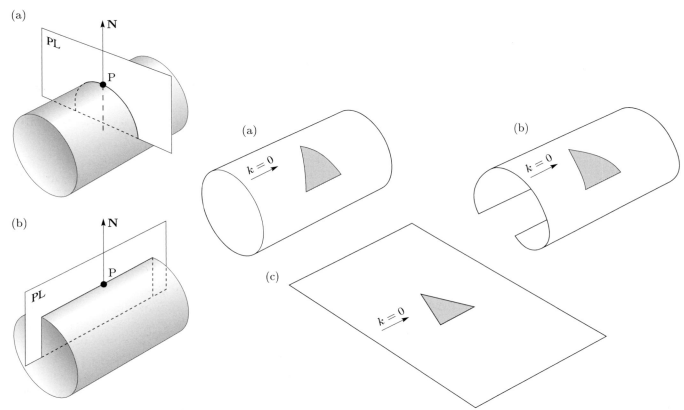

Figure 46   The cylinder as a surface of zero curvature.

Figure 47   Unfolding a cylinder to make it a plane.

definition of flat two-dimensional surface or space

Let us gather together what we have shown so far.

1 $\mathscr{K} = 0$ everywhere for the plane, the cone and the circular cylinder. This is the definition of a flat two-dimensional surface (or space).

2 The geometric properties of the circular cylinder are precisely those of the plane, because they are described by the same metric.

3 $\mathscr{K} \neq 0$ for the surface of a sphere; in fact for a sphere of radius R, $\mathscr{K} = 1/R^2$ everywhere.

4 The geometric properties of the surface of a sphere are essentially different from those of the plane (Sections 5 and 6).

Thus the curvature function, $\mathscr{K}$, is closely connected with the geometric properties. For example: as $\mathscr{K} \to 0$ the geometric properties of a surface approach those of a plane. For the surface of the sphere, $\mathscr{K} \to 0$ as $R \to \infty$, and for any region of a fixed area, as the radius gets larger, the region gets flatter and harder to distinguish from a plane.

Our technical definition of a curvature, curvature$_3$ for a two-dimensional surface makes sense of our geometric ideas. (i) It tells us which surfaces have the same geometric properties as the plane regardless of appearances. (ii) It tells us that the geometry of the surface of a sphere is different from that of a plane. (iii) It allows us to analyse other two-dimensional surfaces to predict their geometric properties.

definition of a curved$_3$ two-dimensional surface or space; $\mathscr{K}_P$

To say that a given two-dimensional surface is 'curved$_3$' means that $\mathscr{K}_P \neq 0$ for some point P in the surface. We *state without proof* that curvature$_3$ has the same content as curvature$_2$: *two surfaces have identical geometric properties if and only if they have identical curvature functions,* $\mathscr{K}$. For example, a surface has the geometric properties of the plane if and only if $\mathscr{K}$ for that surface is identically zero.

One further property of the function $\mathscr{K}$ will be useful in cosmology, Block 4. Figures 43(a–c) and 44(a–c) suggest that surfaces of everywhere negative curvature$_3$ are quite different from surfaces with everywhere positive curvature$_3$. This impression is correct. We have seen that:

1 The sphere has everywhere positive curvature $1/R^2$.

2 The ratio, C/r of circumference to radius of a circle drawn on a sphere is less than 2π.

Remember that the sides of the triangle must be geodesics. N.B. A 'line' of latitude is NOT a geodesic unless it is the Equator.

3 The sum of the interior angles of a triangle drawn on a sphere is greater than π radians.

We state without proof, (i) that these properties are also true of any region of a surface that has positive curvature$_3$ whether constant or not and, (ii), that these inequalities are reversed for regions of surfaces where $\mathscr{K}$ is negative everywhere. That is, for such regions:

1 The ratio C/r is greater than 2π.

2 The sum of the interior angles of a triangle drawn on such a surface (using geodesics as sides, of course) is less than π radians.

These different geometric properties of surfaces of positive and negative curvature$_3$ suggest that we could determine the sign of curvature$_3$ of the space one is in by drawing geometric figures and measuring their geometric properties. The importance of knowing this sign is related to another difference between surfaces of everywhere positive curvature$_3$ and everywhere negative or zero curvature$_3$, the three-dimensional analogy of which is important in cosmology. As is suggested by the sphere, a surface for which $\mathscr{K} > 0$ everywhere can be of *finite area with no edges or boundaries*; the technical word used is *closed* or *compact*. Figures 44(a–c)

closed two-dimensional surface

open two-dimensional surface

and 45 suggest that surfaces of everywhere negative curvature$_3$ (or zero curvature$_3$) cannot be closed round upon themselves in this way; in one direction they rise up while in another they drop away. They are thus described as *open*. As analogies of three-dimensional space, then, closed or open surfaces suggest very different possibilities. On a closed surface a geodesic starting out in one direction can come back to its starting point (as a great circle does on the sphere) whereas the geodesics of an open surface (such as the plane) do not return to their starting points. By analogy, a *closed three-dimensional space* could have remarkable properties. It could have *finite volume and yet have no boundaries*, and you could return to your starting point whilst always travelling on a path that is a three-dimensional geodesic. To picture such a space we would need a four-dimensional imagination, but such a space can be described by a metric (just as we did for the two-dimensional surface of a sphere). In Block 4 you will find that that the Universe itself might just be closed in this sense, in which case it would contain a finite volume of space and yet have no boundaries; this possibility does not appear to be favoured by available astronomical data. We shall return to the question of the openness or closedness of the Universe in Block 4.

Objective 14

SAQ 27   Figure 48 depicts a doughnut-shaped surface called a *torus*, with two points A and B picked out on it. Normal vectors **N** to the torus are drawn at A and B.

(a) What is the sign of $\mathcal{K}_A$?

(b) What is the sign of $\mathcal{K}_B$?

(c) What is the sign of $(C/r - 2\pi)$ for small circles drawn on the torus with centre at point A?

(d) Is the torus an open or a closed surface?

(e) Does the answer to (d) contradict the relationship of openness and negative curvature$_3$?

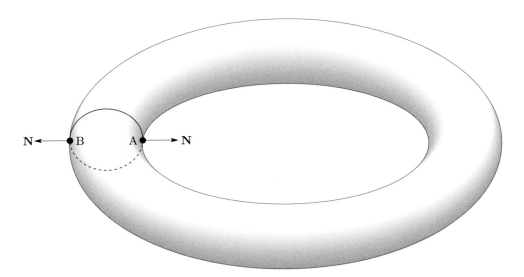

Figure 48   A torus with two points A and B picked out on it.

12.4   The derivation of the curvature of a two-dimensional surface from its metric: curvature₄

We now have a quantity $\mathscr{K}$ which gives us the curvature of a surface. However, the definition of $\mathscr{K}$ involves the perpendicular vector **N** pointing out of the surface. Two-dimensional creatures (you can think of them as ants with two-dimensional vision crawling on the surface) could never see in the direction defined by **N** so they could never use **N** to define $\mathscr{K}$ as we have done. It is only because we have considered the two-dimensional curved surface as embedded in three-dimensional space that we have been able to define curvature₃ in this way.

Suppose now that we dwellers in spacetime wish to define a measure of the curvature of spacetime. Any definition based on erecting a perpendicular to our spacetime is useless to us; we cannot conceive of getting outside spacetime. We are just like the ants who cannot conceive of getting off the two-dimensional surface by climbing in the direction of the vector **N**. However, the ants, though having only two-dimensional perception, *could* have come up with a way of defining curvature for their two-dimensional world. Such a definition will be our model for defining curvature (called curvature₄) for our own four-dimensional spacetime.

What then, can an ant know about the surface on which it is walking? We can most easily answer this question on audio tape while you look at some appropriate diagrams; we present an argument that ants can lay out a coordinate system and in terms of that system determine the appropriate metric — all this without extending their perceptions beyond the surface.

We now seek a way of calculating the curvature of the surface based on what we can say about the surface without leaving it. Curvature is an aspect of the geometric properties of a surface; since we have seen that all the geometric properties of that surface can be deduced from the metric so we should be able to extract the function $\mathscr{K}$ from the metric. So how does the metric determine the function $\mathscr{K}$?

Now turn on AC3, Band 5, and listen to it in conjunction with the 11 frames (Figures 49–59) that follow.

The sufficiently general form of the metric of two-dimensional surfaces that we have been using in this Unit is written again below:

$$\Delta l = [g_1(\Delta q^1)^2 + g_2(\Delta q^2)^2]^{1/2} \tag{68a}$$

where g_1 is a constant and g_2 is a function only of q^1. For any surface describable by such a metric, we give the fourth, last and most important definition of its curvature. To distinguish this *definition* from previous ones we label the curvature defined in this way as *curvature₄*. We *assert* that the *curvature₄* at any point $A = (q_A^1, q_A^2)$ of the surface is given by the value $\mathscr{K}(q_A^1, q_A^2)$ of the function $\mathscr{K}(q^1, q^2)$ at that point, where $\mathscr{K}(q^1, q^2)$ is defined in terms of the first and second derivatives of g_2 to be

Remember that g_2 is a function of q^1.

$$\mathscr{K}(q^1, q^2) = \frac{1}{4g_1(g_2)^2}\left(\frac{\mathrm{d}g_2}{\mathrm{d}q^1}\right)^2 - \frac{1}{2g_1g_2}\left(\frac{\mathrm{d}^2g_2}{\mathrm{d}q^{12}}\right). \tag{68b}$$

definition of curvature₄ of a two-dimensional surface (or space); $\mathscr{K}(q^1, q^2)$

To prove that this formula agrees in general with the curvature₃ definition of $\mathscr{K}_A$ is impossible here. But we can show that it reproduces results that we obtained with the curvature₃ definition of $\mathscr{K}$.

Study comment

You will not be expected to recall Equation 68b from memory, but you should be able to apply it and interpret it.

Let us begin by showing that $\mathcal{K}(q^1, q^2)$ agrees with

$$\mathcal{K}_A = k_A^{\max} \cdot k_A^{\min}$$

for the plane and the surface of the sphere.

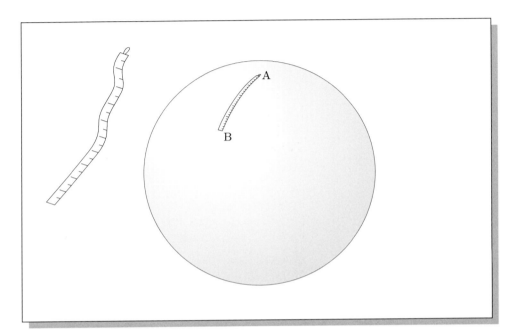

Figure 49   (FRAME 1).

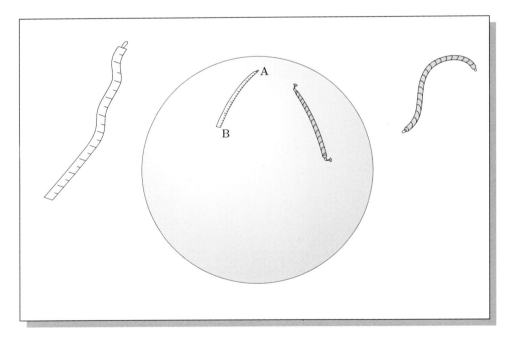

Figure 50   (FRAME 2).

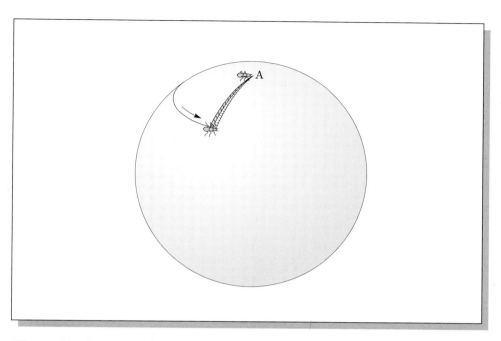

Figure 51   (FRAME 3).

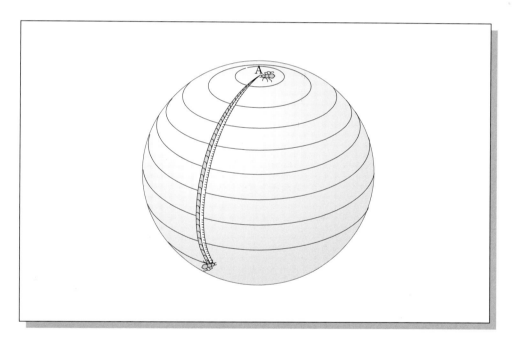

Figure 52   (FRAME 4).

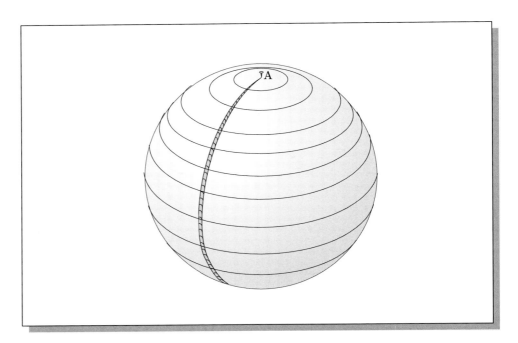

Figure 53   (FRAME 5).

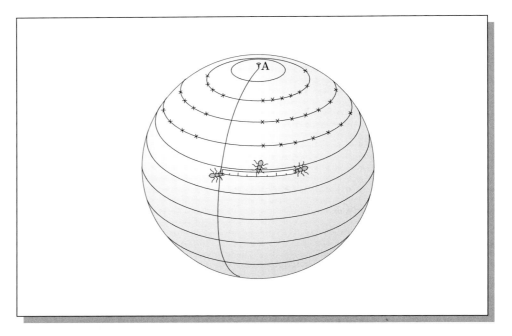

Figure 54   (FRAME 6).

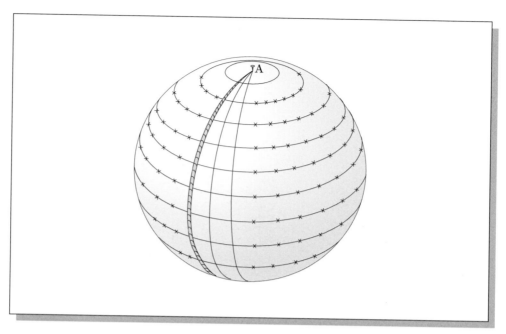

Figure 55   (FRAME 7).

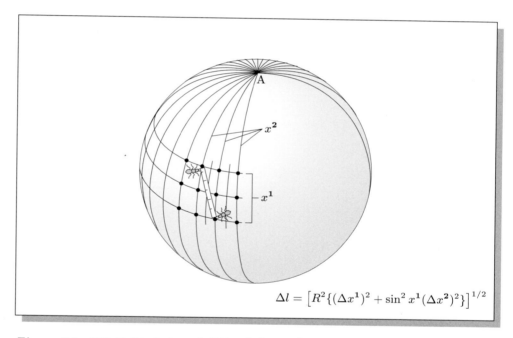

Figure 56   (FRAME 8) $\Delta l = [R^2\{(\Delta x^1)^2 + \sin^2 x^1(\Delta x^2)^2\}]^{1/2}$.

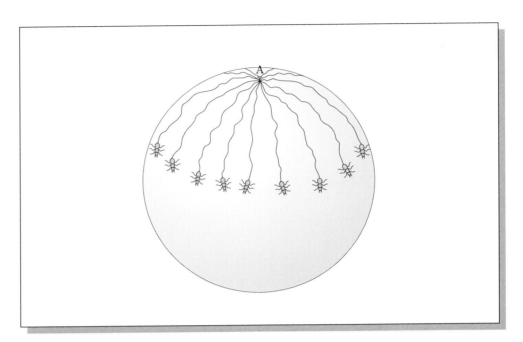

Figure 57   (FRAME 9).

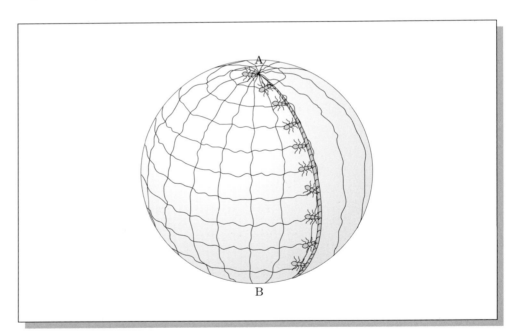

Figure 58   (FRAME 10).

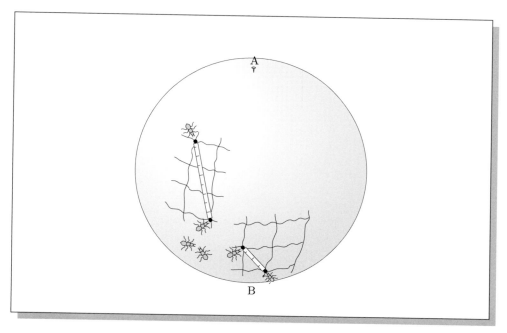

Figure 59 (FRAME 11).

The plane

The appropriate functions g_1 and g_2 for the plane described in Cartesian coordinates are

$$g_1 = 1; \qquad g_2(q^1) = 1 \text{ for all } q^1. \tag{69a and b}$$

From Equation 69b, we get $\qquad \dfrac{dg_2}{dq^1} = 0$

and hence $\dfrac{d^2 g_2}{dq^{12}} = 0$.

Putting these two expressions into Equation 68b gives

$$\mathscr{K}(q^1, q^2) = 0 \quad \text{for all } q^1 \text{ and } q^2.$$

So the plane has zero curvature everywhere according to $\mathscr{K}(q^1, q^2)$ in agreement with the curvature$_3$ result of Section 12.3.

The surface of a sphere of radius R

The functions g_1 and g_2 appropriate to the metric of the surface of the sphere of radius R, described in spherical polar coordinates, are

$$g_1 = R^2; \qquad g_2(q^1) = R^2 \sin^2 q^1. \tag{70a and b}$$

From Equation 70b we get $\dfrac{dg_2}{dq^1} = 2R^2 \sin q^1 \cos q^1$

and hence $\dfrac{d^2 g_2}{dq^{12}} = 2R^2(\cos^2 q^1 - \sin^2 q^1)$. Therefore

$$
\begin{aligned}
\mathscr{K}(q^1, q^2) &= \frac{1}{4g_1(g_2)^2}\left(\frac{dg_2}{dq^1}\right)^2 - \frac{1}{2g_1 g_2}\left(\frac{d^2 g_2}{dq^{12}}\right) \\
&= \frac{1}{4R^2 R^4 \sin^4 q^1}(4R^4 \sin^2 q^1 \cos^2 q^1) - \frac{1}{2R^2 R^2 \sin^2 q^1}2R^2(\cos^2 q^1 - \sin^2 q^1) \\
&= \frac{\cos^2 q^1}{R^2 \sin^2 q^1} - \frac{\cos^2 q^1}{R^2 \sin^2 q^1} + \frac{1}{R^2} \\
&= \frac{1}{R^2} \quad \text{(for all values of } q^1 \text{ and } q^2\text{).}
\end{aligned}
$$

Thus $\mathscr{K}(q^1, q^2)$ confirms what curvature$_3$ tells us: that a sphere of radius R has a constant positive curvature of magnitude $1/R^2$.

Since $\mathscr{K}(q^1, q^2)$ involves the coordinates of the surface, we can use it to show that the curvature is not fooled by a mere change of coordinate system. We do this by means of the following SAQ; if you have difficulty doing the SAQ you should read the answer.

Objective 14   **SAQ 28**   Suppose the metric of a surface is described by the following two functions:

$$g_1 = 1 \qquad \text{and} \qquad g_2(q^1) = (q^1)^2.$$

(a) What is the curvature of an arbitrary point of the surface, according to the function $\mathscr{K}(q^1, q^2)$?

(b) Explain why the answer to part (a) is reasonable.

The above results on the plane and the sphere are examples of the fact that $\mathscr{K}(q^1, q^2)$ associates the same curvature with any two-dimensional surface as $\mathscr{K}_A$ does. Each denotes the same property of a surface and so the associations between geometric properties, visual appearances and $\mathscr{K}_A$ now extend to $\mathscr{K}(q^1, q^2)$. The function $\mathscr{K}(q^1, q^2)$ does not have the intuitive feel of $\mathscr{K}_A$; it simply generates numbers which we associate via $\mathscr{K}_A$ with the bending away of a surface from a given point. $\mathscr{K}_A$ has thus been a pivotal concept, correlating numbers with qualitative properties, but $\mathscr{K}(q^1, q^2)$ solves the problem of the ants: we can determine it from the metric without any appeal to a third dimension. This suggests that the four-dimensional analogue of $\mathscr{K}(q^1, q^2)$ can be defined with no reference to any fifth dimension. So we fix on $\mathscr{K}(q^1, q^2)$ as our definition of curvature.

> We have used curvature$_2$ and curvature$_3$ as stepping-stones to get from our everyday idea of 'curvedness' to this definition; but from now on we use $\mathscr{K}(q^1, q^2)$ as our definition of curvature$_4$ (hereafter written without the subscript), appealing to $\mathscr{K}_A$ or curvature$_2$ for intuition when necessary.

The answer to the following SAQ contains an important piece of information.

Objective 15   **SAQ 29**   (a) Suppose that we specify the metric coefficients g_1 and g_2 of Equation 68a to be

$$g_1 = \frac{1}{c^2} \qquad \text{and} \qquad g_2(q^1) = -\frac{1}{c^2} \qquad \text{for all } q^1.$$

What is the curvature function $\mathscr{K}(q^1, q^2)$ associated with this metric?

(b) Why is it reasonable, on the basis of the answer to part (a), to say that the spacetime of special relativity with one spatial dimension is flat?

12.5 Curvature in two dimensions and in four dimensions

We now have an expression for the curvature of a two-dimensional space which we can calculate within that space from the metric, i.e. without referring in any way to a third dimension. This gives us the second of the two main components of our two-dimensional analogy to general relativity. The first, of course, was the pair of geodesic equations, from which one can calculate the paths of bodies once the metric is known.

Both the curvature and the geodesics are determined from the metric. Indeed, once the metric is known, everything about spacetime is known. So the question is: *how can we determine the metric?* So far, we have just made vague statements, going back to Unit 9 in fact, that somehow the presence of matter determines the curvature of spacetime. Perhaps, since the curvature is a complicated expression involving the metric, if we had an equation relating the curvature to the matter distribution we could solve that equation for the metric coefficients? In a nutshell, that is just what happens. But now, having used our two-dimensional analogy to give us a language, we shall give an account of how the metric is found in four-dimensional spacetime.

Review of what is required in general relativity: to calculate the motion of bodies under gravity, we need to determine geodesics; the geodesic equations require the metric as input (in four dimensions of spacetime, as well as in the familiar case of two dimensions). Hence, before we can solve mechanics problems involving motion under gravity, we must determine the metric. So far we have had a vague statement that matter somehow modifies the metric. So, the key question is: *how does matter determine the metric for the four dimensions of spacetime?* The short answer, which the rest of Section 12 explains, is: *there is a set of equations relating the curvature of spacetime to the mass distribution; since the curvature depends upon the metric, these are in effect a set of equations relating the metric to the distribution of mass; solving them gives us the metric as modified by the presence of mass.* We can then solve the problem of motion given the new metric using the geodesic equations for that metric.

In going from two dimensions to four, there is a major increase in complexity, so that this is the point where our treatment *has* to make reference to the two-dimensional analogy. Nevertheless, we shall give you a glimpse of what is going on, and later give you some very meaningful physics (planetary motion, black holes and the universe as a whole) but on the way there are some places where we have to *describe* rather than *present* the formalism.

Riemann curvature tensor

The big increase in complexity in going from two to four dimensions is exemplified by the fact that instead of *one* number $\mathscr{K}$ (evaluated using Equation 68b, for example) determining the curvature at any point, we now require no less than 20. These 20 numbers collectively are called the *Riemann curvature tensor*, and are denoted $R^{\lambda}_{\mu\nu\kappa}$; yes, there are four indices, each of λ, μ, ν and κ ranges over the values 0, 1, 2, 3 since we are in four-dimensional spacetime. You might then suppose that $R^{\lambda}_{\mu\nu\kappa}$ amounts to $4 \times 4 \times 4 \times 4 = 256$ numbers rather than 20, but they are not all independent. You have already seen that there are only ten independent metric coefficients $g_{\mu\nu}$ (see page 72) rather than 16. This is because $g_{12} = g_{21}$ for example, or in general $g_{\mu\nu} = g_{\nu\mu}$. Similar symmetries reduce the number of independent numbers in $R^{\lambda}_{\mu\nu\kappa}$ from 256 to 20. *If all 20 independent components are zero, then spacetime is flat.* To get some idea how symmetries reduce 256 components to 20, it might help to think

metric tensor

about $g_{\mu\nu}$; if you are familiar with matrices, you can regard the so-called *metric tensor* $g_{\mu\nu}$ as

$$\begin{pmatrix} g_{00} & g_{01} & g_{02} & g_{03} \\ g_{10} & g_{11} & g_{12} & g_{13} \\ g_{20} & g_{21} & g_{22} & g_{23} \\ g_{30} & g_{31} & g_{32} & g_{33} \end{pmatrix}.$$

The independent elements are the four on the diagonal, and the six above and to the right (or, equivalently, the six below and to the left) making 10 in all. The particular form of this which applies to special relativity (i.e. very far from matter, or in a local freely falling frame) is

$$\begin{pmatrix} 1/c^2 & 0 & 0 & 0 \\ 0 & -1/c^2 & 0 & 0 \\ 0 & 0 & -1/c^2 & 0 \\ 0 & 0 & 0 & -1/c^2 \end{pmatrix}.$$

The question is: what does the presence of matter do to this metric tensor of flat spacetime? We already noted in Unit 9 that matter somehow distorts spacetime, so $g_{\mu\nu}$ will no longer have this simple form and must indeed change from place to place. But how can we calculate, given some distribution of mass, the corresponding $g_{\mu\nu}$ and hence the curvature $R^{\lambda}_{\mu\nu\kappa}$?

Einstein solved this problem but in order to describe his solution, we shall have to introduce another object called, somewhat confusingly perhaps, the 'Ricci curvature', (strictly, the *Ricci curvature tensor*) $R_{\mu\nu}$. Like $g_{\mu\nu}$ it has ten independent components. What is it? It consists of certain sums of Riemann tensors; you don't have to remember this, but

Ricci curvature
Ricci curvature tensor

$$R_{\mu\nu} = \sum_{\lambda} R^{\lambda}_{\mu\lambda\nu} = R^{0}_{\mu 0\nu} + R^{1}_{\mu 1\nu} + R^{2}_{\mu 2\nu} + R^{3}_{\mu 3\nu}.$$

All you need to know is that $R_{\mu\nu}$ is a complicated expression involving derivatives of $g_{\mu\nu}$ with respect to the four spacetime coordinates. A key point is this: you could be at a point in spacetime where various components of the Riemann curvature are non-zero (so that spacetime is curved there) yet all the components of the Ricci tensor could be zero. It's just like saying that

$$a + b + c = 0 \tag{71}$$

does not imply that $a = 0, \quad b = 0, \quad c = 0$

since $\quad a = 1, \quad b = 1, \quad c = -2$

satisfy Equation 71. So, crucially, zero Ricci tensor in some local region does not mean zero Riemann tensor (flat spacetime) in that region.

Finally, to present Einstein's solution we require a single number defined for each point in spacetime, the *curvature scalar R*. We shall not write the expression for R, but it is obtained from the Ricci curvature in much the same way that the Ricci curvature is obtained from the Riemann curvature.

curvature scalar

In two-dimensional space, $\mathscr{K}$ varies from point to point, being calculated (Equation 68b) from derivatives of the metric coefficients which in general depend on position; in four-dimensional spacetime, the components of the Riemann tensor are calculated from very complicated expressions involving first and second derivatives of the metric coefficients $g_{\mu\nu}$. We wish to work back from these equations to $g_{\mu\nu}$. How do we do it?

The key is Einstein's field equations. But first we look back to the question posed on p. 77: what does it mean to say that spacetime is flat or that it is

flat spacetime

curved spacetime

curved? We can now say that *spacetime is flat if all 20 independent components of the Riemann curvature are zero at any event in spacetime.* If not, then spacetime is said to be *curved.* The analogous statement for the ants would be to say that they live in a curved two-dimensional space if they found that $\mathscr{K}$ is not zero everywhere. Just as they could test their conclusions by observing the geometric properties of figures drawn with geodesic lines, we can observe the world-lines of test-particles and light rays to decide whether it makes sense to say that we live in a flat or curved spacetime.

Figure 60 Karl Friedrich Gauss (1777–1855) left, and Georg Friedrich Bernhard Riemann (1826–1866) right. Courtesy of the Mansell Collection.

The geometry of Riemann (Figure 60) exploited by Einstein, was itself greatly indebted to the pioneers of non-Euclidean geometry, Gauss (Figure 60) and also János Bolyai (1802–1860) and Nikolai Ivanovich Lobachevsky (1793–1856).

12.6   Matter controls curvature; Einstein's field equations

In Section 12.5 we found that two extra dimensions greatly complicated the specification of curvature. The single curvature function for two-dimensional spaces, $\mathscr{K}(q^1, q^2)$, is replaced by no less than 20 independent functions, known collectively as the Riemann curvature tensor. Each component is a complicated expression involving spatial derivatives of $g_{\mu\nu}$. In special relativity the $g_{\mu\nu}$ were constant; this is no longer true. Certain sums of components of the Riemann curvature gave a ten-component object called the Ricci curvature tensor, and a curvature scalar R was also referred to (in spite of these names, it is the Riemann curvature tensor that you should think of as *the* curvature.) With all this in mind, we now address the following two questions:

1 What is it that makes spacetime curved?

2 How can we find out how curved it is in any given region?

The answers to these questions are at the heart of general relativity and will be crucial for our discussions of cosmology and of black holes.

But before we present Einstein's answer, it is helpful to digress and consider the nature of Maxwell's equations. Recall from Unit 4 that these are a set of differential equations in the field **E** (electric field) and **B** (magnetic field). They can be written with the differentials of **B** and **E** on the left-hand side, and with source terms on the right-hand side. (You might have also encountered source terms as the driving term on the right-hand side of the differential equation for a forced harmonic oscillator.) What are the source terms? They just represent the charges and currents which give rise to the electromagnetic fields; they are literally the sources of the fields. Newton's gravitational theory can also be cast in the form of a differential equation for a scalar field ϕ, the gravitational potential (the mass of a body times the *gravitational potential* gives its *gravitational potential energy* and the gravitational force on a body in any direction is then just minus the rate at which its gravitational potential energy varies in that direction.) The source term for the gravitational potential ϕ is just what you might expect: the mass density $\rho(\mathbf{x})$. After all, mass in Newton's theory is the source of gravity.

Einstein's field equations are analogous. We write them down first (don't panic!), and then comment on them:

$$R_{\mu\nu} - \tfrac{1}{2}g_{\mu\nu}R = -8\pi G T_{\mu\nu}. \tag{72}$$

We refer to *equations*, plural, since there is one for each independent combination μ, ν. They are differential equations for the metric components $g_{\mu\nu}$ since the so-called Ricci curvature $R_{\mu\nu}$ is a complicated expression involving differentials of $g_{\mu\nu}$, as is the scalar curvature R. The right-hand side is a source term with an overall factor of a familiar friend, G: this is Newton's gravitational constant! It still determines the overall strength of gravitational effects. But, in other respects the source term is much more complicated than the single quantity, the mass density $\rho(\mathbf{x})$ at each point, that would appear in Newtonian theory. On the other hand, we have to expect a source term with 10 independent components, since this is the number of independent components in each term on the left-hand side. The key factor in the source term is $T_{\mu\nu}$, with ten independent components

energy–momentum tensor   just like the metric coefficients $g_{\mu\nu}$. It is called the *energy–momentum tensor*. It specifies not only the energy and momentum densities at any point (event) in spacetime, but also the rate at which momentum flows, something to which we refer again when we discuss cosmology.

Einstein's field equations are the last link in the chain of concepts that is the general theory of relativity.

Einstein's field equations embody the answer to question **1**; *mass* makes spacetime curved. The name 'energy–momentum tensor' reminds us that energy has mass (you might have seen the equation $E = mc^2$ somewhere). Since matter is the conspicuous source of mass it is also true that *matter* makes spacetime curved.

It can be shown that the Ricci curvature $R_{\mu\nu}$ is zero in regions of spacetime where the source term is zero. For example if you think of the Sun as a distribution of mass, and that effectively there is zero mass outside it (a very good approximation in many contexts) then the Ricci curvature is non-zero within the Sun, but zero outside. *This does not mean that spacetime is curved within the Sun and flat outside the Sun.* It is the Riemann curvature which determines whether spacetime is curved, and we explained in the last subsection that the Ricci curvature can be zero at a point at which the Riemann curvature is not zero.

To understand what is going on, imagine that there is just one source of mass in the universe, or at least close enough to the region of interest to make a difference. Think of it as a star; let's call it the Sun. What

Einstein's field equations do is determine the metric coefficients $g_{\mu\nu}$ *throughout space*. Without the Sun, they would all be either $\pm 1/c^2$ or zero; consequently all derivatives of all $g_{\mu\nu}$ would be zero and the Riemann curvature would be zero. Spacetime would be flat. If you look at Equation 68b for the two-dimensional curvature, you'll see that if both the coefficients g_1 and g_2 are constants, then $\mathscr{K}$ is zero. The same thing holds in four-dimensional spacetime with the ten $g_{\mu\nu}$ playing the part of g_1 and g_2. But with the Sun as a source, the field equations lead to a solution in which $g_{\mu\nu}$ varies from point to point in spacetime *in a continuous way*. The Riemann curvature will then be non-zero, although the Ricci curvature will be zero outside the Sun. In this case, the Sun is both literally and mathematically the *source* of the curvature of spacetime. Of course, the amount of curvature, the departure of $g_{\mu\nu}$ from constancy, $\pm 1/c^2$ or zero, will fall off with distance from the source. This is a property of the field equations and of course is necessary if Newton's theory of gravitation is to emerge as a good approximation to Einstein's theory.

So now we can answer the second question: how can we determine how curved spacetime is in any region? Step 1: for a given source term, solve Einstein's field equations for $g_{\mu\nu}$ throughout space. Step 2: evaluate the Riemann curvature from $g_{\mu\nu}$ (from complicated equations we have not presented). (You may have realized by now that it is best to think of the Ricci curvature simply as a compact way of expressing a complicated function of differentials of $g_{\mu\nu}$ in terms of the four spacetime coordinates; it is probably not helpful at this stage to give any further meaning to it.)

Is the metric unique? The distribution of mass determines the curvature uniquely, but you should remember that $g_{\mu\nu}$ depends on the coordinate system. Of course, if you know the equations for transforming one set of coordinates to another (such as the polar-to-Cartesian equations like $x^1 = r \sin\theta \cos\phi \dots$) then you can use these to transform the solution $g_{\mu\nu}$ appropriate for one coordinate system to a corresponding $g'_{\mu\nu}$ appropriate to the other coordinates. Of course neither the numerical curvature nor the actual paths in space (geodesics) will depend on the coordinate system used, though the equations representing them will.

Non-linearity of the field equations. There is one point that we have glossed over concerning the source term. We have said that the source has contributions from mass–energy, the flow of energy and the flow of momentum. For some purposes, the overwhelmingly important contribution comes simply from the mass. For example, we expect that Einstein's theory of planetary motion will be dominated by the mass of the Sun as Newton's theory is. But sometimes the other terms are important, and in cosmology they are crucial. In particular, *all* sources of mass contribute, *even the mass-equivalent of gravitational energy itself*. Thus, the solution contributes to the source term! It is this *non-linearity* which can make the solution of the field equations very difficult. In fact, we remind you that the gravitational effect of gravitational energy was mentioned in Unit 9. There we mentioned that the equivalence principle (the $m = \mu$ property) has been verified to the extent that the gravitational binding energy of bound astronomical systems itself has the correct gravitational mass. Remember too, that all energy has mass: we have shown in Unit 4 that the electromagnetic field contains energy and momentum, so that even light contributes a little to the curvature of spacetime!

Let us consider what it means to have solved Einstein's field equations: it means that we know $g_{\mu\nu}$ everywhere (at least in principle; the field equations are notoriously hard to solve except in cases of high symmetry.) These coefficients can then be put into geodesic equations whose solutions are the world-lines of test-bodies and light rays for this particular distribution of energy (or mass), momentum and momentum flux. Therefore, as we have described it, Einstein's theory of motion under gravity comprises two parts: (i) the field equations, which tell us the metric coefficients $g_{\mu\nu}$ appropriate to a given energy–momentum distribution and (ii) the geodesic equations, which tell us how a test-body or a light ray will move in the spacetime described by this metric.

Objective 17   **SAQ 30**   A famous, succinct expression of the content of general relativity is: 'matter tells space how to curve; space tells matter how to move'.

(a) Which of the two parts of Einstein's theory of motion under gravity would you associate with each of the two parts of this expression?

(b) Can you improve the expression, modifying the word 'space' in each part, to make it more truthful to general relativity?

Objective 17   **SAQ 31**   (a) Can you explain why, if the Riemann curvature of spacetime is zero everywhere, the Ricci curvature of spacetime is zero everywhere?

(b) If the Riemann curvature plays the role in four-dimensional spacetime that $\mathscr{K}(q^1, q^2)$ does in two-dimensional spaces, then what does

$$\text{Riemann curvature} = R^{\lambda}_{\mu\nu\kappa} = 0$$

imply about spacetime?

(c) What does

$$\text{Ricci curvature} = R_{\mu\nu} = 0$$

in some region of spacetime imply about that region?

Before we leave the subject of Einstein's field equations, we make three brief comments on the aptness of the term *field equations*.

1   *The motion of a particle is determined by its local environment.*

An uncharged test-particle follows a geodesic in curved spacetime; its motion at the event $(x_A^0, x_A^1, x_A^2, x_A^3)$ in spacetime is dictated by the values of the metric coefficients and their first derivatives in the *immediate vicinity* of the event $(x_A^0, x_A^1, x_A^2, x_A^3)$. The concept of instantaneous action at a distance, implicit in Newton's law of gravitation, is replaced by the (local) geodesic equations. This is analogous to the replacement, in Unit 4, of Coulomb's law by the (local) electric field. As mentioned at the beginning of the Block, the idea of *instantaneous* transmission of force is inconsistent with special relativity.

2   *The geometry of spacetime in a region that contains no sources is influenced by sources in neighbouring regions.*

The geometry of spacetime is determined by the Riemann curvature, which need *not* vanish even if the Ricci curvature does. Thus in a region of spacetime that contains no sources (zero Ricci curvature) the geometry may *not* necessarily be that of special relativity i.e. the Riemann curvature is *not* zero. If there are sources in a *nearby* region, the Ricci curvature and hence the Riemann curvature, cannot be zero there. That means that whatever coordinate system is used, some of the metric coefficients must have non-zero derivatives in the source-free region, *because they vary smoothly as the coordinates vary*. In general, 'Ricci curvature nearby' implies 'Riemann curvature here', as witnessed by the effects of the Sun on planets or light signals that pass nearby.

An analogous situation occurs with the field equations of electromagnetism, Maxwell's equations. These equate certain derivatives of the electric and magnetic field vectors to sources: charges and currents. But the effects of these charges and currents are felt elsewhere, because there must be a smooth variation of electric and magnetic fields from one region of spacetime to another. To complete the analogy with general relativity, one could say that 'charge tells electric and magnetic fields how to vary' and 'electric and magnetic fields tell charge how to move'.

3   *The reality of distortions in spacetime*

Wave-like distortions in spacetime predicted by general relativity are expected to carry energy and momentum. In Unit 4, Section 4.3, we argued that the attributes of energy and momentum gave electromagnetic fields the right to be regarded as part of the *fabric* of the world. In the same way, the detection of gravitational waves would confirm the reality of the spacetime metric as a field. Indeed there has been an indirect but nevertheless convincing demonstration of the existence of gravitational waves for which Hulse and Taylor received the 1993 Nobel prize. In brief, the gradual change in orbital period of a certain binary star (a pair of neutron stars, one of them a pulsar) could be exactly described by the loss of orbital energy as the system radiated gravitational waves. No other mechanism for the loss of energy by the pair has been plausibly suggested. Gravitational waves are further discussed in Unit 12, and there is an associated video band. We simply remark here that whereas in the early 1970's the detection of gravitational waves was spoken of as a test of general relativity, now, in the late 1990's, the gravitational wave detectors under development are described by their builders as 'gravitational-wave telescopes'. This change in language says much for our increased confidence in general relativity.

A pulsar is a 'neutron star' which emits exceptionally regular radio pulses; the Doppler shift due to the orbital motion is readily measurable in the timing of the pulses; therefore one can work back from the timing of the pulses to changes in the orbital motion.

Objective 17   **SAQ 32**   Does the Ricci tensor ever *precisely* vanish?

12.7 Summary of Section 12

1 One of the main aims of the Block is to describe what is meant by saying 'spacetime in the presence of matter is curved'. Our approach is to explain first what is meant by saying that a two-dimensional surface is 'curved' and then describe 'curved spacetime' by analogy.

2 In Unit 10 & 11 we use the word 'curved', as applied to two-dimensional surfaces, in four ways. We label them, in this section, with subscripts, to be clear which one is being referred to. The first two meanings have been introduced in Section 5.

(i) 'Curved₁' means to look curved in three dimensions; this is the everyday definition.

(ii) 'Curved₂' means to have geometric properties that depend on the size of the figure drawn, that differ from Euclidean properties for any figure of finite size, and that approach Euclidean properties as the area enclosed by the figure is reduced to zero.

3 In Sections 12.2 and 12.3 we build up a third way of describing the curvature of a two-dimensional surface.

(i) We begin by assigning a quantitative measure of curvature to each point of a curve in the plane:

$$k_X \equiv \frac{1}{R_X} \tag{66}$$

where R_X is the radius of the circle that best approximates the given curve at X. With this definition we show that:

(a) for a straight line $k_X = 0$ for every point X on the line;

(b) for a circle, $k_X = 1/R$ for every point on the circle, where R is the radius of the circle.

(ii) At any point A on a two-dimensional surface, a variety of one-dimensional curves can be created by intersecting the surface with a plane which contains the vector **N** perpendicular to the surface at A. Varying the orientation of the cutting plane produces the different curves. To each curve so formed, a curvature k may be assigned. Positive curvature must be differentiated from negative curvature. Positive curvature is always considered as being greater than negative curvature. For each point A on the two-dimensional surface we determine the one-dimensional curves of maximum curvature, $k_A^{\max}$, and of minimum curvature, $k_A^{\min}$. We then define *curvature₃* of a two-dimensional surface at the point A to be

$$\mathscr{K}_A \equiv k_A^{\max} \cdot k_A^{\min}. \tag{67}$$

The curvature₃ of a two-dimensional surface is then the function $\mathscr{K}$, which assigns to each point A in the surface the number $k_A^{\max} \cdot k_A^{\min}$.

4 We relate the definition of curvature₃ to that of curvature₁ as follows: if a surface has a large positive or negative value of $\mathscr{K}_A$ at a given point A, then it looks strongly curved in three dimensions; that is, it is strongly curved according to the definition of curved₁. (The converse, however, does not necessarily apply, as illustrated by the cylinder.)

5 We relate the definition of curvature₃ to curvature₂ as follows:

(i) We show that any point A in the plane has $\mathscr{K}_A = 0$. So the plane corresponds to $\mathscr{K}_A = 0$ for all A.

(ii) We show that the circular cylinder, which looks curved but has the same geometric properties as the plane (Section 7), has the same curvature function $\mathscr{K}_A$ as does the plane (i.e. $\mathscr{K}_A = 0$ for all A.)

(iii) We therefore expect surfaces with the same curvature function (curvature₃) to have the same geometric properties (curvature₂) even if they do not look equally curved in three dimensions (curvature₁). This suggests that curvature₂ and curvature₃ refer to the same thing. Curvature₃ does it in quantitative way. That is, specifying $\mathscr{K}$ determines the geometric properties in a local region of the surface.

6 We can use the function $\mathscr{K}$ to give precise definitions of a flat surface and a curved surface:

(i) A flat surface is one for which $\mathscr{K}_P = 0$ for every point P in the surface.

(ii) A curved surface is one for which there exists at least one point for which $\mathscr{K}_P \neq 0$. (For the curved surfaces of concern to us, $\mathscr{K}_P \neq 0$ almost everywhere on the surface.)

This means that a flat surface will have the same geometric properties as the plane, so is not considered curved under the definition of curvature$_2$.

7 The curvature function $\mathscr{K}_X$ provides information about the two-dimensional surface itself, such as a two-dimensional creature crawling over the surface would conclude from making geometric measurements in the surface. But the definition of curvature$_3$ assumes the two-dimensional surface is embedded in three-dimensional space; to even conceive of the vector **N** pointing out of the surface requires the third dimension.

8 Since we have stated that the form of the metric of a surface controls its geometric properties and since we have shown a strong relationship between $\mathscr{K}_X$ and the geometric properties of a surface, there should exist a relationship between the curvature of a two-dimensional surface and its metric. This relationship we designate as curvature$_4$ and we state that, for a metric of a two-dimensional surface of the form

$$\Delta l = [g_1(\Delta q^1)^2 + g_2(\Delta q^2)^2]^{1/2}, \tag{68a}$$

where g_1 is a constant and g_2 a function of q^1, the curvature$_4$ of this surface is given by the function

$$\mathscr{K}(q^1, q^2) = \frac{1}{4g_1(g_2)^2}\left(\frac{\mathrm{d}g_2}{\mathrm{d}q^1}\right)^2 - \frac{1}{2g_1 g_2}\left(\frac{\mathrm{d}^2 g_2}{\mathrm{d}q^{12}}\right). \tag{68b}$$

This function generates the same number for each point in the surface as does the curvature$_3$ function $\mathscr{K}_X$, but makes no appeal to any third dimension.

9 Examples of the fundamental identity of the functions $\mathscr{K}_X$ and $\mathscr{K}(q^1, q^2)$ are provided by calculating the curvature$_4$ of the plane and the sphere from the expressions of their metric coefficients and seeing that they agree with the expressions given by $\mathscr{K}_X$ for the same surface.

10 The answer to SAQ 28 shows that the function $\mathscr{K}(q^1, q^2)$ gives the same expression for the curvature of the plane independently of whether the metric of the plane is written in Cartesian or plane polar coordinates. This illustrates that $\mathscr{K}(q^1, q^2)$ describes a geometric property of the surface which transcends any given coordinate description of that surface.

The answer to SAQ 29 shows that the spacetime of special relativity with one spatial dimension is flat, according to the function $\mathscr{K}(q^1, q^2)$.

11 In four-dimensional spacetime there are, in general,

(i) 10 metric coefficients, written $g_{\mu\nu}$ with $\mu = 0, 1, 2, 3$ and $\nu = 0, 1, 2, 3$, with $g_{\mu\nu} = g_{\nu\mu}$. This is where we need to think of more than 4 of them.

(ii) 20 combinations of $g_{\mu\nu}$ and their first and second derivatives which, as a set of 20, determine the curvature at every event in spacetime; this set forms the Riemann curvature, $R^{\lambda}_{\mu\nu\kappa}$.

(iii) 10 sums of selected elements of the Riemann curvature which, as a set of 10, make up what is called the Ricci curvature $R_{\mu\nu}$, a key element in Einstein's field equations. All 10 elements of $R_{\mu\nu}$ may be zero at some event without all 20 elements of the Riemann curvature being zero there.

12 The curvature of spacetime is determined through Einstein's field equations. These are

$$R_{\mu\nu} - \tfrac{1}{2}g_{\mu\nu}R = -8\pi G T_{\mu\nu}. \tag{72}$$

The quantities that make up the ten components of the source term on the right-hand side are (i) the energy density, (ii) the momentum density, (iii) the momentum flux, of the matter and non-gravitational fields present in spacetime. Einstein's field equations thus enlarge the range of source variables that cause accelerated motion from the simple Newtonian concept of mass to this group of ten. The field equations can be rewritten schematically (or near enough, recalling that the curvature scalar R depends on the Ricci curvature) as

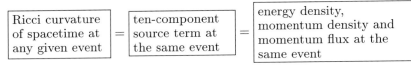

| Ricci curvature of spacetime at any given event | = | ten-component source term at the same event | = | energy density, momentum density and momentum flux at the same event |

13 The field equations, for specific forms of the ten source terms, are a set of second-order differential equations whose solutions are the metric coefficients $g_{\mu\nu}$ that control the geometric properties of spacetime. So *the energy, momentum and momentum flux control the geometry of spacetime.*

14 Although the curvature of spacetime is determined by the energy–momentum tensor, the actual expressions representing the metric coefficients $g_{\mu\nu}$ will depend upon the coordinate system used. In this narrow sense, the $g_{\mu\nu}$ are not unique.

15 While the Riemann curvature specifies the actual curvature of spacetime, it is the Ricci curvature that enters into the field equations. The Ricci curvature is zero within regions where there is no energy, momentum or momentum flux, but this does not mean that spacetime is flat (Riemann curvature = 0) there. The continuity of the Riemann tensor and the field equations ensure that the source terms in one region of spacetime affect the geometric properties of another region of spacetime. (Rather as, in electromagnetism, Maxwell's equations show how charge gives rise to an electric field outside the region of the charges.)

13 The Schwarzschild solution of the field equations

It was possibly Newton's derivation of Kepler's laws that most convincingly established Newton's law of gravitation. In a similar way, it was the solution of the analogous problem in general relativity, the motion of bodies (and light) in the space surrounding a spherical mass distribution (such as the Sun can be considered to be) that first convincingly demonstrated that general relativity is a more accurate theory of gravitation than Newton's.

We envisage a simplified problem of a single planet in motion about the Sun in which the recoil motion of the Sun is ignored. Both in Newton's theory and in general relativity, the procedure for obtaining a solution to this problem begins with certain assumptions:

1 The Sun is assumed to be a spherical distribution of matter.

2 The Sun is stationary at the origin of coordinates.

The Newtonian procedure then takes the following steps:

N1 Assume a given matter distribution for the planet, for example that the planet is a spherical mass that may be treated as a particle.

N2 Use Newton's law of gravitation to evaluate the force that the Sun and planet exert on each other.

N3 Put this force into Newton's second law: $\mathbf{F} = m\mathbf{a}$.

N4 Solve the $\mathbf{F} = m\mathbf{a}$ equations for the trajectory of the planet around the Sun.

In general relativity the procedure for the solution of the same problem is not dissimilar:

GR1   Since the planet's mass is negligible in comparison with that of the Sun (the no-recoil assumption) we consider the planet to be a test-body moving in spacetime determined by the Sun's matter distribution.

GR2   Set up the particular form of Einstein's field equations that is appropriate to the assumption of GR1.

GR3   Solve these equations to obtain the metric coefficients appropriate to this system.

GR4   Put these metric coefficients into the geodesic equations and solve those equations to find the geodesics of the metric of GR3. The planet will follow a world-line that is one of these geodesics.

The concepts of roughly corresponding levels of generality in the two methods are set out side by side in Table 9 below. You have seen the step from 3 to 4 for the metric of spacetime in the absence of matter in Section 9, where we derived the world-lines of test-particles from the geodesic equations for the metric of special relativity. Ideally, we would like to go through the complete planetary motion problem, from point 1 to point 4 of Einstein's programme as outlined in Table 9, but it is beyond the scope of S357. What we shall do for the rest of this section is to examine the *result* of moving from 1 to 2 for the planetary motion problem. That is, we shall write down the solution to Einstein's field equations for a region of spacetime outside a single spherically symmetric mass of magnitude m (the Sun), the centre of which is chosen as the origin of spatial coordinates. The exact solution to this problem was first given

Schwarzschild solution

Figure 61 Karl Schwarzschild (1873–1916). By permission of AIP Emilio Segrè Visual Archives.

by K. Schwarzschild in 1916, and is now known as the *Schwarzschild solution* of the field equations. The properties of this solution are studied to see whether they fulfil reasonable expectations.

TABLE 9   Comparison of Newton's and Einstein's solutions of the problem of motion.

Newton's method	Einstein's method
1 Newton's law of universal gravitation	1 Einstein's field equations
↓	↓
2 Specific force law for given mass distribution	2 Metric from field equations for given source distribution
↓	↓
3 Newton's second law with specific force	3 Geodesic equations with given metric
↓	↓
(solve differential equations)	(solve differential equations)
↓	↓
4 Trajectories, $\mathbf{x}_1(t)$, $\mathbf{x}_2(t)\ldots$ $\mathbf{x}_n(t)$, of parts of the system	4 World-lines $x_1^\mu(\tau)$, $x_2^\mu(\tau)$ $\ldots x_n^\mu(\tau)$ of parts of system

Any solution of Einstein's field equations will be the set of metric coefficients $g_{\mu\nu}$ that corresponds to the given source. In this case where the source has spherical symmetry, it turns out that *providing spherical polar spatial coordinates are used*, there are only four non-zero metric coefficients, g_{00}, g_{11}, g_{22} and g_{33}. Following the lead of earlier in this Unit, we shall write these as g_0, g_1, g_2 and g_3, respectively. The Schwarzschild solution to the field equations, which holds *outside the source* (in this case, the Sun) is then:

$$g_0 = \frac{1}{c^2}\left(1 - \frac{2mG}{c^2 r}\right) \quad \text{and} \quad g_1 = -\frac{1}{c^2\left(1 - \dfrac{2mG}{c^2 r}\right)} \tag{73a and b}$$

$$g_2 = -\frac{r^2}{c^2} \quad \text{and} \quad g_3 = -\frac{r^2 \sin^2 \theta}{c^2} \tag{73c and d}$$

With

$$q^0 = ct, \quad q^1 = r, \quad q^2 = \theta \quad \text{and} \quad q^3 = \phi$$

the general form of the spacetime metric of postulate 1 (p. 72) becomes, in the case of the metric of the Schwarzschild solution, replacing $(\Delta q^0/c)^2$ by $(\Delta t)^2$,

$$\Delta\tau = \left[\left(1 - \frac{2mG}{c^2 r}\right)(\Delta t)^2 - \frac{1}{c^2}\left\{\frac{(\Delta r)^2}{\left(1 - \dfrac{2mG}{c^2 r}\right)} + r^2(\Delta\theta)^2 + r^2\sin^2\theta(\Delta\phi)^2\right\}\right]^{1/2}. \tag{74a}$$

Let us first check that this metric behaves in a way we would expect for a reasonable limiting case. When we get very far away from the mass at the origin, we should expect its effects on spacetime to be negligible. So as $r \longrightarrow \infty$, the Schwarzschild metric should approach in form the metric that corresponds to the complete absence of matter; that is, the metric of special relativity. As r gets large the quantity $2mG/c^2 r$ will become small; at large enough values of r it will be negligible in comparison to 1 and can be dropped. Then Equation 74a becomes

$$\Delta\tau = \left[(\Delta t)^2 - \frac{1}{c^2}\{(\Delta r)^2 + r^2(\Delta\theta)^2 + r^2\sin^2\theta(\Delta\phi)^2\}\right]^{1/2} \tag{74b}$$

The three terms in the curly brackets are simply

$$(\Delta x^1)^2 + (\Delta x^2)^2 + (\Delta x^3)^2$$

written in terms of r, θ and ϕ, the spherical polar coordinates of three-dimensional space. (One can obtain the spherical polar form from the Cartesian form just as the metric of the plane is obtained in plane polar coordinates from the Cartesian form in Section 6.3. Equations 23(a–c), with R corresponding to r and being allowed to vary along with θ and ϕ, provide the equations of transformation.) So the Schwarzschild metric becomes indistinguishable from the metric of special relativity far away from the mass at the origin. Notice also that reducing m, the mass at the origin, to zero, has the same effect on spacetime, as should be the case.

Objective 18   **SAQ 33**   Formulate these last two reasonable properties in a single mathematical statement by providing the 'expression' for insertion in the statement: "As 'expression' $\rightarrow 0$, the Schwarzschild metric $\rightarrow$ mass-free, flat-spacetime, metric."

Thus, a third reasonable property of the Schwarzschild metric is the fact that the extent that it departs from the metric of flat spacetime scales with the factor G, the universal gravitational constant. The origin of this factor is, of course, the fact that the source term on the right-hand side of Einstein's field equations contains this overall factor. Moreover, since the only source of gravitational field in the model is the mass m of the central body, it is reasonable that this too, should be an overall factor in the term which represents a departure from flatness, $2mG/c^2r$.

A fourth satisfying property of the Schwarzschild metric can be seen by looking at the way the time coordinate appears in it. Since there is nothing in our prescription of the physical situation that changes in time, the metric should be invariant under a change in the origin of the time coordinate. Changing the origin of time is done by transforming t to t' by the equation

$$t' = t + t_0 \quad \text{where } t_0 \text{ is a constant.}$$

Now t appears only in the expression $(\Delta t)^2$. If t_1 and t_2 represent the time coordinates of neighbouring events, then

$$\Delta t = t_2 - t_1 = (t_2 + t_0) - (t_1 + t_0) = t'_2 - t'_1 = \Delta t'.$$

So the metric of Equation 74a has the expected time-independence.

It was necessary for us to simply quote the Schwarzschild metric and show that it has reasonable properties since a derivation requires tensor calculus. We can make the g_0 term of the metric plausible, using arguments involving the equivalence principle. But first we face up to a property of coordinates in general relativity which we have hardly touched on.

In the tape-frame section, which showed how one could establish coordinate systems on a sphere, we saw that there are always many possible coordinate systems. So, while the coordinates of the ants work quite well to label each point uniquely, there is, in general, no obvious way of using them to calculate distances. Knowing that two neighbouring points, A and B, have coordinates (q_A^1, q_A^2) and $(q_A^1 + \Delta q^1, q_A^2 + \Delta q^2)$ tells you nothing about the distance between the points. *Only when you know the metric coefficients g_1 and g_2 at the point A can you work out*

$$\Delta l = [g_1(\Delta q^1)^2 + g_2(\Delta q^2)^2]^{1/2}$$

to compute the distance between points A and B. Even for spherical polar coordinates, the distance between two points is no longer simply the square root of the sum of the squares of the coordinate differences, as it is in Euclidean space with Cartesian coordinates.

Now, in the absence of matter, in flat space, you could always convert back to Minkowski coordinates with the standard measure of distance. But the presence of matter changes that: once spacetime becomes curved, and one finds factors like g_1 of the Schwarzschild solution coming in, one *cannot* convert back to Minkowski coordinates for which distance is simply

$$[(\Delta x^0)^2 - (\Delta x^1)^2 - (\Delta x^2)^2 - (\Delta x^3)^2]^{1/2}.$$

Distances now depend on coordinate differences in more complicated ways which depend on the metric. The essential function of coordinates is to label events. This property of coordinates of curved spaces is described by saying that the coordinates have *lost their metrical significance*, where metrical is the adjective associated with measurement of distance.

loss of metrical significance

This loss of metrical significance is a property of coordinate systems used to map out spacetime in general relativity. It is a perplexing idea that spacetime can be criss-crossed with a network of coordinate markers but that the difference, $t_2 - t_1$, of the coordinate marker you call time does *not* correspond to the time elapsed on a clock moving between the events labelled by t_1 and t_2. Einstein found it perplexing too. In his description of how the general theory developed he says:

> The fact of the equality of inert and heavy mass [$m = \mu$ in our notation] thus leads quite naturally to the recognition that the basic demand of the special theory of relativity (invariance of the laws under Lorentz-transformation) is too narrow ... This happened in 1908. Why were another seven years required for the construction of the general theory of relativity? The main reason lies in the fact that it is not easy to free oneself from the idea that coordinates must have an immediate metrical meaning ...

> Schilpp, P.A. (editor) (1969) *Albert Einstein — Philosopher Scientist*, Illinois, Open Court, third edition.

13.1   The origin of gravitational time dilation

The r- and t-coordinates in which we have written the Schwarzschild metric do not have immediate metrical meaning so that we have to distinguish the coordinate interval (say $\Delta t = t_2 - t_1$), between two events labelled with the values t_1 or t_2 and the time elapsed on a clock that moves between these two events. The latter, as you know from Unit 7 and Section 9 of this Unit, is what we call proper time; the former, Δt, is called **coordinate time** *coordinate time*. The necessity of distinguishing intervals of coordinate time from intervals of proper time can be seen if we consider the change in proper time for events that have the same spatial coordinate markers, r, θ and ϕ. That is we try to evaluate $\Delta\tau$ between events $\mathscr{E}_1 = (t, r, \theta, \phi)$ and $\mathscr{E}_2 = (t + \Delta t, r, \theta, \phi)$ so that

$$(\Delta r)^2 = (\Delta\theta)^2 = (\Delta\phi)^2 = 0.$$

Then

$$\Delta\tau = \left(1 - \frac{2mG}{c^2 r}\right)^{1/2}\Delta t. \tag{75}$$

This implies that when r gets very large (i.e. $1/r$ gets very small) there is a simple relationship between coordinate time t, and proper time τ:

$$\Delta\tau = \Delta t \tag{76}$$

in the limit, $r \to \infty$. Two events that are separated by a time interval $\Delta\tau$, as measured on a clock sitting at (r, θ, ϕ) where r is very large, will also have time coordinate labels, in this system of coordinates, that differ by $\Delta t = \Delta\tau$. But suppose we situate our events at a smaller radius r such that

$$A \equiv \frac{2mG}{c^2 r} \neq 0.$$

Then

$$\Delta\tau = (1 - A)^{1/2}\Delta t \neq \Delta t. \tag{77}$$

So events at this spatial point that are separated in time by $\Delta\tau$, as measured on a clock at this point, will have time *coordinates* that differ by $\Delta\tau/(1 - A)^{1/2}$ in the coordinate system in which we have written the Schwarzschild metric.

Objective 18   **SAQ 34**   Why should you not be surprised by the fact that clocks behave as described in Equations 76 and 77?

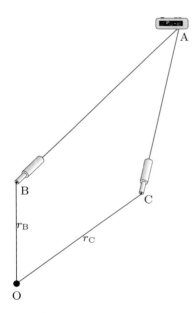

Figure 62 The establishment of coordinate time for observers B and C.

To make this distinction between coordinate time and proper time concrete, we describe a procedure for establishing coordinate time t, for all data takers in the frame. In Figure 62 a clock, A, is set a very great distance from the origin O, where the centre of the spherical mass is situated. Ideally we would like A to be at infinity but 'a very great distance' will do. The time kept by this clock will be our coordinate time, in agreement with Equation 76. How does a data taker, B or C, at a finite distance from O, know what coordinate time is, given that a clock (identical with clock A) that he has with him reads proper time? What data taker B or C does is to observe with a telescope the digital readout of clock A. The succession of numbers seen through the telescope provides a time coordinate with which to label any nearby event. All data takers get a uniform rate of flow of the numbers by sighting the same clock, A. To enable the data taker at B to establish the local coordinate time, A sends a radio signal to B, recording the interval on clock A between sending the signal and receiving the echo from B. Halving this time interval yields C_B, the correction constant for B. A tells B that if clock A is observed through the telescope to read (say) 12.15.27, then 'coordinate time' is actually 12.15.27 $+ C_B$.

We have been at pains to distinguish proper time from coordinate time to illustrate the difference between the *labelling* function of coordinates and the *metrical*, or distance-measuring function of the metric. But time is not special in this regard. With the radial coordinate r, we also must distinguish the proper distance, as measured with metre rods, from the coordinate distance Δr, between neighbouring events that have coordinates (t, r, θ, ϕ) and $(t, r + \Delta r, \theta, \phi)$. Although not pursued here, it is clear from Equation 74a that the radial coordinate r, has no more immediate metrical significance than the time coordinate t.

Equation 77 implies that one effect of matter on spacetime will be that clocks placed at different places outside a large mass will tick at different rates in some sense. This should remind you that in Unit 9 we found that the equivalence principle, EP, leads to a gravitational redshift. We now use Equation 75 to show that indeed, general relativity leads to the expression found in Unit 9 for this redshift.

In what sense is the rate of clocks determined by their position? We shall assume that a clock as seen in its own rest frame is not affected by gravity. That is, it has some intrinsic period Δt_i which is not affected by gravity. A good model to have in mind is an atomic clock, so Δt_i will be the time interval between successive wave crests of light emitted by the clock, as seen close to the clock.

Now place the clock in the region outside a large mass m at some radial distance r from the centre of the mass. Spacetime in the region is described by the Schwarzschild expression for $\Delta \tau$, Equation 74a, but since the clock is fixed in space the ticks are events separated only in time, so $\Delta r = \Delta \theta = \Delta \phi = 0$ and we can use Equation 75. Let us denote by $\Delta \tau_r$ the proper time interval which is the time between successive ticks as measured in the rest frame of the clock; this is the period of the radiation, so $\Delta \tau_r = \Delta t_i$. The frequency of the radiation measured by someone at rest near the clock will be $f_r = 1/\tau_r = 1/\Delta t_i$. The frequency f_∞ of the radiation measured by someone receiving the radiation very far from the mass, i.e. at $r \to \infty$, point A in Figure 62, will be related to the interval between the ticks out there, $\Delta t = 1/f_\infty$ and this will be related to $\Delta \tau_r$ by

$$\Delta \tau_r = \left(1 - \frac{2mG}{c^2 r}\right)^{1/2} \Delta t.$$

It follows that the frequency f_r at radius r is related to f_∞ by

$$f_r = \left(1 - \frac{2mG}{c^2 r}\right)^{-1/2} f_\infty$$

and since $2mG/c^2 r \ll 1$, this can be closely approximated as

$$f_r = \left(1 + \frac{2mG}{c^2 r}\right)^{1/2} f_\infty$$

$$\approx \left(1 + \frac{mG}{c^2 r}\right) f_\infty.$$

We now ask the following question: what will be the measured frequency of the light emitted from our original point at radius r and received at some different radial point $r + \Delta r$. The best way to think of this is to think of a train of waves with period $\Delta \tau_r$ at radius r and period Δt at a point at infinity i.e. Δt is the coordinate time interval corresponding to $\Delta \tau_r$. At whatever radius the radiation is received, the coordinate time interval (and its reciprocal f_∞) will be the *same*, so $f_{r+\Delta r}$, the measured frequency at radius $r + \Delta r$ must be

Of course Δr is the radial distance between two separate fixed points, which is not the meaning of Δr in Equations 74a.

$$f_{r+\Delta r} = \left(1 + \frac{mG}{c^2 (r + \Delta r)}\right) f_\infty.$$

If Δr is small then the measured frequency at $r + \Delta r$ is increased by

$$\Delta f_r = f_{r+\Delta r} - f_r \approx \Delta r \times \frac{\mathrm{d}}{\mathrm{d}r} f_r$$

so that

$$\Delta f_r \approx -\frac{mG}{c^2 r^2} f_\infty \, \Delta r.$$

Now imagine that the gravitating mass m is the Earth and Δr represents a small difference H in height above the Earth's surface, as in Unit 9. So, with $\Delta r = H$ and, for concreteness $r = R$, the radius of the Earth, and since $2mG/c^2 R \ll 1$, we have

$$\frac{\Delta f_R}{f_\infty} \approx \frac{\Delta f_R}{f_R} = -\frac{mG}{c^2 R^2} H.$$

But the acceleration of gravity on the surface of the Earth has magnitude $g = mG/R^2$ so finally:

$$\frac{\Delta f_R}{f_R} = -\frac{gH}{c^2}.$$

This is the difference between the frequency of the emitter in its own rest frame and the frequency that would be measured when it was received in a rest frame at height H. It is exactly the expression we deduced from the EP in Unit 9 for the gravitational redshift *within a local region* (in which g was constant). Hence, the related experimental tests which were presented in Unit 9 as tests of the EP can be seen to be tests of general relativity: if in a local region, it were to be found that $\Delta f/f$ was not $-gH/c^2$, then general relativity would be disproved. Clearly, such tests are important.

Although we have re-derived the EP result from GR, it must be noted that GR says *much more* than the EP. Equation 75 allows conclusions to be drawn that are not confined to a local region where gravity is effectively uniform. If one applies the Schwarzschild solution to the solar system, making the Sun the predominant and only mass (true not too near a planet) then Equation 75 relates the period between the emitted and received frequencies of radiation for two points at rest anywhere in the solar system. This could be points at the radii of Mercury and Pluto: the Unit 9 derivation for a local region based on the EP is quite inapplicable. We reiterate the point made in Unit 9 that we are *not* seeing the effect of gravity on clocks; rather the large mass Sun has distorted spacetime so that local time at a fixed point (proper time) is *no longer* the coordinate time. Indeed, if you sit beside your clock, you will always see it going with the same frequency $f = 1/\tau_i$ where τ_i is the intrinsic period. This leads to our alternative application of Equation 75: if we fix identical clocks at different radii, each with the same proper interval between ticks (or wave crests), it will be the corresponding coordinate time interval Δt that will vary according to Equation 75 depending upon where the clock is placed. In other words, since Δt is the reciprocal of the frequency of the light (or of the ticks) which would be seen at infinity, this frequency will depend upon where the emitting atom (clock) is placed. In this second way of using Equation 75, we now compare different Δt (coordinate times) for fixed $\Delta \tau$ but different positions. Compare this with our redshift derivation where we examined the variation in $\Delta \tau$ for fixed Δt. When we study the radiation of light emitted by atoms near black holes, we shall be much concerned with the variation in Δt for fixed $\Delta \tau$.

13.2   Why the planets stay in orbit; why apples fall

But the metric found by Schwarzschild for the region external to a mass m has other consequences! Since we have promised that general relativity is a metric theory of gravity, should not we be able to derive planetary motion from the metric that Schwarzschild derived from Einstein's field equations? Doesn't the distortion of spacetime which this metric represents account for the path of the Earth around the Sun? Indeed it does, but a derivation is beyond the scope of this course. But we can give some idea of how Einstein's theory correctly predicts how bodies move under *purely radial motion* i.e. motion for fixed θ and ϕ; they move exactly in accord with Newton's theory as long as we keep to speeds which are much less than that of light, and ensure that $2mG/c^2r \ll 1$. These conditions are satisfied pretty well by the planets, but leave open the possibility of some departures from Newtonian behaviour that can be exploited to test Einstein's theory (see Section 14). We now outline the derivation of radial motion, calling upon certain results demonstrated in Appendix 1 (not examinable).

Study comment

You would not be expected to reproduce the following derivation unprompted; the Schwarzschild metric and Equation 78 would be supplied. The important point to remember is in the emphasized sentence near the end.

Specifically, we show that a test-body executing free fall in the spacetime described by the Schwarzschild metric obeys Newtonian equations of motion in the limits of (i) weak gravitational fields, and, (ii) speeds much smaller than the speed of light. First let us consider motion in the radial direction only with the following limits applying: (*a*) large r and (*b*) small speeds, $\dfrac{1}{c}\dfrac{\mathrm{d}r}{\mathrm{d}\tau} \ll 1$. The Schwarzschild metric as applied to this case only contains terms in Δt and Δr, since $\Delta\theta$ and $\Delta\phi$ will be zero for any purely radial movement. The Schwarzschild metric then reduces to

$$\Delta\tau = \left[\left(1 - \frac{2mG}{c^2r}\right)(\Delta t)^2 - \frac{1}{c^2}\frac{(\Delta r)^2}{\left(1 - \dfrac{2mG}{c^2r}\right)} \right]^{1/2}.$$

In Appendix 1 we show that a slight generalization of the geodesic equations introduced in Section 8, when applied to this metric, leads to the following equation which applies to a freely falling body:

$$\left(1 - \frac{k}{r}\right)\frac{\mathrm{d}t}{\mathrm{d}\tau} = N \tag{78}$$

where N is a constant determined by the way the body (e.g. planet) moves at $t = 0$ (obviously the subsequent motion must depend upon how the body sets out). To simplify the equations, we have introduced k given by

$$k = \frac{2mG}{c^2}$$

with which the above expression for $\Delta\tau$ becomes:

$$1 = \left[\left(1 - \frac{k}{r}\right)\left(\frac{\Delta t}{\Delta\tau}\right)^2 - \frac{1}{c^2}\frac{1}{\left(1 - \frac{k}{r}\right)}\left(\frac{\Delta r}{\Delta\tau}\right)^2\right]^{1/2}.$$

In the limit that $\Delta\tau \to 0$, this becomes

$$1 = \left[\left(1 - \frac{k}{r}\right)\left(\frac{dt}{d\tau}\right)^2 - \frac{1}{c^2}\frac{1}{\left(1 - \frac{k}{r}\right)}\left(\frac{dr}{d\tau}\right)^2\right]^{1/2}. \tag{79}$$

From Equations 78 and 79 we can extract a Newtonian equation of motion under gravity for the radial motion of a test-body moving at large r-coordinate values with a speed much less than that of light.

Squaring Equation 79 and using Equation 78 we find

$$1 = \left(1 - \frac{k}{r}\right)\left(\frac{dt}{d\tau}\right)^2 - \frac{1}{c^2}\frac{1}{\left(1 - \frac{k}{r}\right)}\left(\frac{dr}{d\tau}\right)^2$$

$$= \frac{1}{\left(1 - \frac{k}{r}\right)}\left[\left(\left(1 - \frac{k}{r}\right)\frac{dt}{d\tau}\right)^2 - \left(\frac{1}{c}\frac{dr}{d\tau}\right)^2\right]$$

$$= \frac{1}{\left(1 - \frac{k}{r}\right)}\left[N^2 - \left(\frac{1}{c}\frac{dr}{d\tau}\right)^2\right]. \tag{80}$$

Multiplying Equation 80 by $\left(1 - \frac{k}{r}\right)$, we have

$$1 - \frac{k}{r} = N^2 - \left(\frac{1}{c}\frac{dr}{d\tau}\right)^2. \tag{81}$$

To show the correspondence with Newtonian mechanics, we differentiate Equation 81 with respect to τ to obtain

$$\frac{k}{r^2}\frac{dr}{d\tau} = -\frac{2}{c^2}\frac{dr}{d\tau}\frac{d^2r}{d\tau^2}$$

and hence

$$\frac{d^2r}{d\tau^2} = -\frac{c^2}{2}\frac{k}{r^2} = -\frac{c^2}{2}\frac{2mG}{c^2r^2} = -\frac{mG}{r^2} \tag{82}$$

using $k = 2mG/c^2$.

But τ is the time read by a clock moving with a test-particle whose radial coordinate r satisfies Equation 82. For radial motion at speeds much less than c and for values of r which are not too small, this will agree with the Newtonian idea of time. This is because the effects of special relativistic time dilation and gravitational redshift, which in general make τ differ from the coordinate time t, can then be ignored. Also, it is at large enough values of r (so that $k/r \ll 1$) that the radial coordinate r may be identified with the Newtonian idea of radial distance. Under these conditions the left-hand side of Equation 82 can be interpreted as the radial acceleration. The right-hand side of Equation 82 is just the radial acceleration predicted by Newtonian mechanics, if r is the distance from the origin.

Thus general relativity predicts the same results as Newtonian mechanics for radial motion at low speeds and values of r for which $k/r \ll 1$.

This calculation has shown that a test-body executing free fall in the spacetime of the Schwarzschild metric will obey a Newtonian equation of motion if it is moving slowly with respect to the speed of light in a region of the field in which $k/r \ll 1$. Since $k/r \approx 10^{-9}$ at the Earth's surface these approximations are perfectly reasonable to make. Einstein's theory of motion under gravity can then be said to encompass Newton's theory and to reduce to it in this limiting case.

13.3   Remarks on the Schwarzschild solution

We were not able to show you Einstein's field equations in full detail, nor their derivation. But we have been able to show you a solution to these equations (applying in the region outside a single, stationary spherical mass), and this enables us to show you how the motion of bodies near the Sun comes about (albeit restricted to radial motion), how the gravitational redshift comes about, and in the next section, how radar signals are delayed as they pass close to the Sun. In this respect we have gone beyond showing you a two-dimensional analogy to general relativity.

The Schwarzschild metric shows quantitatively how the spacetime around a central mass is *fundamentally* different from the space and time of Block 1. Spacetime itself depends upon the distribution of mass. It is no longer a passive arena in which bodies move and interact, but part of that interaction.

For the case solved by Schwarzschild (that of a single central mass) spacetime itself is distorted in a way that has spherical symmetry. But if we make the Sun's mass the source term, what happens to spacetime near the Earth? To solve the problem of Newton's apple using general relativity, we would model spacetime near the Earth according to the Schwarzschild solution in which the Earth was the source. Near the Earth that would be a good model, but not exact. We know, after all, that both the Sun and Moon contribute to the tides, so they both contribute to the curvature of spacetime near the surface of the Earth. But once one has several bodies contributing to the total source term, the simplicity of the spherically symmetric situation is lost. The exact and complete solution to such problems is in general beyond the technical abilities of physics at present.

Objective 18   **SAQ 35**   (a) Suppose the $\phi = 0$ meridian were moved around by a finite amount ϕ_0, so that a new coordinate system for the Schwarzschild metric was set up: (t, r, θ, ϕ'), where $\phi' = \phi + \phi_0$. Show that the Schwarzschild metric does not change when the new coordinates are substituted for the old ones.

(b) Give a physical justification for the mathematical fact stated in part (a).

Objective 19   **SAQ 36**   Why would it *not* have been in accord with the consensus view of the scientists of the time to say, in 1850, that the geometric properties of space and time are as much part of the solution of any particular problem of motion under gravity as the trajectories of particles are part of the solution?

13.4   Summary of Section 13

1 Newton's method and Einstein's method of solving the problem of motion under gravity can be compared and contrasted. The principal steps in both approaches are set out in Table 9.

2 The field equations for the case of a single spherically symmetric distribution of mass have a simple solution applying to the region outside the mass. This is the Schwarzschild solution, in which there are four non-zero metric coefficients g_0, g_1, g_2, g_3. Written in what are essentially spherical polar coordinates with the mass at the origin, these four functions take the forms

$$g_0 = \frac{1}{c^2}\left(1 - \frac{2mG}{c^2 r}\right) \quad \text{and} \quad g_1 = -\frac{1}{c^2\left(1 - \frac{2mG}{c^2 r}\right)} \tag{73a and b}$$

$$g_2 = -\frac{r^2}{c^2} \quad \text{and} \quad g_3 = -\frac{r^2 \sin^2 \theta}{c^2} \tag{73c and d}$$

where m is the mass of the Sun and G the universal gravitational constant. (Note that the expression for g_0 is that appropriate for the zeroth coordinate $x^0 = ct$; if one used simply t, then g_0 would not have the $1/c^2$ factor.) The metric is:

$$\Delta\tau = \left[\left(1 - \frac{2mG}{c^2 r}\right)(\Delta t)^2 - \frac{1}{c^2}\left\{\frac{(\Delta r)^2}{\left(1 - \frac{2mG}{c^2 r}\right)} + r^2(\Delta\theta)^2 + r^2 \sin^2\theta(\Delta\phi)^2\right\}\right]^{1/2} . \tag{74a}$$

3 The Schwarzschild metric can be seen to have properties that would be expected of a metric that describes the spacetime exterior to a single spherically symmetric mass. For example,

(i) When the radial coordinate is allowed to become very large or the mass m is allowed to go to zero, then the Schwarzschild metric becomes the metric of special relativity.

(ii) The Schwarzschild metric is invariant under time translation.

4 The coordinates t and r in the Schwarzschild metric do not have immediate 'metrical significance' which means that while different values of t, r, θ and ϕ denote distinct events, the time coordinate difference, Δt, between two events (t, r, θ, ϕ) and $(t + \Delta t, r, \theta, \phi)$ does not indicate the difference in proper time registered on a clock present at both those events. Also the difference Δr, in radial coordinate between two events (t, r, θ, ϕ) and $(t, r + \Delta r, \theta, \phi)$ does not indicate the proper length, as measured with rigid metre rods, between those two events. Coordinates in general relativity, such as the (t, r, θ, ϕ) coordinates in which the Schwarzschild metric has been written, serve essentially to *label* events. Elapsed proper time (or proper length, although it does not concern us much in Unit 10 & 11) between events is evaluated using the metric.

5 The constant $2mG/c^2$, which appears in the g_0 term of the Schwarzschild metric, can be made plausible by demonstrating that it leads to the same expression for the gravitational redshift that was found in Unit 9 using the equivalence principle.

6 For bodies moving much slower than light and in regions where the field is weak ($2mG \ll c^2 r$), the geodesic equations for the Schwarzschild solution are just those one finds from Newton's theory. This was demonstrated for the case of radial motion (θ and ϕ constant.)

7 (i) The Schwarzschild metric provides an example of the fact that the geometric properties of spacetime in the presence of matter, as described by general relativity, are not spatially homogeneous. (ii) Other, more complicated matter distributions will determine spacetimes that are not homogeneous in space or time. (iii) Quite simple distributions of matter, such as that of a binary star, produce complicated spacetimes for which there are generally no exact solutions. Thus the geometric structure of spacetime has become as much part of the *solution* to the problem of motion under gravity as the trajectories or world-lines of particles are part of the solution.

14   Experimental tests of general relativity

We have seen in the last section that an explanation of the laws of motion of planets emerged from general relativity, which was based on very general assumptions. Clearly, the derivation of the laws of gravitation from more fundamental principles is a dramatic triumph, but is the theory correct? This is an important question since what is at stake is a root and branch overthrow of our classical understanding of space and time. In this section we outline four ways in which Einstein's general relativity has been tested.

A clue as to how the theory might be tested is to be found in the conditions we put on the demonstration in the last section that bodies do indeed accelerate toward the Sun following Newtonian laws. The derivation stipulated that $k = 2mG/c^2 \ll r$ and that $v/c \ll 1$, so that we might expect departures from Newtonian behaviour to be most appreciable where these conditions are least well satisfied.

Objective 20   **SAQ 37**   For which planet are these conditions least well satisfied?

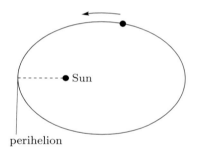

Figure 63   An orbit of an isolated planet around the Sun, according to Newtonian mechanics.

perihelion

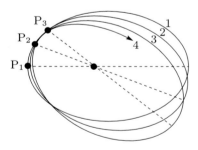

Figure 64   The advance of the perihelion of a planet according to general relativity.

14.1   Test 1: precession of the perihelion of Mercury

A famous consequence of Newtonian mechanics is that the path of an isolated planet moving around the Sun is an ellipse, as illustrated in Figure 63. As well as having a specific size and eccentricity, an ellipse has an orientation. This is specified by the direction of the line joining the focus, representing the Sun, to the point of closest approach of the planet; this point is called the *perihelion*. According to Newtonian mechanics, for a spherically symmetric Sun and an isolated planet this line stays in one position, so the perihelion should occur at the same point in space, orbit after orbit. But by 1845 it was known that the orbit of the planet Mercury does not behave in this manner. With each successive orbit the orientation changes slightly, as shown in exaggerated form in Figure 64. Now a large part of this movement, called the *precession of the perihelion* can be explained using Newtonian mechanics as the effects on Mercury of other planets, but there was a residual effect amounting to a (tiny) *43 seconds of arc per century*. No satisfactory reason for the residual precession could be found on the basis of Newtonian theory. Then in 1915, Einstein, using an approximate form of the Schwarzschild metric (the exact form became known only in 1916) showed that general relativity predicts a perihelion advance of just that amount. It was a confirmation that delighted him immensely. 'I was beside myself with ecstasy for days', he wrote in 1916.

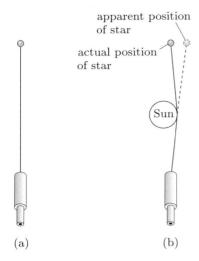

apparent position
of star

actual position
of star

Sun

(a)   (b)

Figure 65   Illustration of the bending of light by the curvature of spacetime in the vicinity of the Sun. (a) The sighting of a star without the Sun nearby. (b) The effect of the Sun on the apparent position of the star.

14.2 Test 2: bending of light by the Sun

The second prediction of the full theory of general relativity is a development of an idea suggested by the principle of equivalence: that the path of a light ray may be changed when it passes through the gravitational field of a massive body such as the Sun. This effect is largest for rays just grazing the Sun. Using the Schwarzschild metric to calculate the world-line of a light ray that just grazes the Sun in coming to us from a star, general relativity predicts that the apparent angular position of the star would shift by 1.75 seconds of arc from the position it would have if the Sun were not there (Figure 65).

The first experimental problem in trying to verify this prediction is that it's not that easy to see any stars when the Sun is around, much less stars that appear just at the edge of the Sun's radius. The expedient of observing these stars at a moment of full solar eclipse eliminates most of the unwanted sunlight. But a considerable number of experimental difficulties, not the least of which is poor weather conditions on Earth during the $7\frac{1}{2}$ minutes maximum total eclipse time, make an accurate determination of the bending of starlight a difficult job. Table 10 lists some attempts at this measurement. Nevertheless, it was the expeditions planned by Sir Arthur Eddington, the first two entries in this table, that gave general relativity its most publicized triumph; it put the word 'relativity' on everyone's lips and made Einstein a world-famous figure.

There seems to be little scope for improving these measurements; for example a measurement in 1975 gave a deflection which was 0.95 ± 0.11 times the prediction of general relativity, which is nicely consistent, but hardly a precision confirmation. A new technology has superceded such optical measurements: radio astronomy, or more precisely *radio interferometry*. The idea is that by using two radio-telescopes separated by a long 'base-line', which might be the width of an ocean, one can measure the very small differences between the times that particular wave crests arrive at the two radio telescopes. Obviously, the farther they are apart the better. Using radio transmission from quasars (which are galaxies so distant as to be almost point sources of radio waves) and measuring differences between directions to pairs of galaxies as one of the pair passes close to the direction to the Sun, the predicted gravitational deflection has been verified to astonishing precision. As a consequence, the deflection of light (or radio waves) is something now taken for granted by astronomers, and indeed must be corrected for. This is because radio interferometry is now precise enough to see bending by the Sun of radio waves coming from sources 175° from the Sun!

The consequences of the gravitational bending of light do not end there: in Unit 12 we briefly mention the important phenomenon of gravitational lensing by galaxies.

TABLE 10 The history of observations of light-bending, 1919–52, attempting to verify the prediction of arc made by Einstein (From Sciama D. W. (1972) *The Physical Foundation of General Relativity*, Heinemann Educational Books).

Observatory and (place of observation)	Eclipse	Number of stars	Minimum distance of star from Sun, in solar radii from center	Maximum distance of star from Sun, in solar radii from center	Mean angle of deflection* (seconds of arc)	Error (seconds of arc)
Greenwich (Brazil)	29 May 1919	7	2	6	1.98	0.16
		11	2	6	0.93	—
Greenwich (Principe)	29 May 1919	5	2	6	1.61	0.40
Adelaide–Greenwich (Australia)	21 Sept 1922	11–14	2	10	1.77	0.40
Victoria (Australia)	21 Sept 1922	18	2	10	1.75 1.42 2.16	—
Lick I (Australia)	21 Sept 1922	62–85	2.1	14.5	1.72	0.15
Lick II (Australia)	21 Sept 1922	145	2.1	42	1.82	0.20
Potsdam I (Sumatra)	9 May 1929	17–18	1.5	7.5	2.24	0.10
Potsdam II (Sumatra)	9 May 1929	84–135	4	15	—	—
Sternberg (U.S.S.R.)	19 June 1936	16–29	2	7.2	2.73	0.31
Sendai (Japan)	19 June 1936	8	4	7	2.13 1.28	1.15 2.67
Yerkes I (Brazil)	20 May 1947	51	3.3	10.2	2.01	0.27
Yerkes II (Sudan)	25 Feb 1952	9–11	2.1	8.6	1.70	0.10

* This is the value estimated for a light ray grazing the Sun, obtained by an extrapolation of the shift in apparent position of a number of stars.

14.3 Test 3: gravitational redshift

The third prediction of general relativity, also made in the earliest days, was that of the gravitational redshift. This was only verified in 1960 in an experiment described in Unit 9 made possible by the discovery of the Mössbauer effect. Prior to that, attempts had been made to measure the redshift of the spectral lines of dense stars, but the effect sought was quite small compared to such dominant effects as the Doppler shifts due to the turbulent currents in the hot gases on the surface of the stars. In spite of the fact that general relativity completely changed our understanding of space and time, there were remarkably few really decisive tests until the 1960s.

14.4   Test 4: time delay of signals passing the Sun

A new test of general relativity was proposed in 1964 by I. I. Shapiro, exploiting exceptionally high-powered radar. The principle is illustrated in Figure 66(a), where an aircraft is located with radar by recording the direction of transmission of a radar pulse and observing the time delay between transmitting a given pulse and receiving its echo. The same observations can be made of one of the nearby planets, such as Mercury or Venus, as shown in Figure 66(b), if the radar transmitter is powerful enough and the receiver sensitive enough.

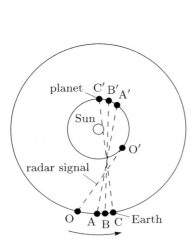

Figure 67   Radar time delay experiment between the Earth and a nearby planet. Successive positions of the Earth are marked as O, A, B and C. Successive positions of the planet are marked as O′, A′, B′ and C′.

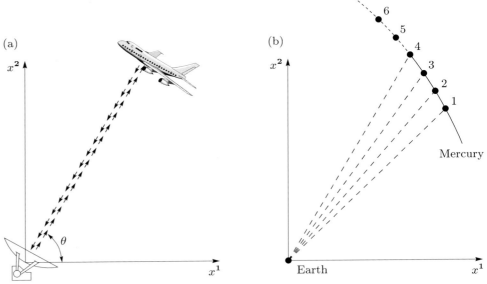

Figure 66   (a) The determination of an aircraft's position by means of radar. (b) The determination of the orbit of a planet by means of radar.

The basic idea of the experiment is to record the travel times of radar signals from Earth to the planet and back and to observe especially the travel times of those echoes that come just as the planet is slipping around the back of the Sun (see path C–C′ in Figure 67). These particular pulses just graze the Sun's edge as they go and come back so they probe the region where the Schwarzschild metric differs most from the flat spacetime of special relativity. If we assume that the orbit of the planet is well known from other astronomical observations, then we can predict the travel times for all pulses going to and returning from the planet at any point in its orbit. If we make predictions assuming that spacetime is flat, we would find that they would agree with experiment for all pulses except those that go close enough to the Sun's edge during the passage. Those pulses take a slightly *longer* time than expected to come back.

To predict the times of travel of light pulses we exploit the results of the last few sections. The geometry of spacetime in the Solar System is dominated by the Sun. Spacetime containing the world-lines of radar pulses between the Earth and one of the nearby planets is thus described by the Schwarzschild metric. Radar pulses, like any other electromagnetic signal or test-body, travel along geodesics of this metric. If we therefore extract the geodesic equations from the Schwarzschild metric, in a way analogous to that used in Sections 8 and 9 to obtain the geodesic equations for the plane, the sphere and flat spacetime, these new geodesic equations should contain the information we need. That is, the geodesic equations should lead to an expression for the time a radar pulse takes to travel from the Earth to a planet while just grazing the surface of the Sun (see Figure 67). This expression will depend upon R_E, R_p and R_S, respectively the distances of the Earth and planet from the Sun, and the radius of the Sun. The world-lines of the radar pulses as they graze the Sun are solutions of geodesic equations which should allow us to calculate any effect on the transit time which is due to the curvature of spacetime near the Sun. If the pulse leaves the antenna at time t_E and reaches the planet at time t_p we want an expression of the form

$$t_p - t_E = f(R_E, R_p, R_S).$$
(83)

The quantity R_S enters because we are concerned with the trajectory which just grazes the Sun. Other trajectories would be expected to be less affected by the curvature of spacetime.

The simplest calculation that follows the method just outlined is only just within the capability of the techniques that we have presented in this Unit. We have to derive, by the methods used in the *optional* portion of Section 8.1, the geodesic equations of a somewhat more general metric than that presented in Sections 7 and 8. This has been done in the *optional* Appendix 1 (results from this Appendix have been used in Section 13.2). Further we have to use a selection of calculus techniques to transform the metric and the geodesic equations into the desired result.

14.4.1   Derivation of the time of travel of radar signals passing close to the Sun

We present here a method, based on a simplified model of an Earth–Sun–planet system, for calculating the time of travel that general relativity predicts for a radar pulse which goes from Earth to a nearby planet on a path that just grazes the Sun's surface. We know that spacetime in the presence of the Sun (neglecting the Earth and the planet as having much smaller masses) is described by the Schwarzschild metric of Section 13. We know that light travels within the Solar System along geodesics of this metric. Therefore the geodesic equations written in terms of the Schwarzschild metric coefficients should provide us with the means to make a quantitative prediction of this time delay.

Figure 68 shows the simplified model of the Earth–Sun–planet system that we use in this calculation. We assume that, for the 40 minutes that it takes a signal to go from the Earth to the planet and back again, the Earth and the planet stay approximately in the same positions. The Earth, the Sun and the planet thus are considered to sit in one plane, which we choose for mathematical convenience to be the plane given by $\theta = \pi/2$. This will eliminate one variable θ, from the Schwarzschild metric as it applies to this problem.

The Schwarzschild metric is

$$\Delta\tau = \left[\left(1 - \frac{2mG}{c^2 r}\right)(\Delta t)^2 - \frac{1}{c^2}\left\{ \frac{(\Delta r)^2}{\left(1 - \frac{2mG}{c^2 r}\right)} + r^2(\Delta\theta)^2 + r^2\sin^2\theta(\Delta\phi)^2 \right\} \right]^{1/2}.$$

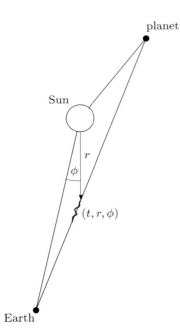

Figure 68 Illustration of the trajectory of a radar pulse, travelling between the Earth and a nearby planet, that just grazes the Sun.

Non-assessable ▼
optional text

Since $\theta = \pi/2$ and $\Delta\theta = 0$ in this problem, this metric may be rewritten, with $2mG/c^2$ denoted by k, as

$$\Delta\tau = \left[\left(1 - \frac{k}{r}\right)(\Delta t)^2 - \frac{(\Delta r)^2}{c^2\left(1 - \frac{k}{r}\right)} - \frac{r^2}{c^2}(\Delta\phi)^2\right]^{1/2}. \tag{84}$$

It is the geodesic equations of this metric that describe the world-line of the radar pulse. This reduced Schwarzschild metric is of the general type studied in Appendix 1.

Study comment

The following derivation of the time-of-travel formula (the explicit version of Equation 83) is optional reading and is non-assessable. We would dearly like you to follow through this derivation because it shows the ideas of general relativity at work. But if you don't wish to do so, you may, without loss to any further reading, jump to the final formula, Equation 95, different facets of which we can examine without reference to the derivation.

We have shown in Appendix 1 that two of the geodesic equations of this metric are of quite a simple form: they are

$$\left(1 - \frac{k}{r}\right)\frac{dt}{d\tau} = N \tag{78}$$

and

$$r^2\frac{d\phi}{d\tau} = c^2 J \tag{85}$$

where N and J are constants. The definition of k and Equations 78, 84 and 85 are all we need to calculate the time delay.

Figure 68 illustrates the method we follow. With some artistic licence, we have drawn a radar pulse at one point of the trajectory from the Earth to the planet. To each point along the trajectory between the Earth and the limb of the Sun, we can associate a unique r-coordinate, ϕ-coordinate and time coordinate, t. If we could determine how the time coordinate varies with r, that is, if we could find an expression for dt/dr in terms of r, then we could integrate it to find the time of travel of a pulse from the Earth to the Sun and from the Sun to the planet,

$$\Delta T(\text{Sun to Earth}) = \int_{R_S}^{R_E} \frac{dt}{dr}\,dr \tag{86a}$$

and

$$\Delta T(\text{Sun to planet}) = \int_{R_S}^{R_P} \frac{dt}{dr}\,dr \tag{86b}$$

where R_S, R_E, and R_p are the radial coordinate values of the Sun's surface, the Earth and the planet in the coordinate system that has its origin at the centre of the Sun. To do this we must eliminate the variables τ and ϕ from Equations 84, 78 and 85; so this is our next task.

The variable τ in Equation 84 can be eliminated by realizing that it is the world-line of an electromagnetic signal that we are looking for. Such world-lines are what we have called null geodesics (p. 71); the elapsed proper time along any

Optional text ▽ segment of such a world-line is zero. So Equation 84, applied to neighbouring events on the pulse's world-line, becomes

$$\left(1 - \frac{k}{r}\right)(\Delta t)^2 - \frac{(\Delta r)^2}{c^2\left(1 - \frac{k}{r}\right)} - \frac{r^2}{c^2}(\Delta\phi)^2 = 0. \tag{87}$$

We divide by $(\Delta t)^2$ and rearrange terms to get

$$\left(\frac{\Delta r}{\Delta t}\right)^2 = c^2\left(1 - \frac{k}{r}\right)^2 - r^2\left(1 - \frac{k}{r}\right)\left(\frac{\Delta\phi}{\Delta t}\right)^2.$$

We take the limit in this equation as $\Delta t \longrightarrow$ zero, and take the positive square root to obtain

$$\frac{dr}{dt} = \left[c^2\left(1 - \frac{k}{r}\right)^2 - r^2\left(1 - \frac{k}{r}\right)\left(\frac{d\phi}{dt}\right)^2\right]^{1/2} \tag{88}$$

which is the first of the reworked versions of the metric of which we shall have need. In the same way we can find the inverse equation:

$$\frac{dt}{dr} = \frac{1}{\left[c^2\left(1 - \frac{k}{r}\right)^2 - r^2\left(1 - \frac{k}{r}\right)\left(\frac{d\phi}{dt}\right)^2\right]^{1/2}}. \tag{89}$$

From Equations 86a and 86b it is obvious why we shall need this quantity. If we could eliminate $d\phi/dt$ from Equation 89 in favour of some quantity involving only r, we would be ready to perform the integrations of Equations 86a and 86b. The other equation involving ϕ that is at our disposal, Equation 85 is written in terms of $d\phi/d\tau$. But we can use the other geodesic equation, (78), both to eliminate the variable τ and to obtain the derivative $d\phi/dt$ that we need.

To evaluate $d\phi/dt$ we use the standard result of calculus that $d\phi/dt = d\phi/d\tau(dt/d\tau)^{-1}$. Using Equation 85 for $d\phi/d\tau$ and Equation 78 for $dt/d\tau$, we get

$$\frac{d\phi}{dt} = \frac{d\phi}{d\tau}\frac{d\tau}{dt} = \frac{c^2 J}{r^2}\left(1 - \frac{k}{r}\right)\frac{1}{N} = \left(1 - \frac{k}{r}\right)\frac{1}{r^2}A \tag{90}$$

where A is the constant $c^2 J/N$.

In fact, J and N are both infinite for a radar pulse which travels on a null geodesic with $\Delta\tau = 0$. But A, which depends on the ratio of J to N, is finite.

We establish the magnitude of the constant A from the condition that $dr/dt = 0$ just as the light grazes the Sun. We first insert $d\phi/dt$ from Equation 90 into Equation 88 for dr/dt, getting

$$\frac{dr}{dt} = \left(1 - \frac{k}{r}\right)\left[c^2 - \frac{A^2}{r^2}\left(1 - \frac{k}{r}\right)\right]^{1/2}. \tag{91}$$

Putting this expression to zero at $r = R_S$ (i.e. just as the light grazes the surface of the Sun) we get:

$$\left(1 - \frac{k}{R_S}\right)\left[c^2 - \frac{A^2}{R_S^2}\left(1 - \frac{k}{R_S}\right)\right]^{1/2} = 0.$$

Since

$$\frac{k}{R_S} = \frac{2mG}{c^2 R_S} \approx 2 \times 10^{-6}$$

it is the term in the square bracket that must be zero, and solving for A^2 gives

$$A^2 = c^2 R_S^2/(1 - k/R_S). \tag{92}$$

Optional text   ▽   Now we can put Equations 92 and 90 into Equation 89 to give

$$\frac{dt}{dr} = \frac{1}{c\left(1 - \dfrac{k}{r}\right)\left[1 - \left(\dfrac{R_S}{r}\right)^2 \dfrac{(1 - k/r)}{(1 - k/R_S)}\right]^{1/2}} \equiv \mathscr{F}(r) \tag{93}$$

where $k = 2mG/c^2$. This is the function we need to evaluate the total time of travel of the radar pulse from Earth to the planet. Putting Equations 86a, 86b and 93 together, we get

$$\Delta T(\text{Earth to planet}) = \int_{R_S}^{R_E} \mathscr{F}(r)\, dr + \int_{R_S}^{R_P} \mathscr{F}(r)\, dr. \tag{94}$$

The total travel-time from transmission to reception back on Earth will be twice the value of the integrals of Equation 94. The integrals on the right-hand side of Equation 94 are not elementary, but the idea of performing such integrations does not raise any conceptual difficulties; it is only a matter of finding the appropriate technique. The result of an approximate evaluation is given below (Equation 95) End of optional text   ▲   and it is on this equation that we shall concentrate.

The explicit version of the expression for twice the quantity that we have labelled $(t_p - t_E)$ in Equation 83 (and as ΔT (Earth–planet) in the optional derivation) is given in Equation 95. It gives the total round-trip time of a radar pulse sent from Earth to the planet and back that just grazes the Sun's surface, in terms of the parameter k of the Schwarzschild metric and the radial coordinates R_S, R_E and R_p of the Sun's surface, the Earth and the planet respectively:

$$\Delta T(\text{Earth–planet–Earth}) \approx \frac{2}{c}([R_E^2 - R_S^2]^{1/2} + [R_p^2 - R_S^2]^{1/2}) + \frac{2k}{c}\left\{\ln\left(4\frac{R_E R_p}{R_S^2}\right) + 1\right\}. \tag{95}$$

The first thing to notice is what happens to this result if we set $k(= 2mG/c^2)$ equal to zero. This corresponds to saying that spacetime is everywhere like that of special relativity. The total travel-time reduces in this case to

$$\Delta T = \frac{1}{c}[2([R_E^2 - R_S^2]^{1/2} + [R_p^2 - R_S^2]^{1/2})]$$

which is just what you would expect. The distance of the Earth from the planet is computed with the Euclidean formula from the coordinates (see Figure 69) and the total distance there and back (contained in the square bracket) is divided by c to get the total travel-time of the pulse. It is therefore the term in the curly brackets of Equation 95, multiplied by $2k/c$, which represents the effects of curved spacetime on ΔT.

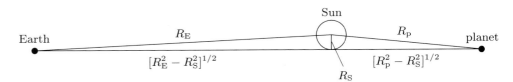

Figure 69   A radar pulse from the Earth, E, just grazing the Sun as it travels to a planet, p. In Shapiro's experiment, p was the planet Mars which is in fact more distant from the Sun than is the Earth.

Equation 95 allows us to estimate the extra time delay. We know that light from the Sun takes about 8 minutes to get to the Earth. Thus the first term of Equation 95 will be of order of 16 to 40 minutes, depending on the planet used. Now k/c $(= 2M_S G/c^3)$ is about $10\,\mu s$; so unless the term in the curly bracket is very large (which it won't be—typical values are 10 to 15) the extra time delay predicted by general relativity is a tiny fraction of the total travel time. This is an example of the fact that general relativity predicts extremely small departures from Newton's theory everywhere within the solar system; there are simply not large enough concentrations of mass within the solar system for it to be otherwise.

We can also see that the effect of the expression in the curly brackets of Equation 95 is to *increase* the time of travel of the pulse from that expected for the spacetime of special relativity; general relativity predicts a time *delay*. The quantity whose logarithm is to be taken can be written as

$$4 \left(\frac{R_E}{R_S} \right) \left(\frac{R_p}{R_S} \right).$$

Since

$$R_E \gg R_S \quad \text{and} \quad R_p \gg R_S$$

then

$$4 \left(\frac{R_E}{R_S} \right) \left(\frac{R_p}{R_S} \right) \gg 1$$

and natural logarithms of numbers greater than unity are positive. So the whole term in curly brackets is positive.

Finally, we can put in some typical values of R_E, R_p and the value of R_S to get a quantitative estimate of the time delay caused by the effect of the Sun on the spacetime near it. At the outset of this calculation we should mention that the experimental problems involved in measuring radar-pulse travel-times are considerable and they come from a variety of sources and we cannot do justice to the experiments here. We mention as an example results from experiments conducted during the Viking satellite mission to Mars. So we use as R_p the mean distance of Mars from the Sun: 2.254×10^{11} m. Putting this quantity along with

$$R_E = 1.495 \times 10^{11} \text{ m}, \quad R_S = 6.960 \times 10^8 \text{ m} \quad \text{and} \quad \frac{k}{c} = 9.838 \times 10^{-6} \text{ s}$$

into the expression

$$\frac{2k}{c} \left\{ \ln \left(\frac{4 R_E R_p}{R_S^2} \right) + 1 \right\}$$

gives a predicted maximum time-delay of $266.2 \, \mu\text{s}$. The maximum delay observed in the Viking experiment was $250 \, \mu\text{s}$; so our simple general relativistic calculation does predict a time-delay effect of the Sun on a radar pulse of the right order of magnitude.

14.5 Are the effects of general relativity always small?

There is a sense in which, as we have noted, the effects of general relativity within the solar system are extremely small. But of course the very fact that the planets stay in their orbits, and the fact that apples fall to earth, are explained in terms of general relativity. What is true is that additional phenomena which go beyond what Newtonian physics would predict (gravitational redshift, perihelion precession, bending of light, time-delay of radar signals) are so small that extremely delicate experiments are required to establish that Einstein's picture is truer than Newton's. Of course, general relativity has the virtue of predicting Newton's theory (as well as the corrections to it) on very general grounds, but it certainly still requires testing to the limits. So there is also a sense in which the effects of general relativity are large; a tightrope walker presumably thinks of nothing but these effects while she is on the job. But you might have some problem reconciling in your own mind two situations: firstly, the tiny deflection of light grazing the Sun, which seems to accord with our idea that after all, the curvature of spacetime is small, and secondly, the effects which pre-occupy our tightrope walker, and, indeed, keep planets in their orbits. The point is this: planets and tightrope walkers move extremely slowly according to nature's intrinsic scale of speed; planets and people have speeds $\ll c$. Light grazing the Sun, however, does travel at c and is deflected little, in line with the very small curvature of spacetime. Planets moving many orders of magnitude more slowly than the speed of light have time for the small curvature of spacetime to do its work, keeping the planets in orbit, among other things.

Where might the curvature of spacetime be large? Some measure of the departure of spacetime from flatness outside a large mass is the departure of

$$g_0 = 1 - \frac{2mG}{c^2 r}$$

from unity. Now remember that m is the mass of the large source of gravitation. Let us consider a small test body of mass m_t and multiply both the numerator and denominator in the second term of g_0 by it. We get

$$g_0 = 1 - \frac{2mGm_t}{rm_t c^2} = 1 + \frac{2\phi(m_t)}{E_t}$$

where $\phi(m_t) = -mGm_t/r$ is the gravitational potential energy of the test body at distance r from the centre of the mass m, and $E_t = m_t c^2$ is the energy associated with the mass of the test body. You should be well aware of how much larger this rest energy of a body (think of a lump of uranium!) is than its gravitational potential energy. On the surface of the Sun the ratio is about 4.8×10^5 and on the surface of the Earth, it is about 1.45×10^9.

Objective 20　　　**SAQ 38**　　Given that the mass and radius of the Earth are $5.98 \times 10^{24}\,\text{kg}$ and $6.38 \times 10^6\,\text{m}$ respectively, verify the ratio 1.45×10^9 given above.

So to find situations where the curvature of spacetime is large, we need to find either a very massive object (m large) or one of small radius (r small at its surface): this takes us to black holes, the topic of the next unit.

If you wish to read more about the subject of testing general relativity, you may wish to consult a most readable little book: Will, C.M. (1988) *Was Einstein right?* Oxford, Oxford University Press ISBN 0-19-282203-9.

14.6 Summary of Section 14

Newton's theory works so exceptionally well that it is obvious that any replacement of it should fulfil two criteria: the first is that it must predict Newton's results on the basis of assumptions that somehow seem deeper and more general, perhaps avoiding theoretical weaknesses of Newton's theory (such as the lack of Lorentz invariance of any theory that implies instantaneous transmission of force). The second criterion is that it should make some predictions which measurably disagree with Newtonian results. These latter form the basis of tests of general relativity.

The four tests discussed here are:

1 The precession of the perihelion of Mercury;

2 The gravitational redshift;

3 The bending of light from stars by the Sun;

4 The time-delay of radar signals bounced off planets passing behind the Sun.

In the case of the fourth of these, we were able to give an account of the time-delay on the basis of the Schwarzschild solution.

We remind you also of the radiation of gravitational waves from the Hulse Taylor binary star (two neutron stars, of which one is a pulsar), briefly mentioned in Section 12.6. In Unit 12 certain other tests of general relativity will be briefly mentioned.

15   Summary of Unit 10 & 11

Unit 10 & 11 has been very long and we shall not duplicate the section summaries here. You should freely refer back to these as you review and consolidate your understanding of this Unit: our introduction to the theory which cost Einstein seven years of intense labour to produce. That, of course is Einstein's general theory of relativity, or, as it is often called, Einstein's theory of gravitation.

Over the course of Unit 10 & 11, we have witnessed a profound change in our understanding of space and time — few of the 14 postulates concerning space and time listed in Block 1 survive.

The two key ideas of the double Unit are these: firstly, that spacetime in the presence of matter becomes curved, and, secondly that the motion under gravity of bodies or light, can be described in terms of the effects of that curvature. Those effects have been formulated geometrically, so that motion under gravity has become motion along geodesics of curved spacetime.

Of course, these ideas are easy to state vaguely in words, but we must have a quantitative formulation. What, for example do we mean by curved spacetime? We found that one of the basic geometric properties of any space that can be deduced from the metric of the space is the curvature — a property that can vary from point to point throughout the space. For example, for the two-dimensional space that is the surface of the sphere, the curvature is the same at all points, whereas spacetime near a mass becomes more strongly curved close to the mass. The metric is the expression by which the distance between two neighbouring points can be related to the differences in their coordinates. The geometry of any space can be calculated from the metric of that space; in the case of spacetime, this is an expression for the invariant proper time interval $\Delta\tau$ in terms of intervals of spatial coordinates and the time coordinate. The coefficients $g_{\mu\nu}$ which enter into the metric are constant far from any matter (corresponding to the flat spacetime of special relativity) but otherwise depend on location with respect to matter, (or other source of mass). The very idea of distance is no longer simple, and the key idea that we have taken over from Block 2 is the concept of proper time. The concept of proper time is something of a lifeline as we travel through the unfamiliar waters where 'metric significance' fails. It is always the case that (i) light travels along worldlines having zero change in proper time, and, (ii) if you have a clock with you in your frame, it will tell you proper time. But don't expect always to know coordinate time, that is, time measured by someone far from any mass.

If we know the metric coefficients, we can calculate everything else (which is part of the theory) from them: e.g. the curvature of spacetime, the geodesics and so on. The metric coefficients can be found by solving differential equations known as Einstein's field equations in which the source terms represent mass and other sources of gravity. These equations are difficult to solve in general, but Schwarzschild solved them for the highly symmetric case involving a central mass. Although we were not able to show the derivation of the Schwarzschild solution, its statement is in some ways the climax of this Unit. With it, by applying the geodesic equations to the metric coefficients, we were able to demonstrate that indeed, one does obtain (although we could show it only for purely radial motion) the same particle motion near the Sun that Newton's theory would predict. Of course, the assumptions made in this derivation suggest that, in extreme cases, we would not get exactly the Newtonian results. This is very important since this gives us the opportunity actually to see whether Einstein's theory is superior to Newton's. As Einstein himself discovered, his theory is indeed superior just where the assumptions we have mentioned break down. So, for example, with the motion of Mercury, it is Newton's predictions which fail.

We were also able to show directly from the Schwarzschild solution that the gravitational time-dilation effects follow as predicted by the equivalence principle. Indeed, we get a much more general time-dilation effect than that which we could find from the equivalence principle, since that principle was only able to make predictions in local regions. The full significance of this will appear later when we study black holes, but the time-dilation effect showed explicitly for the case of t how the coordinates lose their metric significance. In the cosmology block, we shall face this phenomenon again, in particular with regard to the position coordinates.

Band 6 of AC3 comments on this Unit.

16 Appendix 1: Some useful results concerning geodesic equations

We here use the methods developed in the optional part of Section 8.1 to derive two of the geodesic equations for a somewhat more general metric than is used in the main text. These two equations can be used as follows:

1 The two geodesic equations will be directly applied to show that Equations 78 and 85 in Sections 13.2 and 14.4.1 are justified.

2 One of the geodesic equations and the more general metric of this Appendix can be used to show that a body in free fall in the spacetime described by the Schwarzschild metric undergoes Newtonian motion in the limits (i) weak gravitational fields and (ii) speeds $\ll c$. The details, based on results presented here, are given in the main text, Section 13.

We assume here that you have read the optional derivation in Section 8.1, where the method of derivation is described in detail.

Derivation of geodesic equation

In this appendix, arguments are *always* retained in functions in equations, e.g. $g_2(q^1)$.

Consider a metric containing three independent coordinates, q^1, q^2, q^3 (they could be three of the coordinates in the Schwarzschild metric), of the form

$$\Delta l = [g_1(q^1)[\Delta q^1]^2 + g_2(q^1)[\Delta q^2]^2 + g_3(q^1)[\Delta q^3]^2]^{1/2}.$$

(If we set $g_1(q^1)$ to be a constant and $g_3(q^1)$ to be zero, we return to the metric of Sections 7 and 8.) Then we pick five points A–E very close together on a geodesic $\mathscr{C}$ in this three-dimensional space. The length of the segment A–E of $\mathscr{C}$ is

$$\mathscr{L}_\mathscr{C}(A,E) = \mathscr{L}_\mathscr{C}(A,C) + \mathscr{L}_\mathscr{C}(C,E) \tag{96}$$

where

$$\mathscr{L}_\mathscr{C}(A,C) \approx [g_1(q^1_B)[q^1_C - q^1_A]^2 + g_2(q^1_B)[q^2_C - q^2_A]^2 + g_3(q^1_B)[q^3_C - q^3_A]^2]^{1/2} \tag{97a}$$

and

$$\mathscr{L}_\mathscr{C}(C,E) \approx [g_1(q^1_D)[q^1_E - q^1_C]^2 + g_2(q^1_D)[q^2_E - q^2_C]^2 + g_3(q^1_D)[q^3_E - q^3_C]^2]^{1/2}. \tag{97b}$$

We can now distort the curve segment from A to E into neighbouring curves by separately varying one of the three coordinates of the point C, while keeping the end-points, A and E, fixed. The manner in which the coordinates of B and D vary will be discussed later. If curve $\mathscr{C}$ is a geodesic then

$$\frac{\mathrm{d}}{\mathrm{d}q^i_C}\mathscr{L}_\mathscr{C}(A,E) = 0 \quad \text{where } i = 1, 2 \text{ or } 3. \tag{98}$$

Choose $i = 2$. Applying Equations 96, 97a and 97b to Equation 98 gives

$$\frac{\mathrm{d}}{\mathrm{d}q^2_C}\mathscr{L}_\mathscr{C}(A,E) = \frac{1}{\mathscr{L}_\mathscr{C}(A,C)}g_2(q^1_B)(q^2_C - q^2_A) - \frac{1}{\mathscr{L}_\mathscr{C}(C,E)}g_2(q^1_D)(q^2_E - q^2_C) = 0. \tag{99}$$

This equation is identical in form to Equation 57. Since Equation 62b can be derived directly from Equation 57, Equation 99 must similarly lead to the equation

$$\frac{\mathrm{d}}{\mathrm{d}s}\left(\frac{g_2\dot{q}^2}{L}\right) = 0 \tag{100}$$

where, in this case,

$$L(s) = [g_1(q^1(s))[\dot{q}^1(s)]^2 + g_2(q^1(s))[\dot{q}^2(s)]^2 + g_3(q^1(s))[\dot{q}^3(s)]^2]^{1/2}.$$

Equation 100 is the first of our three geodesic equations.

Optional text ▽ Similarly, choose $i = 3$. Performing the same form of calculation as led from Equations 96 and 97 to Equation 99, we get

$$\frac{d}{dq_C^3}\mathscr{L}_\mathscr{C}(A,E) = \frac{1}{\mathscr{L}_\mathscr{C}(A,C)}g_3(q_B^1)(q_C^3 - q_A^3) - \frac{1}{\mathscr{L}_\mathscr{C}(C,E)}g_3(q_D^1)(q_E^3 - q_C^3) = 0.$$

(101)

If Equation 100 follows from Equation 99, then Equation 101 must lead to

$$\frac{d}{ds}\left(\frac{g_3\dot{q}^3}{L}\right) = 0$$

(102)

the second of our geodesic equations.

Let us now apply these two geodesic equations to deal with the first of our two substantive points. To justify the claims in Sections 14.4.1 and 13.2 that

$$r^2\frac{d\phi}{d\tau} = c^2 J \quad \text{and} \quad \left(1 - \frac{2mG}{c^2r}\right)\frac{dt}{d\tau} = N$$

(where J and N are constants) are two of the geodesic equations of the reduced Schwarzschild metric of the radar time-delay problem, let us begin by writing the reduced Schwarzschild metric. It is

$$\Delta\tau = \left[-\frac{1}{c^2\left(1 - \dfrac{2mG}{c^2r}\right)}(\Delta r)^2 + \left(1 - \frac{2mG}{c^2r}\right)(\Delta t)^2 - \frac{r^2}{c^2}(\Delta\phi)^2\right]^{1/2}$$

because θ is set equal to $\pi/2$ and hence $\Delta\theta = 0$ for this problem.

Now compare this metric with our general metric

$$\Delta l = [g_1(q^1)[\Delta q^1]^2 + g_2(q^1)[\Delta q^2]^2 + g_3(q^1)[\Delta q^3]^2]^{1/2}.$$

The reduced Schwarzschild metric *is* of this form with

$$q^1 = r; \quad q^2 = t; \quad q^3 = \phi$$

(103a–c)

$$g_1(q^1) = -\frac{1}{c^2\left(1 - \dfrac{2mG}{c^2q^1}\right)}; \quad g_2(q^1) = \left(1 - \frac{2mG}{c^2q^1}\right); \quad g_3(q^1) = -\frac{1}{c^2}(q^1)^2.$$

(104a–c)

Our first geodesic equations, (100) and (102), are

$$\frac{d}{ds}\left(\frac{g_2\dot{q}^2}{L}\right) = 0 \quad \text{and} \quad \frac{d}{ds}\left(\frac{g_3\dot{q}^3}{L}\right) = 0.$$

If we choose the parameter s to be the proper time τ, then L becomes identically equal to unity, as discussed in Section 9.2, and these equations read

$$\frac{d}{d\tau}(g_2\dot{q}^2) = 0 \quad \text{and} \quad \frac{d}{d\tau}(g_3\dot{q}^3) = 0$$

or

$$g_2\dot{q}^2 = N \quad \text{and} \quad g_3\dot{q}^3 = -J.$$

(We chose the constant as $-J$ with foresight.) Rewriting these equations with the help of Equations 104b, 104c, and 103b and 103c gives

$$\left(1 - \frac{2mG}{c^2r}\right)\frac{dt}{d\tau} = N \quad \text{and} \quad -\frac{1}{c^2}(r)^2\frac{d\phi}{d\tau} = -J \quad \text{or} \quad r^2\frac{d\phi}{d\tau} = c^2 J$$

End of optional text ▲ which are exactly the equations required.

17 Appendix 2: The derivation of Equation 38a

Non-assessable ▼
optional text

In this Appendix, we shall show that the geodesic equation (38b), derived in the optional portion of Section 8.1, and Equation 38c can be manipulated to derive the second geodesic equation of the main text of this Unit, Equation 38a. Equation 38b can be written in the form

$$\frac{g_2(q^1)}{L}\dot{q}^2 = N \quad \text{(a constant)} \tag{105}$$

In this appendix, arguments are always retained in functions in equations, e.g. $g_2(q^1)$.

and Equation 38c is

$$L(s) = [g_1[\dot{q}^1(s)]^2 + g_2(q^1(s))[\dot{q}^2(s)]^2]^{1/2} \tag{106}$$

where g_1 is a constant. In the manipulations to follow, we leave the dependence of q^1 and q^2 on s as understood, to make the equations neater.

We begin by squaring L to obtain

$$L^2 = g_1[\dot{q}^1]^2 + g_2(q^1)[\dot{q}^2]^2. \tag{107}$$

From this expression we eliminate $\dot{q}^2$ by using Equation 105 in the form

$$\dot{q}^2 = \frac{NL}{g_2(q^1)}. \tag{108}$$

Combining Equations 107 and 108 gives

$$L^2 = g_1[\dot{q}^1]^2 + g_2(q^1)\left(\frac{NL}{g_2(q^1)}\right)^2$$

$$= g_1[\dot{q}^1]^2 + L^2\frac{N^2}{g_2(q^1)}$$

which we can rewrite as

$$g_1[\dot{q}^1]^2 = L^2\left(1 - \frac{N^2}{g_2(q^1)}\right). \tag{109}$$

Multiplying both sides of Equation 109 by g_1/L^2, we get

$$\left(\frac{g_1\dot{q}^1}{L}\right)^2 = g_1\left(1 - \frac{N^2}{g_2(q^1)}\right).$$

Next we differentiate this expression with respect to s to obtain

$$2\frac{g_1\dot{q}^1}{L}\frac{\mathrm{d}}{\mathrm{d}s}\left(\frac{g_1\dot{q}^1}{L}\right) = \frac{g_1N^2}{(g_2(q^1))^2}\frac{\mathrm{d}g_2}{\mathrm{d}q^1}\cdot\dot{q}^1.$$

The factor $g_1\dot{q}^1$ cancels from both sides. Multiplying both sides of the above expression by $L/2$ and the right-hand side by $L/L(=1)$ gives

$$\frac{\mathrm{d}}{\mathrm{d}s}\left(\frac{g_1\dot{q}^1}{L}\right) = \frac{1}{2L}\frac{\mathrm{d}g_2}{\mathrm{d}q^1}\left(\frac{NL}{g_2(q^1)}\right)^2. \tag{110}$$

Finally we apply Equation 108 to the right-hand side of Equation 110 to obtain:

$$\frac{\mathrm{d}}{\mathrm{d}s}\left(\frac{g_1\dot{q}^1}{L}\right) = \frac{1}{2L}\frac{\mathrm{d}g_2}{\mathrm{d}q^1}(\dot{q}^2)^2$$

End of optional text ▲   which is the desired geodesic equation (38a).

Self-assessment questions — answers and comments

SAQ 1 The square of an interval in spacetime is $(c\Delta t)^2 - ((\Delta x^1)^2 + (\Delta x^2)^2 + (\Delta x^3)^2)$ whereas for an interval in space it is $(\Delta x^1)^2 + (\Delta x^2)^2 + (\Delta x^3)^2$. A zero interval in spacetime corresponds to zero elapsed proper-time, as is the case for two spacetime points on the same light cone.

SAQ 2 (a) The curve is a straight line. An easy way to identify a curve in a parametric form is to set up a table of values and plot a graph. For the functions $x^1(t) = t + 1$, $x^2(t) = 2t + 3$, we set up Table 11. The values are plotted in Figure 70 and the curve is a straight line.

(b) The curve is a half-circle of unit radius centred at the origin; the half-circle sits totally in the upper half-plane. To demonstrate this we set up a table of values of the two functions (Table 12), which are plotted in Figure 71.

TABLE 11 Values of $x^1(t)$ and $x^2(t)$ for SAQ 2(a).

t	$x^1(t)$	$x^2(t)$
0	1	3
2	3	7
5	6	13
10	11	23
15	16	33

TABLE 12 Values of $x^1(t)$ and $x^2(t)$ for SAQ 2(b).

t	$x^1(t)$	$x^2(t)$
0.95	0.95	0.31
0.90	0.90	0.44
0.80	0.80	0.60
0.60	0.60	0.80
0.40	0.40	0.92
0.20	0.20	0.98
0.00	0.00	1.00
−0.20	−0.20	0.98
−0.40	−0.40	0.92

SAQ 3 A quick way of finding out what kind of curve is represented by a given pair of parametric equations is to eliminate the parameter t between the two of them. We shall do this for the two curves given in SAQ 2.

(a) From $x^1(t) = t + 1$ we get

$$t = x^1 - 1.$$

We then put this into the second equation:

$$\begin{aligned} x^2(t) = 2t + 3 &= 2(x^1 - 1) + 3 \\ &= 2x^1 - 2 + 3 \\ &= 2x^1 + 1 \end{aligned}$$

or

$$x^2 = 2x^1 + 1$$

which is the equation of a straight line.

(b) If we square both equations of SAQ 2(b) we get

$$(x^1)^2 = t^2 \quad \text{and} \quad (x^2)^2 = 1 - t^2.$$

We substitute $(x^1)^2$ for t^2 in the second equation to get

$$(x^2)^2 = 1 - (x^1)^2 \quad \text{or} \quad (x^1)^2 + (x^2)^2 = 1.$$

That is the equation of the circle of unit radius. Because x^2 is limited to positive values, this gives the upper half-circle.

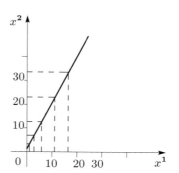

Figure 70 Illustration of the answer to SAQ 2(a).

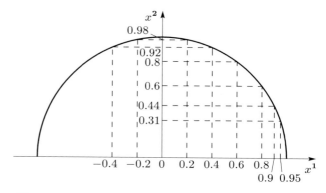

Figure 71 Illustration of the answer to SAQ 2(b).

SAQ 4 (a) The equation of a straight line is usually written in the form

$$x^2 = ax^1 + b \tag{111}$$

and the constant a is identified as the slope of the line. The parametric equations given in the question can be written in this form by eliminating the parameter t between them, as done in SAQ 3. From

$$x^1(t) = at + b$$

we get

$$t = \frac{x^1 - b}{a}.$$

We put this expression for t into the x^2-equation to get

$$\begin{aligned} x^2 &= c\left(\frac{x^1 - b}{a}\right) + d \\ &= \frac{c}{a}x^1 + \left(d - \frac{bc}{a}\right). \end{aligned}$$

Comparing this equation with Equation 111 (or simply computing $\mathrm{d}x^2/\mathrm{d}x^1$) shows us that the slope is c/a.

(b) Parallel lines must have equal slopes. Then

$$\frac{j}{g} = \frac{c}{a}$$

if the two lines are parallel. If they are not to be two equations for the same line, their x^2 values must be different when their x^1 values both take the value 0. Therefore

$$\left(k - \frac{j}{g}h\right) \neq \left(d - \frac{bc}{a}\right)$$

if the equations are to describe different lines which are parallel.

SAQ 5 (a) To use Equation 8b to evaluate Δl_C we must compute the derivatives $\dot{x}^1$ and $\dot{x}^2$.

$$\dot{x}^1(s) = 6s \quad \text{and} \quad \dot{x}^2(s) = 8s.$$

We then work out the right-hand side of Equation 8b.

$$[(6s_A)^2 + (8s_A)^2]^{1/2} = [100(s_A)^2]^{1/2} = 10s_A.$$

Thus

$$\Delta l_C \approx 10 s_A \cdot \Delta s.$$

For

$$s_A = 1.00 \quad \text{and} \quad \Delta s = 1.50 - 1.00 = 0.50$$

we get

$$\Delta l_C \approx 10 \times 1.00 \times 0.50 = 5.00.$$

(b) For

$$s_A = 1.00 \quad \text{and} \quad \Delta s = 1.10 - 1.00 = 0.10$$

we get

$$\Delta l_C \approx 10 \times 1.00 \times 0.10 = 1.00.$$

SAQ 6 (a) To evaluate the length of a curve we must complete the right-hand side of Equation 11. So we work out $\dot{x}^1$ and $\dot{x}^2$ for the given coordinate functions

$$\dot{x}^1(s) = 6s \quad \text{and} \quad \dot{x}^2(s) = 8s$$

so that

$$[(\dot{x}^1)^2 + (\dot{x}^2)^2]^{1/2} = [100s^2]^{1/2} = 10s$$

so

$$\mathscr{L}_\mathscr{C}(P,Q) = \int_{s_P}^{s_Q} 10s \, ds = [5s^2]_{s_P}^{s_Q} = 5(s_Q^2 - s_P^2).$$

For $s_P = a$ and $s_Q = b$, this gives
$\mathscr{L}_\mathscr{C}(P,Q) = 5(b^2 - a^2).$

(b) For part (a) of SAQ 5, the approximate answer is wrong by 20 per cent. For part (b) of SAQ 5 the approximate answer is in error by about 5 per cent. We calculate these numbers below.

(i)

$$\mathscr{L}_\mathscr{C}(P,Q) = 5[(1.50)^2 - (1.00)^2] = 6.25$$

Thus the percentage error in Δl_C is

$$\frac{6.25 - 5.00}{6.25} \times 100 \, \text{per cent}$$
$$= 20 \, \text{per cent}.$$

(ii)

$$\mathscr{L}_\mathscr{C}(P,Q) = 5[(1.10)^2 - (1.00)^2] = 1.05.$$

Thus the percentage error in Δl_C is

$$\frac{1.05 - 1.00}{1.05} \approx 5 \, \text{per cent}.$$

SAQ 7 The metric is:

$$\Delta l = [(\Delta x^1)^2 + (\Delta x^2)^2 + (\Delta x^3)^2]^{1/2}.$$

The length $\mathscr{L}_\mathscr{C}(P,Q)$ of the curve $\mathscr{C}$ between the points P and Q is given by

$$\mathscr{L}_\mathscr{C}(P,Q) = \int_{s_P}^{s_Q} [(\dot{x}^1(s))^2 + (\dot{x}^2(s))^2 + (\dot{x}^3(s))^2]^{1/2} \, ds.$$

SAQ 8 $\rho(0) = \dfrac{1}{\cos(0)} = 1 \quad \text{and} \quad \phi(0) = 0.$

Therefore the point $(\rho = 1, \phi = 0)$ is one unit from the origin along the positive x^1-axis.

SAQ 9 The equation of the circle of unit radius is

$$\rho(s) = 1 \quad \text{and} \quad \phi(s) = s.$$

This means that

$$\dot{\rho} = 0 \quad \text{and} \quad \dot{\phi} = 1.$$

The length of a curve written in plane polar coordinates is given by the formula

$$\mathscr{L}_\mathscr{C}(P,Q) = \int_{s_P}^{s_Q} [(\dot{\rho})^2 + \rho^2(\dot{\phi})^2]^{1/2} \, ds$$
$$= \int_0^d [1]^{1/2} \, ds = d.$$

SAQ 10 (a) If you use the north pole as a centre and draw circles of larger and larger radius, as in Figure 72, you will find the circumference increasing with increasing radius until you draw the circle that is the equator. Then increasing the radius further forces you to draw a circle of smaller circumference than the equator, as shown in Figure 72.

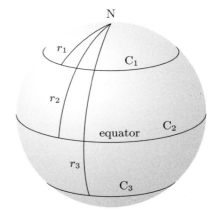

Figure 72 Illustration of the answer to SAQ 10.

So the radius r, of the largest circle on a sphere of radius R, is the length of the geodesic from the equator to the north pole, which is a quarter of the length of a great circle on this sphere.

$$r = \frac{1}{4} \cdot 2\pi R = \frac{\pi R}{2}.$$

(b) Since C for the equator is $2\pi R$, we have

$$\frac{C}{r} = \frac{2\pi R}{\dfrac{\pi R}{2}} = 4$$

quite different from the value 2π, we are used to on the plane.

SAQ 11 There are no parallels on a sphere according to definition 1. Figure 73 gives a way to obtain this answer. If we can take any line on a sphere (consider the equator in Figure 73) we can draw lines perpendicular to this line at different points on it.

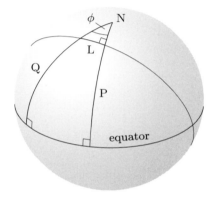

Figure 73 For SAQ 11.

The two meridians P and Q shown in Figure 73 are examples. So the equator intersects the two meridians at right angles. But do all other lines do the same? Consider the line L, which intersects the meridian P at right angles very close to the north pole. The lines L, P and Q form a triangle of very small area. Its properties should therefore be almost those of a Euclidean plane triangle. Now the sum of the interior angles of a Euclidean triangle is $180°$. Thus the angle of intersection of L with Q is

$$180° - 90° - \phi < 90°.$$

So the line L does not intersect both P and Q at right angles and thus P and Q are not parallel according to definition 1.

SAQ 12 (a) $\mathscr{C}_1$ is the curve DF. It is one quarter of the equator.

(b) $\mathscr{C}_2$ is the curve NE.

SAQ 13 To obtain the Cartesian coordinate functions of curve $\mathscr{C}_1$ of SAQ 12, we put the plane polar coordinate functions of $\mathscr{C}_1$ into Equations 24(a–c).

$$x^1(s) = R\sin\frac{\pi}{2}\cos s = R\cos s \quad \text{for all } s.$$

$$x^2(s) = R\sin\frac{\pi}{2}\sin s = R\sin s \quad \text{for all } s.$$

$$x^3(s) = R\cos\frac{\pi}{2} = 0 \quad \text{for all } s.$$

SAQ 14 For each of the curves given, we evaluate the integrand of $\mathscr{L}_\mathscr{C}(P,Q)$ of Equation 29, and then complete the integration.

(a)
$$\theta(s) = \frac{\pi}{2}; \text{ thus } \dot\theta = 0.$$
$$\phi(s) = s; \text{ thus } \dot\phi = 1.$$
$$\mathscr{L}_\mathscr{C}(P,Q) = \int_0^{\pi/2} R\left[0 + \sin^2\frac{\pi}{2}\cdot(1)^2\right]^{1/2} ds$$
$$= \int_0^{\pi/2} R\,ds = \frac{\pi R}{2}.$$

(b)
$$\theta(s) = s; \text{ thus } \dot\theta = 1.$$
$$\phi(s) = 0; \text{ thus } \dot\phi = 0.$$
$$\mathscr{L}_\mathscr{C}(P,Q) = \int_0^{\pi/4} R[(1)^2 + \sin^2 s\cdot(0)]^{1/2} ds$$
$$= \int_0^{\pi/4} R\,ds = \frac{\pi R}{4}.$$

SAQ 15 The required metric is that of plane polar coordinates in the plane, Equation 19:

$$\Delta l = [(\Delta\rho)^2 + \rho^2(\Delta\phi)^2]^{1/2}.$$

SAQ 16 With θ represented by q^1 and ϕ by q^2, we have that the curve A is given by the equations

$$q^1(s) = s; \quad 0 \leqslant s < \frac{\pi}{2}$$
$$q^2(s) = 0.$$

We must first compute the form of L for this curve

$$\dot q^1 = 1; \quad \dot q^2 = 0$$
$$L = [R^2(\dot q^1)^2 + R^2\sin^2 q^1(\dot q^2)^2]^{1/2}$$
$$= [R^2 + R^2\sin^2 s\cdot(0)]^{1/2}$$
$$= R.$$

Putting the expressions for q^1, $\dot q^1$, $\dot q^2$ and L into Equation 46a gives

$$\frac{d}{ds}\left(\frac{R^2\cdot 1}{R}\right) - \frac{R^2}{R}\sin s\cos s\cdot(0)^2 = 0$$

or

$$0 - 0 = 0.$$

So the first geodesic equation is satisfied. Putting the expressions for q^1, $\dot q^2$ and L into Equation 46b gives

$$\frac{d}{ds}\left(R^2\frac{\sin^2 s\cdot(0)}{R}\right) = 0$$

or

$$0 = 0.$$

So the second geodesic equation is satisfied.

SAQ 17   The equation $\mathcal{P}_{\mathcal{W}}(\mathcal{E}_P, \mathcal{E}_Q) = 0$ says that the proper time elapsed along a world-line $\mathcal{W}$, between two events $\mathcal{E}_P$ and $\mathcal{E}_Q$, on it is zero. From Unit 7 you know that (i) from $\Delta S = c \Delta \tau$, the elapsed proper time is proportional to the invariant interval ΔS, between events, and (ii) ΔS is zero between two events that are connected by a light signal. So the equation $\mathcal{P}_{\mathcal{W}}(\mathcal{E}_P, \mathcal{E}_Q) = 0$ tells you that $\mathcal{W}$ is the world-line of a light signal (or other electromagnetic signal) rather than that of a material particle.

SAQ 18   The answer to this SAQ is contained in the main text immediately following the SAQ.

SAQ 19   As essential feature of geodesics of concern to us, in any of the applications that we wish to make of them, is the following. Taking the geodesics of the sphere as examples, from any given point on the sphere the geodesic that leaves in a given direction is a unique curve. No two geodesics can meet the same point while moving in the same direction. Now if we want to associate the geodesics of some form of spacetime with the world-lines of free fall, then from a given point and starting with a given initial velocity, there must be only one possible world-line that is associated with the free-fall of a test-body.

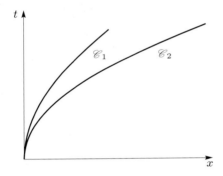

Figure 74   The world-lines of ordinary matter and the 'amazing compound'.

But if our 'amazing compound' exists, then there can be two world-lines (as shown in Figure 74) that start at the same event with the same initial velocity. Because of the different accelerations the world-lines of test-bodies of ordinary matter and 'amazing compound' will differ as the test-bodies leave the initial event. Because there is no longer a unique world-line to associate with a unique geodesic, we cannot associate the world-line of a test-body in free-fall with a geodesic in the natural way that general relativity does.

SAQ 20   **(a)**   An essential difference between the geometric properties of a plane and those of a curved surface, that is revealed by taking larger regions of the surface to draw figures on, is this: the geometric properties of a plane are independent of the size of the region in which they are observed but the geometric properties of a figure on a curved surface depend on the size of that figure. For example, the sum of the interior angles of any triangle drawn on a plane is π radians. But the sum of the interior angles of a triangle drawn on a curved surface depends on the area enclosed by that triangle.

(b)   The essential difference between free-fall motion in outer space and that near a large mass is this: the basic properties of the motion in empty space do not depend on how large a spacetime volume is used to observe these motions. Two particles that initially have parallel paths in free fall in empty space will continue to have parallel paths on any scale of observation. But for free fall near a large mass the properties of the motion depend on how large a spacetime volume the motion takes place in.

(c)   Term (i) should be paired with term (iii); term (ii) should be paired with term (iv).

SAQ 21   The answer to this SAQ is contained in the main text immediately following the SAQ.

SAQ 22   The statement that the curvature is constant means that at every point the curve can be approximated by a circle of the same radius. The magnitude of the radius can be worked out from the formula $k = 1/R$:

$$R = \frac{1}{k} = \frac{1}{0.2\,\mathrm{cm}^{-1}} = 5\,\mathrm{cm}.$$

Suppose, in Figure 75, we pick a point A, which we assume to be on the curve. We approximate the curve through A by a segment of a circle of radius 5 cm. On the circle segment we pick a point B near A. The curve in the neighbourhood of B must look like a circle segment of radius 5 cm as well, so we show the extension of the approximating circle as a dashed curve. On this extension we pick a point C. We can repeat this procedure again and again. The curve we generate by doing so is a complete circle of radius 5 cm. So a curve of constant curvature, $k = 0.2\,\mathrm{cm}^{-1}$, is a circle of radius 5 cm.

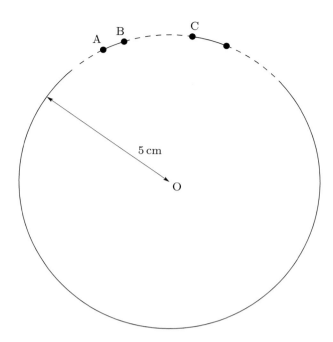

Figure 75 Illustration of the argument to show that a circle is a curve of constant curvature.

SAQ 23 The answer is almost self-evident from Figure 76. We draw a straight line GD, we pick a point A on it and we try to approximate the straight line near A with a series of circles $C_1, \ldots C_5$ whose radii increase from R_1 to R_5.

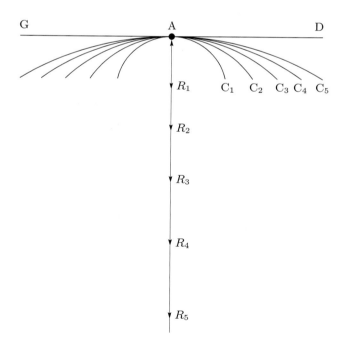

Figure 76 Illustration of the argument to show that a straight line is a curve of zero curvature.

As the radius increases, the circle lies closer to line GD for a larger extension around the point A. The approximation gets better as R increases, without limit; that is, as the curvature of the approximating circles, $k = 1/R$, gets closer to zero. For any finite radius R, there is a circle of larger radius that does the approximating better; so the curvature of the straight line must be smaller than $1/R$ for all possible R. That means it is zero.

SAQ 24 You can make a nice cone out of a piece of paper by cutting it into the shape shown in Figure 77. From the outer rectangular shape, cut the inner shape and tape the two straight edges together with point 1 touching point 2. Now because you can make a cone out of a flat piece of paper without tearing or crushing the paper in any way, the geometric properties of a cone must be those of a flat piece of paper, the two-dimensional plane. The curve of shortest length between two points on a cone must be the same as the curve of shortest length between those two points when the cone was a flat piece of paper — that is, a straight line in the ordinary sense of the word. This argument applies to the properties of triangles and circles drawn on a cone as well. So the cone and the plane have the same geometric properties.

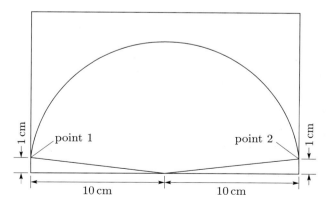

Figure 77 Pattern for making a cone out of a plain piece of paper.

SAQ 25 The argument is contained in Figure 78(a), which shows a cone on which an arbitrary point G has been picked. An arrow **N** is erected at G perpendicular to the surface of the cone. A plane ABCD containing **N** and the vertex of the cone, E, cuts the cone along the line FE. This line FE is a straight line. (Roll a piece of paper into a cone and simulate Figure 78(a) if this is hard to visualize.) Thus one of the curvatures associated with the point G is zero, because a straight line has zero curvature. As Figure 78(b) shows, any other orientation of the plane through G containing **N** cuts the cone in such a way as to produce a curve, FGH, of positive curvature. This means that the zero curvature line FGE of Figure 78(a) is the curvature of minimum curvature through the point G. Thus

$$\mathscr{K}_{\mathrm{G}} = k_{\mathrm{G}}^{\max} \cdot k_{\mathrm{G}}^{\min} = k_{\mathrm{G}}^{\max} \cdot 0 = 0.$$

The curvature of any point G (excluding the vertex) on the cone is zero; therefore the cone is flat.

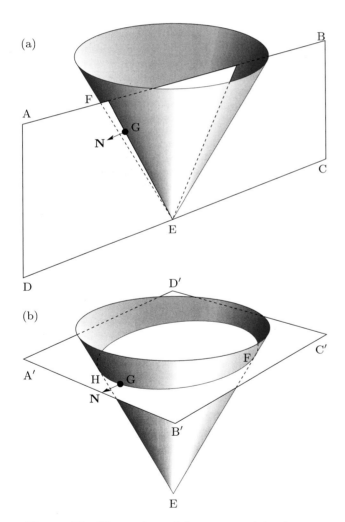

(a)

(b)

Figure 78 Illustration of the argument to show that a cone is a surface of zero curvature₃.

SAQ 26 Take a sphere of radius R, as shown in Figure 79, and pick any point P on it. Erect an arrow **N** perpendicular to the surface at the point. The extension of this arrow goes through O, the centre of the sphere. Any plane cutting the sphere that contains the arrow also contains O. Therefore

the curve that the plane makes in cutting the sphere is a great circle, a circle of radius R. Thus all curves through the point made by this cutting procedure have the same curvature, $k = 1/R$. Thus

$$\mathscr{K}_{\mathrm{P}} = k_{\mathrm{P}}^{\max} \cdot k_{\mathrm{P}}^{\min} = \frac{1}{R} \cdot \frac{1}{R} = \frac{1}{R^2}$$

and this is true for all points P on the sphere.

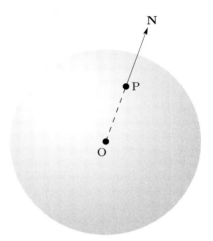

Figure 79 Illustration of the argument to show that the sphere is the surface of constant positive curvature₃.

SAQ 27 **(a)** At point A, cutting the torus with horizontal and vertical planes produces the curves shown in Figure 80. The curve in the vertical plane has a positive curvature $k_{\mathrm{A}}^{\mathrm{v}}$ with respect to the normal vector **N**. The curve in the horizontal plane has negative curvature $k_{\mathrm{A}}^{\mathrm{h}}$ with respect to **N**. Now $k_{\mathrm{A}}^{\max}$ must be greater than or equal to $k_{\mathrm{A}}^{\mathrm{v}}$ and $k_{\mathrm{A}}^{\min}$ must be less than or equal to $k_{\mathrm{A}}^{\mathrm{h}}$. Thus

$$\mathscr{K}_{\mathrm{A}} = k_{\mathrm{A}}^{\max} \cdot k_{\mathrm{A}}^{\min} < 0.$$

(b) Any plane cutting the torus at point B and containing the normal vector **N** makes a curve that has positive curvature with respect to **N**. Thus

$$\mathscr{K}_{\mathrm{B}} = k_{\mathrm{B}}^{\max} \cdot k_{\mathrm{B}}^{\min} > 0.$$

(c) Since $\mathscr{K}_{\mathrm{A}} < 0$, C/r for small circles on the torus about A as centre is greater than 2π, as stated in the text. Thus $(C/r - 2\pi)$ is positive.

(d) The torus is a closed surface: it is smoothly closed round on itself, being of finite area with no bounding edges.

(e) There is no contradiction between the answer to (d) and the relationship between openness and negative curvature₃. It is only a surface of negative curvature₃ *everywhere* that cannot be closed. As we have shown in part (b) there are points of positive curvature₃ on the torus; it is not therefore a surface of negative curvature₃ *everywhere* and hence can be closed.

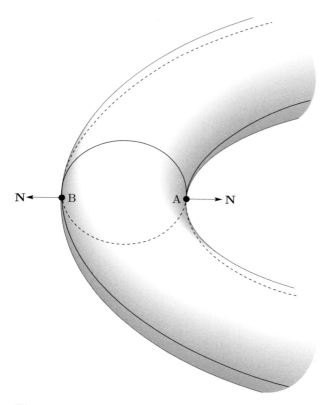

Figure 80 Illustration of the argument to show that the point A of the torus of Figure 48 is a point of negative curvature$_3$ and that point B of the same torus is a point of positive curvature$_3$.

SAQ 28 (a) If $g_1 = 1$ and $g_2(q^1) = (q^1)^2$ then

$$\frac{dg_2}{dq^1} = 2q^1 \quad \text{and} \quad \frac{d^2g_2}{dq^{12}} = 2.$$

Thus

$$\mathscr{K}(q^1, q^2) = \frac{1}{4g_1(g_2)^2}\left(\frac{dg_2}{dq^1}\right)^2 - \frac{1}{2g_1g_2}\left(\frac{d^2g_2}{dq^{12}}\right)$$

$$= \frac{1}{4[(q^1)^2]^2}(2q^1)^2 - \frac{1}{2(q^1)^2} \cdot 2$$

$$= \frac{1}{(q^1)^2} - \frac{1}{(q^1)^2} = 0.$$

Therefore $\mathscr{K}(q^1, q^2) = 0$ for all values of q^1 and q^2, for the surface defined by the metric coefficients of this SAQ.

(b) The answer to part (a) is reasonable because: (i) the functions $g_1 = 1$ and $g_2(q^1) = (q^1)^2$ are the metric coefficients of the plane in plane polar coordinates; (ii) the curvature$_4$ of the plane is everywhere zero; (iii) the curvature$_4$ is a geometric property of the surface which does not change just because we change the coordinate system in which to describe the plane.

SAQ 29 (a) If $g_1 = 1/c^2$ and $g_2 = -1/c^2$ then

$$\frac{dg_2}{dq^1} = 0 \quad \text{and} \quad \frac{d^2g_2}{dq^{12}} = 0$$

so that

$$\mathscr{K}(q^1, q^2) = 0 \qquad \text{for all } q^1, q^2.$$

(b) The metric of Equation 68a becomes the metric of the spacetime of special relativity that has one spatial dimension if we make the following substitutions:

$$\Delta l \longrightarrow \Delta\tau; \quad q^1 \longrightarrow x^0; \quad q^2 \longrightarrow x^1;$$
$$g_1 = \frac{1}{c^2}; \quad g_2 = -\frac{1}{c^2}$$

to get

$$\Delta\tau = \left[\frac{1}{c^2}(\Delta x^0)^2 - \frac{1}{c^2}(\Delta x^1)^2\right]^{1/2}$$

$$= \frac{1}{c}[(\Delta x^0)^2 - (\Delta x^1)^2]^{1/2}.$$

We have shown in part (a) that the curvature function associated with this metric is

$$\mathscr{K}(x^0, x^1) = 0 \qquad \text{for all } x^0, x^1.$$

Since an identically zero curvature function defines a flat space in Section 12.4, it is reasonable to describe the spacetime of special relativity that has one spatial dimension as 'flat spacetime'.

Additional note: The restriction to one spatial dimension is only imposed because we have a metric and curvature$_4$ defined for two-dimensional surfaces. The four-dimensional spacetime of special relativity is also flat but a more general curvature function is needed to show it.

SAQ 30 (a) 'Matter tells space how to curve' is a colloquial description of the field equations since mass density, or energy density, is one of the source variables that determine the Ricci curvature through the field equations. But it is only part of the story since the momentum density and the momentum flux also help determine the Ricci curvature. 'Space tells matter how to move' is a somewhat closer description of general relativity as a metric theory of gravity. One could say that it is the geometric properties of space as reflected in the metric coefficients that control the movement of test-bodies through the role they play in determining the geodesic equations.

(b) It would be more truthful to general relativity to say 'matter tells spacetime how to curve; spacetime tells matter how to move'.

SAQ 31 (a) The Ricci curvature has ten components, each one made up of sums of selected members of the 20 components of the Riemann curvature. If the Riemann curvature is zero everywhere, that is, all 20 components of it are zero everywhere, then the Ricci curvature must be zero everywhere.

(b) If the Riemann curvature plays the role for spacetime that $\mathscr{K}(q^1, q^2)$ does for two-dimensional space, then to set the Riemann curvature to zero must imply that the spacetime is flat. This would be true of the spacetime of special relativity although we have not produced expressions for the Riemann curvature of four-dimensional spacetime with which we could prove it.

(c) It implies that the density of mass (and momentum etc.) is zero in that region. It does not imply that the region of spacetime in question is flat. That is only true if the Riemann curvature of the region is zero.

SAQ 32 If 'precisely' means *precisely*, the answer is 'no'. The Ricci tensor is non-zero at those points in spacetime where there is no mass–energy, momentum etc . . . . For many purposes, there are lots of places where this is true. For example, in calculating the orbit of the Earth, one might consider a model in which the only source of spacetime curvature is the mass of the Sun. In such a model, the Ricci tensor is zero outside the Sun. But there are no places in the Universe where the energy density is exactly zero. For one thing, the light of the stars, however distant, will contribute the energy of EM fields. Moreover, however far you are from a galaxy, there will be some gravitational energy due to it. Recall the discussion of how gravitational energy makes the field equations non-linear. Finally, in the cosmology Block you will meet (and you are likely to have heard of) the so called cosmic microwave background radiation, that fills the Universe, and which must have mass density.

SAQ 33 The required expression is

$$\frac{2mG}{c^2 r}.$$

SAQ 34 You should not be surprised because, in Unit 9, we discussed the fact that clocks in a gravitational field are observed to run slower the nearer they get to the source of that gravitational field. Equations 76 and 77 are another expression of the gravitational redshift.

SAQ 35 (a) The only place where the coordinate ϕ appears in the Schwarzschild metric is in the term

$$\frac{r^2}{c^2}\sin^2\theta(\Delta\phi)^2$$

where

$$\Delta\phi = \phi_1 - \phi_2$$

for neighbouring events. Since we can write

$$\Delta\phi = \phi_1 - \phi_2 = (\phi_1 + \phi_0) - (\phi_2 + \phi_0)$$
$$= \phi_1' - \phi_2' = \Delta\phi'$$

then the term

$$\frac{r^2}{c^2}\sin^2\theta(\Delta\phi)^2 = \frac{r^2}{c^2}\sin^2\theta(\Delta\phi')^2.$$

The Schwarzschild metric will thus take the same form when written in the coordinates (t, r, θ, ϕ') as it does when written in the coordinates (t, r, θ, ϕ), where $\phi' = \phi + \phi_0$ (ϕ_0 is a constant).

(b) Since the mass that controls the Schwarzschild metric is spherically symmetrical, we should not expect that moving the meridians around would produce a new description of spacetime. In the case of the ϕ-coordinate this turns out to be especially true in that it does not even change the *form* of the metric.

SAQ 36 Most scientists in the nineteenth century, basing their ideas of space and time on their understanding of Newtonian mechanics, would have said that the properties of space and time had been established once and for all. Space and time were for them a fixed background within which physical systems moved. Any concept of the geometric properties of space and time changing with individual situations would have been entirely foreign to their way of thinking.

SAQ 37 For Mercury. For the purposes of the argument here we can consider Mercury to have circular orbit of radius r. (1) $2m_{\text{Sun}}G/c^2 r$ must be largest for the planet with the lowest r. (2) v/c is greatest for the planet with the lowest r, as can be seen from the balance of forces equation $m_{\text{planet}}v^2/r = m_{\text{Sun}}m_{\text{planet}}G/r^2$.

SAQ 38 Simply insert the given M and r for Earth's mass and radius together with the value for G given on the back of the units into

$$\frac{mc^2}{GMm/r}.$$

The mass m of the test body in question cancels, yielding a ratio of 1.45×10^9.

Unit 12 Black holes and other consequences of general relativity

Prepared by the Course Team

Contents

Aims

In this Unit, we intend to:

1 Show that spacetime can have closed spatial volumes from which neither matter nor radiation can escape, and relate the properties of such '*black holes*' to the metric of spacetime near a very compact body.

2 Describe how the centre of a black hole is beyond the scope of general relativity in being a region in which matter is compressed to such densities that 'quantum gravity' is necessary for a proper description of it.

3 Indicate in broad outline the ways that black holes might be formed in the Universe and present evidence for their actual existence.

4 Briefly introduce three further applications of general relativity: gravitational lenses, gravitational waves and subtle effects on gyroscopes.

Objectives

When you have finished studying this Unit, you should be able to:

1 Use the Schwarzschild metric to give an account of the general features which are relevant to the occurrence of spherical black holes. (This objective is basically reinforcement of content from Unit 10 & 11.)

2 Explain the existence of an event horizon given the Schwarzschild metric; calculate the Schwarzschild radius corresponding to a given mass.

3 Explain and calculate redshift and time dilation effects near and at the event horizon for a spherical black hole.

4 Discuss the different kinds of black hole and give an account of how they are thought to come into existence.

5 Describe what an external observer would see as a space probe falls freely towards (i) a stellar black hole, and (ii) a galactic-centre black hole. Assume the space probe is attempting continuously to communicate with the observer by radio.

6 Describe the effects of a spherical black hole on space and time outside and within the event horizon.

7 Describe the experiences of a traveller on board a space probe falling freely towards (i) a stellar black hole, and (ii) a galactic-centre black hole. In each case, assume the black hole is spherical.

8 Discuss the deflection of light by a spherical black hole, making use of the concept of photon sphere.

9 Discuss in general terms the properties of rotating black holes; explain the significance of the Kerr metric (without writing it down). Explain the term 'static limit'.

10 Discuss the significance of the central singularity in spherical and rotating black holes.

11 Briefly describe the principles of the Hawking process of radiation from mini (primordial) black holes.

12 Give an account of the evidence for stellar black holes. Give a brief account of such phenomena as those associated with Cygnus X-1.

13 Give an account of the evidence for galactic-centre black holes; give a brief account of objects like M87 and the processes understood to give rise to quasars.

14 Include in an essay on the consequences of general relativity brief but apposite accounts of: the Lense–Thirring effect and 'Gravity Probe B'; gravitational lenses; gravitational waves.

Study comment

There are two video sequences in Videotape VC3 related to this Unit. Band 4 is a general illustration of black hole phenomena and supports Section 2 of this Unit. Band 5, made in 1996 at Glasgow University, discusses attempts to detect gravitational waves and eventually to make a gravitational wave telescope. This band supports Section 6.2.

At certain points in the Unit, non-elementary integrals are introduced. You would not be expected to remember these. You should be aware of the numerical data printed on the back cover of the block; this will be required for solving problems from time to time.

You are not expected to write down the Schwarzschild metric from memory, but you should be able to perform manipulations with it which demonstrate an understanding of its meaning. Likewise, a number of equations from Unit 10 & 11 are quoted (Equation 4 and Equation 8) and you would not be expected to memorize them, but you could be asked to use them. Although you will not be expected to remember the Schwarzschild metric for the exam, it might be a good idea to memorize it, at least for as long as you are studying this Unit. It will make you aware of its structure, and also speed up your understanding since it is referred to frequently.

There are a number of interesting applications of general relativity which are treated in only qualitative fashion. You are not expected to have more than a qualitative understanding of them, but you should have a general awareness of their significance so that, for example, you could mention them where relevant in an essay about the importance of, and tests for, general relativity.

1   Introduction

Band 7 of AC3 introduces this Unit

No consequence of general relativity has caught the public imagination more than 'black holes'. The imagination of the scientific world has also been grabbed by these objects, particularly since Roger Penrose showed in the 1960s that there is a 'singularity' at the centre of each black hole, and also since it has become probable that certain celestial phenomena do indeed entail black holes. Science has no understanding at present of what happens at singularities. Speculations that black hole singularities lead via 'worm holes' to other universes have been seriously put forward but such ideas are not discussed here. It is thought that understanding black hole singularities will go hand in hand with understanding the first great singularity, the big bang, and that each will require a theory of 'quantum gravity'. This unification of quantum theory and general relativity is still the holy grail of modern physics. Although some people think they know where the grail might be found, we still seem to be far from discovering it.

But there are aspects of black holes which are now well understood. Your labours over Unit 10 & 11 will reward you with an opportunity to get some genuine understanding of these extraordinary objects. The main tool will be the Schwarzschild solution to Einstein's field equations. Indeed, we begin the next section with a refresher on the Schwarzschild solution.

Following black holes, the Unit briefly introduces two other dramatic phenomena, also associated with general relativity, which promise to be of key importance to astronomy and cosmology: gravitational lensing and gravitational waves. The Unit also briefly discusses what has been described as the longest experiment in history, the Gravity Probe B experiment. Originally proposed in 1960, this is scheduled to go into space in 1999. It will detect the way the rotating Earth drags spacetime round with it ... very slightly!

2 The Schwarzschild solution and spherical black holes

In this section, we consider only the idealized case of spherical, non-rotating black holes. Probably, real black holes are rotating (dragging around spacetime in their vicinity, making it rotate too!) and we shall discuss these in Section 3. Nevertheless, the study of spherical, non-rotating black holes is a good starting point since they exhibit many of the startling and well-publicized phenomena associated with black holes.

In this section, we introduce spherical black holes in five steps:

1 We briefly review the Schwarzschild metric and use it to show that *something* weird must happen close to very massive bodies. The key concept will be the 'event horizon'. (Section 2.1)

2 We then discuss the three broad classes of black holes that might actually exist. This will give us specific references to draw on in the more formal discussion. (Section 2.2)

3 We discuss the surprising properties of spacetime near a black hole. (Section 2.3)

4 We then discuss how the properties of spacetime change at the event horizon. (Section 2.4)

5 Finally, we discuss what would happen to spacecraft entering black holes of different kinds. (Section 2.6)

2.1 Spacetime near an isolated mass

An isolated mass m attracts any other mass and this can be understood as an effect of the distortion of spacetime by m. If we have a body with mass m which is spherically symmetric, we know exactly how the exterior spacetime is distorted. In Unit 10 & 11, we saw that the Schwarzschild solution to Einstein's field equations gave us the metric describing spacetime outside the body:

$$\Delta\tau = \left[(1 - k/r)\,(\Delta t)^2 - \frac{1}{c^2}\left\{\frac{(\Delta r)^2}{(1 - k/r)} + r^2(\Delta\theta)^2 + r^2\sin^2\theta(\Delta\phi)^2\right\}\right]^{1/2} \quad (1)$$

Definition $k = 2mG/c^2$

where $k = 2mG/c^2$.

The motion of bodies under the influence of mass m is given by the geodesic equations of the above metric; we saw some examples in Unit 10 & 11.

Study comment

Having the answers to the following SAQs well understood will be very helpful in understanding the rest of this Unit.

Objective 1   **SAQ 1**   In Equation 1, which quantity corresponds

(a) to the time as measured on a clock carried by a body which moves from (t, r, θ, ϕ) to $(t + \Delta t, r + \Delta r, \theta + \Delta \theta, \phi + \Delta \phi)$?

(b) to the time measured by stationary clocks a very large distance from the mass m?

Objective 1   **SAQ 2**   A pulse of light passes close to the mass m. What can be said about the total integrated change in τ along the path of the pulse in spacetime?

Objective 1   **SAQ 3**   The following refer to Equation 1:

(a) Write down an expression for the interval $\Delta \tau$ between two distinct events in spacetime which are at the same spatial position.

(b) Write down an expression for $(\Delta \tau)^2$ between two events in spacetime which occur at the same time as registered by a clock far enough from the mass for $1 - k/r$ to be effectively unity, but which are separated by Δr along the same radial line from the mass. Is this interval space-like or time-like?

(c) Write down the metric for the case where $m = 0$. What is another name for this metric and what is its spacetime curvature? Write it in Cartesian coordinates.

Now let us consider an observer O at a fixed point (r, θ, ϕ) in the vicinity of mass m. We know that an interval of time measured on a clock held by O is not equal to the corresponding time Δt measured by an observer at infinity. It is of course just $\Delta \tau = (1 - k/r)^{1/2} \Delta t$. We saw in the last Unit that using this expression we get back the gravitational redshift expression originally deduced for uniform gravitational fields from the equivalence principle in Unit 9. And we also get more: a complete account of the gravitational effects on time measurements extending throughout regions as large as the Solar System over which the gravitational field is manifestly non-uniform. These phenomena are sometimes referred to as the effects of gravitational fields on clocks. But you will understand from the SAQs that the time between ticks as seen by an observer holding a clock is *not* affected by the gravitational field, whereas observers at different distances from m *will* observe the clock going at different rates; this is the basis of the gravitational redshift.

> We always assume that gravitational fields (hence accelerations) do not affect the internal workings of clocks.

Now, if you have been staring imaginatively at this expression for $\Delta \tau$, you might have asked yourself just what happens if O is at the particular radius $r = k$. It would seem that $\Delta \tau$ is zero. But if we think of the equation as expressing intervals of time at infinity Δt in terms of fixed intervals of proper time $\Delta \tau$, $\Delta t = (1 - k/r)^{-1/2} \Delta \tau$ (after all, gravity does not affect the innards of clocks, see marginal note above), we would come to the conclusion that, corresponding to $r = k$, we have $\Delta t = \infty$ for any interval $\Delta \tau$. So any time interval on O's clock would be an *infinite* interval for an observer 'at infinity'. This seems to be the ultimate redshift: any light signal emitted by O at $r = k$ would be redshifted all the way to *zero* frequency according to an observer at infinity.

The obvious next question is, do situations exist where $r = k$? Even without calculating k for particular cases (you will do this in SAQ 4 below) you might guess that we are far from finding $r = k$ anywhere in the Solar System simply because gravitational redshifts are very small, even at the surface of the Sun. But what about deep inside the Sun? Surely as r gets smaller, we must find a place where $r = k$? Well, it's not that simple ... remember that k depends on m, and the Schwarzschild metric applies to the region *outside* the mass (see the box below concerning Birkhoff's theorem). As you go deeper and deeper into the Sun, then (assuming constant density within the Sun) the mass m_r, defined as that mass which is at a *smaller* radius than r, is proportional to r^3. So it is not hard to see that if $r > k$ at the Sun's surface, then r/k actually *increases* as r corresponds to radii deeper and deeper within the Sun. In other words, as you go down into the Sun, trying to reach the Schwarzschild radius, the Schwarzschild radius corresponding to the mass 'below' you (the mass at a lesser distance from the Sun's centre) shrinks even faster.

But, you might be wondering, what if we could somehow *compress* the Sun, so that its entire mass was contained within a much smaller volume? Since k depends only on the mass m, it would be the same however small we squashed the Sun. Then, perhaps we could find values of r which were outside the Sun and for which $k = r$? Would we then get the ultimate redshift? To discuss this, it is useful to introduce a new term: *event horizon*. This is the name given to the spherical shell for which $r = k$. To make possible the ultimate redshift, then, 'all' that is required is that sufficient mass m be contained within the radius $2mG/c^2$ (which becomes the event horizon). In the next section, we discuss how (whether?) the apparently far-fetched idea of squashing down stars might actually happen, but first we briefly look at some consequences.

event horizon

If bodies having their mass entirely within their event horizons do exist, then we shall see that general relativity makes certain unambiguous statements about their properties. Firstly, we have already shown that we get the ultimate redshift for light emitted from a body located on the spherical shell with $r = k$. More dramatically, if any object somehow reaches radii $r < k$, it will never get out. This includes photons. No light can 'get out' from radii less than the event horizon. Such a region of extreme distorted spacetime around a large mass, from which nothing can escape, is what Wheeler in the 1960s called a 'black hole'. The radius of the event horizon, $r = k = 2mG/c^2$ is known as the *Schwarzschild radius*.

Schwarzschild radius

Birkhoff's theorem

Birkhoff proved that the Schwarzschild metric holds everywhere entirely outside a spherical distribution of matter of mass m. Thus, for example, if mass m were contained within a sphere of radius r_1, then the Schwarzschild metric applies everywhere for $r > r_1$. If the mass were to shrink to a smaller radius r_2, spacetime would be unaffected for $r > r_1$ but now the Schwarzschild metric for mass m would hold also for all $r > r_2$. In particular, the mass could be cyclically shrinking and expanding but outside the furthest extent of the mass, the spacetime curvature would be constant and that given by the Schwarzschild metric. We must not think of $2GM_\odot/c^2$ as defining an event horizon for the Sun, deep within the Sun ... it would however define the event horizon were the mass of the Sun to be compressed to any radius which is less than this. One consequence of Birkhoff's theorem is relevant to the question of *gravitational waves* mentioned later in this Unit and in the video sequence: if a spherical distribution of mass suddenly undergoes a reduction in radius from r_1, say, to some lesser value, then spacetime for $r > r_1$ is unaffected. As a consequence, a supernova in which a star undergoes spherically symmetric collapse to a neutron star or black hole will not emit gravitational waves. Another aspect of Birkhoff's theorem which is of cosmological significance is the fact that the metric in a spherical system is unaffected by an external spherically symmetric mass distribution. This is analogous to Newton's demonstration that the gravitational field at any point in a spherically symmetric distribution of matter is exactly that of all the matter lying at a smaller radius concentrated at a point. For example, the Earth's orbit around the Sun would be unaffected if the Solar System outside (say) the outer limit of the orbit of Pluto were solid gold, distributed isotropically to an indefinite distance.

$M_\odot$ represents the mass of the Sun

If nothing ever comes out of a black hole, how might we ever learn of its existence, particularly as it will be remote like all astronomical objects? Well, the very existence of the event horizon is a consequence of the distortion of spacetime described by the Schwarzschild metric. Birkhoff's theorem assures us that this distortion extends beyond the event horizon. So black holes have a gravitational effect on external objects and it is this fact that opens the way to their detection, as we shall see.

Objective 2   **SAQ 4**   (a) Using data found on the back of your units, calculate the Schwarzschild radius for a mass equal to that of the Sun. To what size would (b) the Earth and (c) a 10 kg mass have to be compressed before they would fit within their Schwarzschild radii?

One property of the Schwarzschild radius which has been implicit, and which you probably used in solving the last SAQ, is that it is proportional to m. This is an important feature.

2.2   Three possible types of black hole

2.2.1   Stellar black holes

The original proposal for the existence of black holes arose from a consideration of the life cycle of stars. In brief, it was realized that some stars at the end of their lives might indeed become compressed into the volume within their event horizons. How could this happen? To give you some idea, we make a rapid and superficial traversal of basic astrophysics.

First we ask: why doesn't ordinary matter collapse down to a very much greater density? After all, couldn't all those atomic electrons collapse down into the nuclei and neutralize them, permitting the attractive nuclear force to attract all the resulting neutral nuclei together? A full answer takes us too far afield, but the two key ideas are both quantum mechanical: Heisenberg's uncertainty principle and Pauli's exclusion principle. The way they keep an atom from collapsing is as follows: If an atom were to be squeezed into a smaller volume, the volume in which an electron might be found would be reduced ... in other words its 'position uncertainty' would be reduced. But Heisenberg says that a decrease in uncertainty in position must be accompanied by an increase in uncertainty in momentum. It turns out that increasing the *uncertainty in momentum* increases the *average momentum* and this in turn increases the *energy*. Energy must come from somewhere to increase the energy of the electrons: work must be done to squash atoms; they resist squashing. Now, if the atom has many electrons, another effect comes into play: each electron goes into a different 'state' or 'orbital' and only one electron can go into each orbital. Moreover, successive orbitals get larger in size as the orbital energy increases. This suggests that atoms would get larger and larger on going up through the Periodic Table. The main reason they don't is that the positively charged nucleus exerts an inward force which increases with the nuclear charge. The outcome of this interplay is the typical size of atoms and this in turn determines the typical densities of matter that we see around us.

A normal star like the Sun is kept from squashing down under the enormous gravitational forces by a different effect: the nuclear processes which generate the star's heat thereby exert an outward pressure, effectively 'holding up' the star. But the fuel for stellar nuclear reactions must eventually be exhausted. This happens in a progression which corresponds to the life cycle of a star. Very briefly, first, all the hydrogen undergoes fusion to give helium, then the star undergoes a number of transformations as successively helium fuses to give carbon and so on. The life cycle of stars is a huge and mature scientific subject which we cannot go into here apart from one or two key points. One key point is the fact that the life story of a star is critically determined by its mass. The mass of a star can be from about $M_\odot/10$ to about $100M_\odot$. (The symbol $M_\odot$ represents the mass of the Sun.) A star of mass near $M_\odot$ will, after a few billion years of shining, successively expand enormously to become a 'red giant', tenuously filling the space comparable to the inner Solar System (see Figure 1a), and subsequently shrink to become a 'white dwarf' (see Figure 1b) with density of about $10^9 \, \text{kg m}^{-3}$ or some 40 000 times the density of the densest metals on Earth.

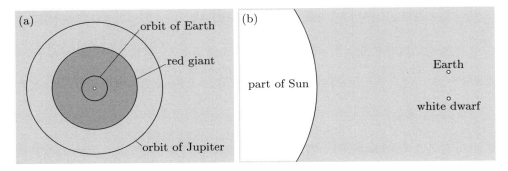

Figure 1 (a) Comparing the dimension of a red giant star to the Solar System. A star of mass $M_\odot$ goes through the red giant phase for some 50 million years after about 10 billion years as a normal star. (b) Comparing a white dwarf star with the Earth and the Sun.

White dwarf stars are not supported by internal pressure due to nuclear reactions, but by the same quantum mechanical effects that support atoms. In particular, the electrons in a white dwarf are not associated with particular nuclei, but move through the star as a whole. A white dwarf star is like a huge atom, held up by the combined repulsive effect of the Pauli exclusion principle and the Heisenberg uncertainty principle known as 'degeneracy pressure'. However, when degeneracy pressure balances the enormous pull of gravity within a white dwarf star, the resulting density far exceeds that of ordinary solid matter.

Chandrasekhar (1910–1995) received the Nobel prize in physics in 1983.

Chandrasekhar limit
$1.4M_\odot$ is the accepted value of refined modern theory.

In 1930 a young astrophysicist, Subrahmanyan Chandrasekhar made an extraordinary theoretical discovery: a white dwarf star, he found, cannot be more massive than just above $M_\odot$. This is the so-called *Chandrasekhar limit*. Although it is understood that a star sheds much mass in the various stages (such as being a red giant) leading up to becoming a white dwarf, it is clear that there are many stars which are just too massive to be held up by degeneracy pressure. What happens to them? The clue came with the discovery in 1932 of the neutron. Instead of the star becoming a white dwarf, a more drastic transition occurs. Under the immense pressure in massive stars, the electrons are absorbed by the protons to become neutrons! The radius of the star collapses, releasing huge amounts of energy, mainly in the form of *neutrinos*. These come from the process in which a proton absorbs an electron to become a neutron with the emission of a neutrino:

A **neutrino**, symbol ν, is a very weakly interacting particle that is involved in beta decay processes. It is possibly massless and certainly almost massless.

$$\mathrm{p} + \mathrm{e}^- \rightarrow \mathrm{n} + \nu.$$

This sudden immense release of energy gives rise to a 'supernova' event, during which the star briefly shines with the brightness of a galaxy (some 10^{11} stars). Left behind is what is, in effect, a huge atomic nucleus: a 'neutron star'. Since stars in general spin, the conservation of angular momentum means that neutron stars, being very compact, spin very rapidly. This opens the way to their detection as follows: They often emit beams of radio waves from their magnetic poles. Since these poles do not necessarily lie on the axis of rotation, the radio beams can sweep around searchlight fashion. The resulting regular pulses picked up on Earth led to the sources being called 'pulsars' before they were identified as the neutron stars predicted by Oppenheimer and Volkov in 1938. A typical neutron star has something like $1.5M_\odot$ (i.e. just above the Chandrasekhar limit) within a radius of some 10 km, see Figure **??**. This represents a density some 10^{15} times greater than water — many orders of magnitude denser even than white dwarf stars.

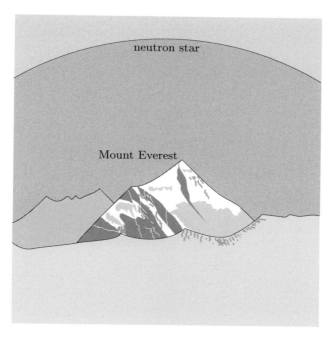

Figure 2   The size of a typical neutron star compared to Mount Everest

Now, history repeats itself: less than a year after Oppenheimer and Volkov in 1938 put forward the basic idea of a neutron star, Oppenheimer and Snyder then asked if there was a limit to the size of such an object — as there had been in the case of white dwarf stars. The answer was 'yes'. Applying Schwarzschild's metric and certain assumptions (such as a spherical distribution of matter) Oppenheimer and Snyder predicted that a stellar object above a certain mass would not only continue to contract to densities exceeding that of a neutron star, but *would collapse to a volume within the event horizon and thence to a singularity at the centre of mass!* It was not until the 1960s that this idea began to be taken seriously by Wheeler, Kruskal, Penrose and their students. We shall later review evidence that such compressed stars do exist in the Universe.

stellar black hole

To summarize: the end point in the evolution of a sufficiently massive star is a *stellar black hole*. The limiting mass above which neutron stars cannot exist is not known very well, but is thought to be about $3.5M_\odot$. However, Nature teases us since the upper limit of *measured* neutron star masses is at present very little above the Chandrasekhar limit. This suggests that $3.5M_\odot$ might be an overestimate, but new observations could alter the picture at any time. It is thought that very massive stars, 10–$100M_\odot$, could become stellar black holes at the end of their lives (i.e. as their thermonuclear fuel is exhausted) even if they shed much of their material in the final supernova explosion. Indeed, it is the enormous compressive forces on the central core of the star, during a supernova explosion, that starts a sufficiently massive star on the compressive transition which ends up as a one-way plunge through the event horizon. In what follows, we shall consider a typical stellar black hole to have a mass of about $10M_\odot$.

2.2.2   Galactic-centre black holes

It is now believed that, at an early stage in the evolution of most galaxies, very massive black holes form at the galactic centre. Presumably, when stars or early generation stellar black holes collided in these regions, where the density of stars was very high, a process of coalescence produced very massive black holes. This process is cumulative since the more massive the black hole, the more effective it is in sucking in other stars, and so on, leading eventually to a huge black hole at the centre of a galaxy, dominating everything taking place in its vicinity. The swirling infall of stars into the galactic-centre black hole can be a maelstrom in which up to 10% of the mass of the stars is liberated as energy just before they fall through the event horizon. This is particularly the case early in the life of a galaxy, and gives rise to the quasar phenomenon, in which very compact regions (of the size of the Solar system) emit far more energy than whole normal galaxies.

There is now evidence that 'quasars', 'active galaxies' and even relatively placid galaxies such as our own Galaxy and our neighbour the Andromeda galaxy all contain *galactic-centre black holes* at their centres. These are on a quite different scale to stellar black holes, having masses in the range 10^7–$10^9 M_\odot$ or higher! Such black holes can have spectacular consequences, making far off galaxies, otherwise too faint to be seen, visible over truly extraordinary distances. The evidence for galactic-centre black holes will be presented later.

As we shall see in the cosmology Units, the most distant galaxies are seen at a very early stage in their life cycle, owing to the immense time it has taken for the light to arrive.

galactic-centre black hole

Objective 2   **SAQ 5**   Calculate the Schwarzschild radius of a galactic-centre black hole of mass $10^9 M_\odot$. Express your answer in terms of the radius of the Earth's orbit around the Sun.

2.2.3 Mini (primordial) black holes

The definition of 'black hole' places no lower limit on the mass. However, whether Nature has ever created a black hole with the mass of the Earth, or a grand piano or a proton, we don't know. In the case of stellar or galactic-centre black holes, we have some idea of how the immense compressive forces necessary for creating them might have arisen. But a grand piano will not come near to collapsing under its own self-gravity. After all, we know how weak is the gravitational attraction between two laboratory scale objects, and that applies to the different parts of a grand piano! Nevertheless, two facts have kept alive interest in the possibility of 'mini black holes' existing. The first is the idea that during the initial 'big bang' in which everything came into being (see Block 4), there *might* have been inhomogeneities and compressive effects sufficient to create primordial black holes. Secondly, mini black holes of the 'right' mass would have certain extraordinary properties predicted by cosmologist Stephen Hawking which we shall discuss in Section 4. Mini black holes would be objects of great density: In SAQ 4, you showed that the Schwarzschild radius for an object with the mass of the Earth would be about the radius of a golf ball. If the Earth *were* compressed to that radius, its density would far exceed that of an atomic nucleus.

mini black holes
We hazard no guess as to what the mass of such an object might be!

Objective 4   **SAQ 6**   Write notes for an essay discussing the different kinds of black hole and give an account of how they are thought to come into existence.
[Try to do this without looking back through Section 2.2.]

2.3   The spacetime of a spherical black hole

Since it is the key to understanding spherical black holes, we repeat the Schwarzschild solution of the Einstein field equations for an isolated spherical mass m. It is the following metric describing spacetime around such a mass:

$$\Delta\tau = \left[\left(1 - \frac{k}{r}\right)(\Delta t)^2 - \frac{1}{c^2}\left\{\frac{(\Delta r)^2}{(1 - k/r)} + r^2(\Delta\theta)^2 + r^2\sin^2\theta(\Delta\phi)^2\right\}\right]^{1/2}$$

where $k = 2mG/c^2$ and m is the mass of the spherically symmetric, static object exterior to which the Schwarzschild metric applies. Because the spacetime of the Schwarzschild solution is spherically symmetric, and to simplify our equations, let us consider only radial motion. That is, we only consider world-lines for which $\Delta\theta = \Delta\phi = 0$. Under this restriction, the metric can be written

$$(\Delta\tau)^2 = (1 - k/r)(\Delta t)^2 - \frac{1}{c^2}\frac{(\Delta r)^2}{(1 - k/r)}. \tag{2}$$

You will recall that in Unit 10 & 11 we applied a similar restriction to radial motion of a body under the influence of a central mass. Doing this, we succeeded in showing that the geodesics of the Schwarzschild metric lead to Newtonian radial motion of the body to a very good approximation. The approximation was only valid, however, if (i) the speed of the object was much less than c, and (ii) the gravitational field is 'weak' (spacetime curvature small) over the path of the body. Of course, near a black hole the gravitational field is by no means weak, so we should not be surprised if the radial motion of a body near a black hole is far from Newtonian.

Newtonian physics works pretty well, everywhere in the Solar System. Even on the surface of the Sun, k/r is only $\sim 0.4 \times 10^{-5}$.

We now present four remarkable consequences of the distortion of spacetime around a black hole:

1 The coordinate time taken for a light signal to travel a distance outwards along a radius from a point r just outside the event horizon $(r \gtrsim k)$ becomes *infinite* as $r \to k$.

2 The time taken for an object in free fall near a black hole to reach the event horizon *as recorded by a clock moving with the object* is finite, as indeed is the time to reach the singularity at $r = 0$.

3 The *coordinate* time taken for an object in free fall near a black hole to reach the event horizon from any point outside is *infinite*. This, remember, is the time recorded by an observer (effectively) at infinity.

4 Space itself becomes markedly curved around a black hole.

In connection with point 2, you may well have heard that an observer falling through an event horizon (and so taking readings on the clock in his own local inertial frame) will be torn apart as he does so. In fact, it depends on whether he falls into a stellar black hole or a galactic-centre black hole, a point we discuss in more detail later.

1   Light emitted from near the event horizon

For light travelling radially outwards, we can apply Equation 2. Since light travels on world-lines for which proper time intervals are zero, we can put $\Delta\tau = 0$ and light satisfies

$$0 = (1 - k/r)(\Delta t)^2 - \frac{1}{c^2}\frac{(\Delta r)^2}{(1 - k/r)}$$

which can be rewritten in the limit as

$$c\,dt = \frac{dr}{(1 - k/r)}.$$

This can easily be integrated to find the coordinate time taken for light emitted at r_1 and received at r_2:

$$t_2 - t_1 = \int_{t_1}^{t_2} dt = \frac{1}{c}\int_{r_1}^{r_2}\frac{dr}{1 - k/r}.$$

It turns out that this is a standard integral, and we get

$$t_2 - t_1 = (r_2 - r_1)/c + \frac{k}{c}\ln\frac{r_2 - k}{r_1 - k}. \tag{3}$$

The first thing to notice about this is that the coordinate time interval is *not* simply $r_2 - r_1$ over c, there being an additional term involving logarithms. In this sense, light appears not to be going at the speed of light! In fact, this is perfectly acceptable since, firstly, as we shall see, radial *coordinate intervals* $r_2 - r_1$ do not exactly correspond to *distances* $r_2 - r_1$ due to the curvature of space near a black hole (see Equation 12 below). Secondly, it remains true that in a *local inertial frame* special relativity remains true, and light *does* travel at speed c, but we are looking at light from an external point of view which most certainly is *not* a local inertial frame.

Now notice that $t_2 - t_1$ is always greater than $(r_2 - r_1)/c$, and in particular, the excess time $\to \infty$ as $r_1 \to k$. This remarkable fact can be seen from the denominator of the logarithmic second term in Equation 3.

Recall from Unit 9 that the equivalence principle tells us that local inertial frames exist in which special relativity applies.

Objective 3, revision   **SAQ 7**   The gravitational slowing down of light is actually not new in this course. Which test of general relativity described in Unit 10 & 11 effectively involves the same effect, albeit in a less extreme form?

Remember that coordinate time intervals are those recorded by a very distant observer for whom $r \gg k$.

Let us restate this finding: the coordinate time taken for light signals to reach an observer situated at $r = r_2$ from a point along the same radius at $r = r_1$ near a black hole becomes longer and longer the closer point r_1 is to the event horizon and becomes *infinite* for points *at* the event horizon, $r_1 = k$. So, not only are signals from points on the event horizon infinitely reddened, as we saw above, but infinitely delayed, too. Signals from the event horizon never get anywhere: even for any given r_2 arbitrarily close to the event horizon, the time taken to reach r_2 from an even smaller radius r_1 becomes *infinite* as $r_1 \to k$. No signals can escape from the event horizon (nor, it turns out, from anywhere within it). This is one way in which we can view the statement that light never escapes from the event horizon. This is a primary sense in which 'black holes' are, in fact, black.

An interesting qualification of the blackness of black holes, due to Hawking, is mentioned later.

2   Body falling freely according to observer falling with it

In Section 13.2 of Unit 10 & 11, we showed that bodies moving radially near a mass m obeyed Newtonian motion as long as the speed was not too great or the spacetime curvature too large. This was an important confirmation that Einstein's theory agrees in an appropriate limit with the classic combination of Newtonian gravity and Newton's second law of motion. Now we lift the restrictions. We imagine a body or voyager starting from rest some way out from a black hole and falling inwards. We study the dependence of radial distance r on proper time τ, the time shown on the voyager's own clock. Our starting point is Equation 81 of Section 13.2 in Unit 10 & 11 (an equation involving no approximations):

$$1 - \frac{k}{r} = N^2 - \left(\frac{1}{c}\frac{dr}{d\tau}\right)^2. \tag{4}$$

The constant N is fixed by the way the body starts out: we assume the body starts from rest, $dr/d\tau = 0$, at some large radius, $r = R$. Thus $N^2 = 1 - k/R$.

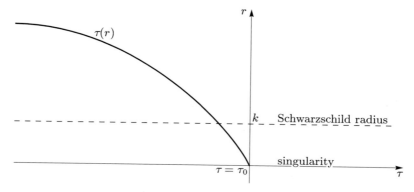

Figure 3   The relationship between radial distance and proper time for a body freely falling into a black hole of Schwarzschild radius k.

The equation of motion of the body is therefore

$$\frac{dr}{d\tau} = -c\sqrt{k}\sqrt{\frac{1}{r} - \frac{1}{R}} = -c\sqrt{k}\sqrt{\frac{R-r}{Rr}} \tag{5}$$

where we have taken the negative square root because we are studying inward motion. To integrate this equation, we rewrite it as

$$d\tau = -\frac{1}{c}\sqrt{\frac{R}{k}}\sqrt{\frac{r}{R-r}}\,dr$$

which leads to a tricky integral. We simply state the result which follows from the assumption that $r \ll R$ (we are interested in what happens fairly near the black hole, i.e. at distances much less than those which the body had when it started out):

$$\tau(r) - \tau(R) = \frac{1}{c}\left(\frac{R}{k}\right)^{1/2}R\left[\frac{\pi}{2} - \frac{2}{3}\left(\frac{r}{R}\right)^{3/2}\right]. \tag{6}$$

Here $\tau(R)$ is the proper time at which the body is released. We see, therefore, that the *proper* time required for a body released from rest at a finite distance R to reach the centre of a black hole, $r = 0$, is *finite*. From Equation 6, it is just

$$\text{time to reach centre} = \frac{\pi R^{3/2}}{2ck^{1/2}}.$$

If we redefine our zero of time so that $\tau = \tau_0$ when $r = 0$, we can recast Equation 6 as:

$$\tau = \tau_0 - \frac{2}{3c}\frac{r^{3/2}}{k^{1/2}}. \tag{7}$$

The motion then follows the solid line in Figure 3; nothing strange happens as the body crosses the event horizon, $r = k$. It also follows from Equation 6 that the interval of proper time required for a body released from rest at the event horizon to reach the singularity at $r = 0$ is $\pi k/2c$ which for a stellar black hole of mass $5M_\odot$ is just 7.85×10^{-5} s.

Objective 7   **SAQ 8**   Verify the statements in the last sentence. (You can exploit the result of SAQ 4.) What would the corresponding time interval be for a galactic-centre black hole of mass $10^9 M_\odot$?

3   Body falling freely according to external observer

We use dr and Δr etc. interchangeably, the former being the infinitesimal limit of the latter. This will not lead to errors here.

We now ask how the motion of a body falling radially into a black hole would be described by a distant external observer, i.e. an observer very far away whose clocks tick in intervals of coordinate time, t. To answer this question, we need an expression relating intervals dt to intervals $d\tau$. Of course, one cannot obtain such a relationship simply by setting $\Delta r = \Delta \theta = \Delta \phi = 0$ in the Schwarzschild metric, as the following SAQ brings out.

Objectives 3, 6   **SAQ 9**   What would we find for $dt/d\tau$ by setting $\Delta r = \Delta \theta = \Delta \phi = 0$ in the Schwarzschild metric? Write it down and explain why it is not appropriate here.

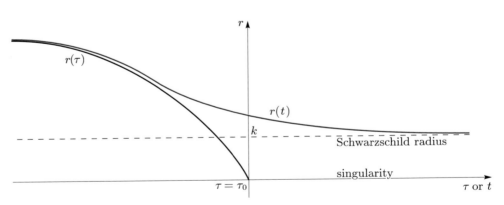

Figure 4   Like Figure 3 but showing also the relationship between coordinate time t and r for the same body. Note that as the body starts out, for early times and large radii t and τ are the same.

The required expression relates dt to $d\tau$ for a freely falling object (i.e. *not* at a fixed point with $\Delta r = \Delta\theta = \Delta\phi = 0$), and is found from the geodesic equations for the Schwarzschild metric to be (see Section 13.2 of Unit 10 & 11):

$$(1 - k/r)\frac{dt}{d\tau} = N \tag{8}$$

where N is the constant determined from the initial conditions, $N = \sqrt{1 - k/R}$, see after Equation 4.

Using Equation 8 to replace $d\tau$ by dt in Equation 5, we get the following differential equation:

$$\frac{dr}{dt} = \frac{dr}{d\tau}\frac{d\tau}{dt} = -ck^{1/2}\frac{1 - k/r}{\sqrt{1 - k/R}}\left(\frac{R - r}{Rr}\right)^{1/2}. \tag{9}$$

We shall not solve this equation here, but the result is illustrated by the blue line in Figure 4. Naturally, for large r, coordinate time t and proper time τ do not greatly differ, as can be seen in this figure where the two lines match at very early times. But as the body arrives near the black hole a dramatic difference appears: as r falls toward the event horizon value $r = k$, the corresponding coordinate time becomes longer and longer. Indeed, as $r \to k$, $t \to \infty$. In other words, *according to an external observer, it takes an infinite time for a body falling into a black hole to reach the event horizon.*

Objective 5, 7   **SAQ 10**   Briefly contrast the way in which the distance of a spacecraft falling into a black hole varies with proper time of an observer on board and with the time of a remote observer.

Not the least weird thing about black holes is the fact that observers on board a falling spacecraft see themselves rapidly fall through the event horizon whereas to external observers the spacecraft never quite reaches the event horizon. Of course, this latter fact is directly related to the extreme time dilation effect near the event horizon. In order to get a clearer view of what actually happens at the event horizon, we shall have to confront the fact that the Δr term in the metric becomes infinite when $k = r$. This we do in Section 2.4.

4   The curvature of space near a black hole

The properties of spacetime that we have seen so far near a black hole relate mostly to the 'time' aspects of spacetime. What about space itself? For example, one of the things that we have learned to expect of curved space is that the circumference C of a circle of radius r is not the $2\pi r$ of flat space. Does something like that happen near a black hole? In fact, this does indeed happen near a black hole.

Once more, we turn to the Schwarzschild metric for enlightenment. We wish to consider spacetime intervals corresponding to zero change in coordinate time, i.e. $\Delta t = 0$. As usual, we will simplify things so that we keep to the equatorial plane with $\Delta\theta = 0$ and $\theta = \pi/2$ so that the non-zero parts of the metric can be written:

$$c^2(\Delta\tau)^2 = -\frac{1}{1 - k/r}(\Delta r)^2 - r^2(\Delta\phi)^2. \tag{10}$$

At or outside the event horizon, $r \geqslant k$ so both terms on the right side of Equation 10 are negative. $\Delta\tau$ here is a space-like interval and we take $|c\,\Delta\tau|$ as an interval of 'proper length'. This is the length you would measure if you could somehow place rulers along the path to be measured at some single instant in time. Thus, the proper distance L_{12} along a *radial* path, i.e. with $\Delta\phi = 0$ from r_1 to r_2 is

Alternatively, the method of Unit 10 & 11 is always valid: define a geometric path $r = s$, $\phi = \phi_0$ (constant), $\theta = \pi/2$, with parameter s going from r_1 to r_2. You get the same answer. The parametric method applies to paths of any shape.

$$L_{12} = \int_{r_1}^{r_2} \frac{\mathrm{d}r}{\sqrt{1 - k/r}}. \tag{11}$$

It turns out that this integral can be evaluated to give:

$$L_{12} = \sqrt{r_2(r_2 - k)} - \sqrt{r_1(r_1 - k)} + k \ln \frac{\sqrt{r_2} + \sqrt{r_2 - k}}{\sqrt{r_1} + \sqrt{r_1 - k}}. \tag{12}$$

Now we use Equation 12 to evaluate the proper radial distance between the event horizon, $r_1 = k$, and a circle, $r_2 = 2k$. We find $L_{12} = k(\sqrt{2} + \ln(1 + \sqrt{2}))$ or $L_{12} = 2.296k$. This is remarkable. For, we note that the same metric, Equation 10, gives for the circumference of a circle centred at the black hole simply

$$C = r \int_0^{2\pi} \mathrm{d}\phi = 2\pi r$$

so that circles with $r = k$ and $r = 2k$ and hence circumferences $2\pi k$ and $4\pi k$ respectively, are separated by a radial distance *not* equal to k but $2.296k$. This corresponds to a vastly greater distortion of space than one would find anywhere in the Solar System, even at the surface of the Sun.

Objective 6   SAQ 11   Calculate the proper radial distance between two circles centred on a black hole, and in the same plane, of circumferences $C_1 = 2n\pi k$ and $C_2 = 2(n + 1)\pi k$, where k is the Schwarzschild radius. Calculate the case of $n = 10$, and repeat for $n = 20$. Is space effectively getting flatter as r increases?

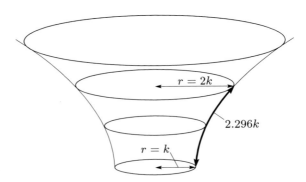

Figure 5 By embedding in three-dimensional space the two-dimensional 'equatorial' surface through the black hole, it is possible to visualize how curvature can modify the relationship between the radius and circumference of circles. The significant feature of a figure like this is that proper distances between points are proportional to the shortest (geodesic) distance on the surface. The two circles shown have values of r equal to k and $2k$ and circumferences $2\pi k$ and $4\pi k$ respectively, but the proper radial distance between them is much greater than k.

In Figure 5, we embed in three-dimensional space the two-dimensional $\theta = 0$ equatorial plane through the centre of a black hole in a way that suggests the curvature. Note that the up–down direction of the figure is not up–down in a gravitational field, so although the diagram suggests the way something is sucked into a black hole, we could just as well have drawn the figure the other way up. Always remember that gravitational attraction is due to the curvature of *spacetime*.

2.4   What happens at the event horizon?

We have already remarked that something odd happens when $r = k$: intervals Δt corresponding to given intervals $\Delta \tau$ seem to approach infinity. Moreover, the Δr term in the metric becomes infinite at $r = k$ ... it *looks* as if spacetime develops catastrophic geometric properties at events with values of r equal to k. In other words, there is apparently a *singularity* at $r = k$. In fact this is *not* a real singularity, because it can be eliminated by re-expressing the metric in a new set of coordinates, r and t' known as Eddington–Finkelstein coordinates.

Study comment

You will not be expected to recall the mathematical form of this coordinate transformation, but you should be aware of its consequences.

The new time coordinate t' is related to the customary coordinates, r and t, by the equation

$$t' = t + \frac{k}{c} \ln \left| \frac{r}{k} - 1 \right|.$$

This new coordinate t', instead of t, will give us a metric in which no infinite increments in proper time, $\Delta \tau$, are produced by small changes in the coordinates, Δr and $\Delta t'$. It is possible to show that small changes in t are related to small changes in t' by

$$\Delta t = \Delta t' - \frac{k \, \Delta r}{cr \, (1 - k/r)}.$$

It is straightforward to verify that putting this expression back into the metric gives:

$$(\Delta \tau)^2 = \left(1 - \frac{k}{r} \right) (\Delta t')^2 - \frac{2k \, \Delta t' \, \Delta r}{cr} - \frac{(\Delta r)^2}{c^2} \left(1 + \frac{k}{r} \right)$$

which has no singularities apart from the *essential* singularity at $r = 0$.

In terms of the r–t' coordinates, the metric does *not* behave badly at $r = k$, so an apparent difficulty in the Schwarzschild metric has been removed. On the other hand, the presence of the term involving $\Delta t' \, \Delta r$ makes the metric harder to interpret, but we do not pursue that here. However, the fact that there is a continuous relationship between τ and r all the way down to the essential singularity suggests that there should exist a non-singular form of the metric, and that you have now seen. This continuity across the event horizon will be invoked shortly.

Nevertheless, something very odd does happen at the event horizon. Refer, for example to Equation 2. Outside the event horizon, the coefficient for the 'time' component is positive and that for the $(\Delta r)^2$ component is negative. This is just the same arrangement of $+$ and $-$ signs as that for the Minkowski metric of flat spacetime; it was just those signs that gave us our picture of light cones and our concepts of space-like and time-like intervals.

Objective: Revision   **SAQ 12**   Classify space-like and time-like intervals according to whether they lie inside or outside light cones for flat Minkowski spacetime.

But consider what happens *inside* the event horizon. The term $(1 - k/r)$ becomes negative, so that we get a negative value of $(\Delta\tau)^2$ for an interval with $\Delta r = 0$. Two neighbouring events cannot lie on the world-line of a particle (or photon) if their separation is space-like, i.e. $(\Delta\tau)^2 < 0$. But if we had a particle at rest within the event horizon, then $\Delta r = \Delta\theta = \Delta\phi = 0$, and so, because of the reversal in the sign of the 'time' term, the interval would be space-like. It follows that *nothing can be stationary for $r < k$*. What would be a time-like interval outside the event horizon has become a space-like interval. Similarly, what would have been space-like intervals outside the event horizon become time-like within.

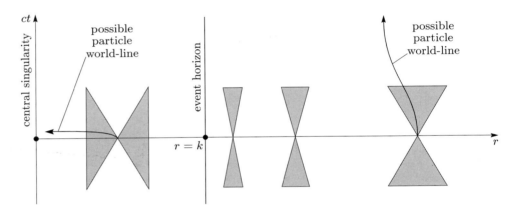

Figure 6   Light cones just outside and just inside the event horizon of a black hole. The vertical coordinate is $x^0 = ct$ and the horizontal coordinate is r, but this is the same as $x = x^1$ if we assume $\theta = \pi/2$ and $\phi = 0$ (i.e. somewhat like being on the equator at the Greenwich meridian).

The effect of this switch is to rotate light cones through a right-angle. In Figure 6, we show sample light cones just inside and just outside the event horizon. Shortly we shall consider quantitative features of these light cones, but there is just one dramatic feature that stands out: the light cones within the event horizon are rotated through $\pi/2$ and appear to face *inwards*. In order for successive points on the world-line of a body to be time-like separated, world-lines of any body must always be within the light cone, just as was the case in flat Minkowski spacetime. Another fact in flat spacetime was that since time goes forward, world-lines must move upwards within light cones. Now, with light cones on their sides, as it were, what constraint is placed on world-lines? The answer is that world-lines are still confined to be within the light cones and, for bodies located inside the event horizon, *bodies must lie on inwardly directed world-lines*. Because both the $1 - k/r$ and $1/(1 - k/r)$ factors change sign inside the event horizon, r plays the role of time, and 'forward' time-like intervals point toward the origin. In other words, *all* world-lines within the event horizon end up at the central singularity at $r = 0$. So motion towards $r = 0$ is as unavoidable within the event horizon as 'going forward in time' is inevitable outside. Once within the event horizon, the fate of any traveller is sealed. Although we haven't shown it here, motion must be inward (toward smaller r) within the light cones for objects within the event horizon. This can be shown by considering light cones involving the Eddington–Finkelstein coordinates which behave in a continuous fashion at the event horizon.

Before leaving this discussion, we look at the light cones in Figure 6 more quantitatively. Let us keep with the metric in the form of Equation 2, i.e. consider only radial motion. Remember that the light cone is defined by the world-lines of light (or photons, as we now understand it). The motion of light is, as we have stressed several times, defined by zero intervals of proper time (light travels on null geodesics). Thus we should be able to find the light cones by setting $\Delta \tau = 0$ in Equation 2. This gives us:

Remember: light travels on null geodesics.

$$\frac{\Delta t}{\Delta r} = \pm \frac{1}{c} \frac{1}{(1 - k/r)}. \tag{13}$$

The $+$ sign corresponds to r increasing with time, i.e. to outwards directed light, with the $-$ sign indicating ingoing light. To see that Equation 13 makes sense, first consider a value of r corresponding to a great distance from the black hole. Then we can take $k/r = 0$ and we get the customary $45°$ light cone of special relativity:

$$\frac{\Delta t}{\Delta r} = \pm \frac{1}{c} \tag{14}$$

or, equivalently,

$$\frac{\Delta ct}{\Delta r} = \frac{\Delta x^0}{\Delta r} = \pm 1. \tag{15}$$

As we would expect, far from the black hole, where spacetime is flat, the lines defining the light cone have unit slope (with $x^0 = ct$ ordinate of course) corresponding to speed c. However, as k/r becomes finite, nearer to the event horizon, see Equation 13, the magnitude of the slope becomes greater so that the cones get narrower. In Figure 6, this becomes increasingly evident as the event horizon is approached from outside.

Objective 6   **SAQ 13**   What does this say about the apparent speed of light just outside the event horizon of a black hole? How does this relate to what we have seen earlier in the Unit?

Again, we stress that this behaviour of light is not in conflict with special relativity since in a *freely falling local inertial frame,* light would still be measured to have speed c.

Now consider what happens inside the event horizon. Let us suppose that we are at quite small radius, $r \ll k$, then

$$\frac{\Delta ct}{\Delta r} = \pm \frac{1}{k/r - 1} \approx \pm \frac{r}{k}. \tag{16}$$

Now the slope becomes $\pm$(a number that tends to zero as $r \to 0$) and the light cones get narrower and narrower about the horizontal direction as one approaches the central singularity at $r = 0$. The last moments of something destined for the singularity at $r = 0$ are fleeting indeed!

2.5   The deflection of light by a spherical black hole

We now discuss the way in which light is deflected by a black hole. Since spacetime near a black hole is very much more distorted than spacetime near the Sun, we should not be surprised to find light passing near a black hole deflected by *much* more than the 1.75 seconds of arc that is suffered by light grazing the Sun. The results we present here are computer simulations by Cohn based on the Schwarzschild metric, and you would certainly not be expected to derive them.

H. Cohn, *American Journal of Physics*, **45** (1977) 239.

Suppose we project a bundle of light rays that are parallel at infinity past the origin of a coordinate system with no matter situated at it; the rays should continue along parallel paths as in Figure 7. The initial x^2-coordinate of each of the light rays, given in Figure 7 in arbitrary units, is called its *impact parameter*. Now we place a black hole of mass m at the origin of spatial coordinates and send in the same bundle of light rays. We imagine that we are confined to the 'equatorial' plane, i.e. $\theta = \pi/2$. The resulting paths are shown in Figure 8. The shading, interior to $r = k (\equiv 2Gm/c^2)$ represents space inside the event horizon. Even a light ray of impact parameter $4k$ is strongly deflected. For light with impact parameter $2.6k$ the bending is so severe that the light is captured in a circular path of radius $r = 1.5k$ where it would orbit forever unless perturbed. Light rays with impact parameter less than $2.6k$ are drawn in through the event horizon to the singularity. So any light ray that crosses the sphere at radius $r = 1.5k$ *from the outside* is captured by the black hole; this sphere is called the *photon-sphere* of the black hole.

impact parameter

photon-sphere

Objective 8   **SAQ 14**   What is the essential difference between the photon-sphere and the event horizon?

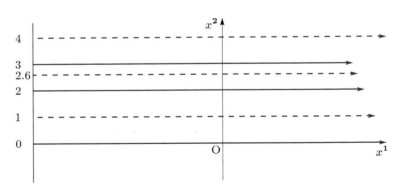

Figure 7   Parallel light rays passing the origin of coordinates of a space containing no matter; their initial x^2-separations (marked on the scale at the left in arbitrary units) remain unchanged as they pass the origin O.

There is a crucial difference between the photon-sphere and the event horizon. Suppose there exists an object in the region between the photon-sphere and the event horizon, say with radial coordinate $r = 1.2k$. If this object emits light in the outward radial direction, the light will emerge through the photon-sphere and escape. If, however, the object is inside the event horizon, then whatever the initial direction, the light must eventually reach the central singularity. The light can never escape the event horizon. Altogether, the behaviour of light rays near a black hole makes a strong contrast with the tiny effects in the Solar System that Eddington, Shapiro and others worked so hard to detect.

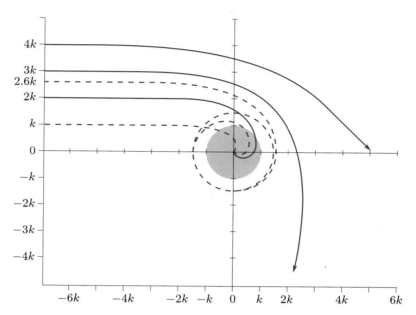

Figure 8   The bending of light rays by a spherical black hole of mass m. The distance scales are in units of $k = 2Gm/c^2$; the event horizon is the sphere at $r = k$, and the space interior to the event horizon is shaded. The light ray with impact parameter $2.6k$ goes into a circular orbit of radius $1.5k$ about the black hole. Any slight disturbance that decreases its radial coordinate will cause it to spiral into the central singularity. Light rays with impact parameter less than $2.6k$ spiral into the singularity without orbiting. The photon-sphere is at $r = 1.5k$.

2.6   Falling into a black hole

We have mentioned bodies falling through the event horizon, and you might have been puzzled if you have heard in popular accounts of black holes that anything entering a black hole is destroyed in the process. In fact, it does (for a while) make a difference whether you fall into a galactic-centre black hole or a stellar black hole. The difference relates to the fact that the Schwarzschild radius of a black hole is proportional to its mass, and so is many orders of magnitude greater for a galactic-centre black hole than for a stellar black hole. The tidal forces at the event horizon are much less for a galactic-centre black hole. But if an astronaut falls feet-first into a stellar black hole, he will be stretched horribly by the difference between the pull on his feet and his head and at the same time squashed sideways. Note the stretching effect is real in the sense that it has observable consequences in the unfortunate astronaut's rest frame. What causes these physical effects of stretching and squeezing? Of course the torture will end quickly as the astronaut is compressed to zero volume at the central singularity.

Recall from Unit 9 that tidal forces arise from the gradient of the gravitational force. Consider, as is permissable for the present argument, the Newtonian gravitational force on a mass μ at a distance r from a central mass m. The magnitude of this force is

$$F(r) = \frac{Gm\mu}{r^2} \tag{17}$$

Figure 9   Tidal forces near a stellar black hole make the medieval rack torture benign by comparison.

Contrast this with the length contraction effects of special relativity which are manifestations of coordinate transformations and which will not be felt to squeeze a subject in his inertial frame.

and taking the derivative we find for small displacements that

$$F(r + \Delta r) - F(r) = \frac{\mathrm{d}F}{\mathrm{d}r}\Delta r = -\frac{2Gm\mu}{r^3}\Delta r. \tag{18}$$

This is a measure of the tidal force across an object of dimension Δr. It is *very* large near the event horizon of a stellar black hole both by virtue of the large mass of the black hole, but more particularly because r is very small near the (small) Schwarzschild radius. As the physicist Luminet puts it, speaking of the forces on an astronaut at the horizon ($k = 30\,\mathrm{km}$) of a $10M_\odot$ black hole:

The book 'Black holes' by J-P Luminet is highly recommended as a vivid non-mathematical account of black holes.

> At the horizon the stretching effect would be the same as if he was hanging from a girder of the Eiffel tower with the entire population of Paris suspended from his ankles!
>
> J-P Luminet *Black Holes* Cambridge, 1992

Now, note that the tidal force goes like $1/r^3$ but the radius of the event horizon is proportional to the mass. It follows that the tidal force at the event horizon goes like $1/m^2$ and would therefore be almost imperceptible for a traveller passing through the event horizon of a galactic-centre black hole. Of course, his fate would be sealed once he passed through, just as surely as it would for a stellar black hole. He would not escape tidal forces for long; as he approached the singularity these would become immense. But he could not tell us of his brief experiences within the event horizon since, once inside, he could get no message out.

Closely related to the tidal force is the question of the spacetime volume of a 'local' inertial frame of the traveller. We have said that whereas light does not travel at speed c in the (non-inertial) (ct, r, θ, ϕ) frame, we know that the core of the equivalence principle (actually the weak equivalence principle of Unit 9) is that special relativity holds in a freely falling local inertial frame. It is clear that the spacetime volume which corresponds to 'local' will be extremely small for a traveller passing into a stellar black hole. Such a traveller would scarcely have the space or the time to verify that light had speed c in a local inertial frame as he fell through the event horizon.

2.7   The central singularity

The term $1 - k/r$ in the Schwarzschild metric clearly becomes infinite at $r = 0$; this is a real central singularity which *cannot* be eliminated by a clever choice of coordinates. Once anything or anyone penetrates the event horizon, *its* or *his* or *her* world-line ends up at the singularity. It can not overshoot since then it would be going the wrong way on the other side, so it seems (and can be proved to be) inescapable that we have a region of finite mass but zero volume. At least that is the picture to which we are impelled by general relativity: infinite density. Of course, such a singularity is deeply alien to physics and, as mentioned above, it was the proofs by Penrose, Hawking and other that such singularities existed which aroused much of the interest in black holes.

There is, however, a possible quantum escape route: general relativity breaks down in this region and a theory of 'quantum gravity' might provide a way that the volume would be non-zero, though still very small. A brief discussion is given in Section 4.

3 Rotating black holes and the Kerr solution

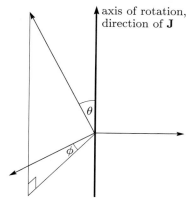

Figure 10   For a rotating black hole, we take the polar axis (from which θ is measured) as the axis of spin. The light deflection to be described below takes place on the 'equatorial plane' with $\theta = \pi/2$.

We also assume zero electrical charge, a point to which we shall return.

So far, we have considered only a spherically symmetric black hole. In practice, a black hole formed from a star will normally retain much of the angular momentum of its parent and so, thanks to its reduced size, may spin quite rapidly. The black hole then possesses an axis of rotation and is no longer spherically symmetric. The metric of spacetime outside such a rotating black hole is not the Schwarzschild solution but a new solution of Einstein's field equations discovered only in 1963 by Roy Kerr. This discovery is of immense importance since it has opened the way to a much more realistic description of black holes. Indeed, a whole new range of fascinating phenomena arise, the most striking of which is the way a rotating black hole *drags nearby spacetime itself* around with it.

Let us assume that the black hole has angular momentum $\mathbf{J}$ and that we choose our coordinates with $\theta = 0$ aligned along $\mathbf{J}$. This very natural choice is indicated in Figure 10.

Detailed analysis of the Kerr solution shows that there is a maximum value for the magnitude $J = |\mathbf{J}|$ that a black hole of given mass can have. It turns out that $J \leqslant m^2 G/c = mck/2$. It also turns out that the event horizon is now at the smaller radius, r_- where

$$r_- = \frac{k}{2} + \left[\left(\frac{k}{2} \right)^2 - \rho^2 \right]^{1/2} \tag{19}$$

where $\rho = J/mc$.

Objective 9

SAQ 15   What value does r_- take when J has its maximum value? What value does it take when the angular momentum of the black hole is zero?

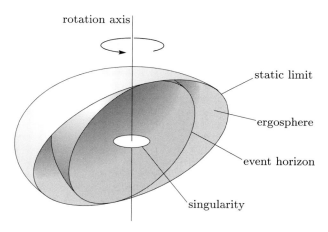

Figure 11   The regions around a rotating black hole showing the ergosphere and the static limit.

ergosphere

static limit

There is a second surface surrounding a rotating black hole, further dividing space into two regions. This surface delimits the *ergosphere* and is not spherical, although it is axially symmetric, i.e. independent of ϕ. The surface of revolution defined by $r_+(\theta)$ and shown in Figure 11 is the boundary of the ergosphere and is called the *static limit* of the black hole, for a reason which will become apparent shortly. It is

$$r_+(\theta) = \frac{k}{2} + \left[\left(\frac{k}{2} \right)^2 - \rho^2 \cos^2 \theta \right]^{1/2}. \tag{20}$$

From Equation 20, we can see that r_+ ranges from r_- at $\theta = 0$ or π (the 'poles') to $r_+ = k$ at $\theta = \pi/2$. The relationships between the different distances are indicated on Figure 12.

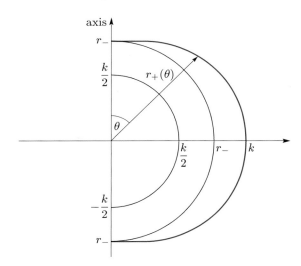

Figure 12   A plane including the polar axis through the black hole (half a black hole) indicating the relationship between k, r_- and $r_+(\theta)$ for a rotating black hole with $J = 0.9$ times the maximum permitted value.

Referring back to Figure 11, you will note that there is an inner horizon and also the inner singularity takes the form of a flat ring rather than a point. Unfortunately, it is not possible to discuss these interesting phenomena with the mathematical tools at our disposal. The book by Luminet cited above has a qualitative discussion.

Study comment

You will not be expected to describe phenomena occurring within the event horizon of a Kerr black hole.

The characteristic property of the ergosphere, the region between the event horizon, and the static limit, is that nothing there can be at rest *...angular motion is compulsory*. This is because spacetime itself is being dragged around with extreme violence. If light cones were to be drawn in this region, they would tip forward so far in the whirlpool of spacetime that the world-lines of particles would be compelled to rotate in the direction of increasing azimuthal angle ϕ. (Recall that for successive points on a world-line of a particle to be at time-like intervals, the world-line must be within the forward light cone.) With the expenditure of energy, voyagers within the ergosphere could avoid the event horizon, but once the event horizon has been penetrated, their fate is sealed just as in the static case. Spacetime is also dragged around outside the ergosphere, but not to the extent that rotation is compulsory, and clearly the rotation must fall off smoothly with distance from the black hole.

Outside the ergosphere a sufficiently powerful spacecraft could avoid being swept around.

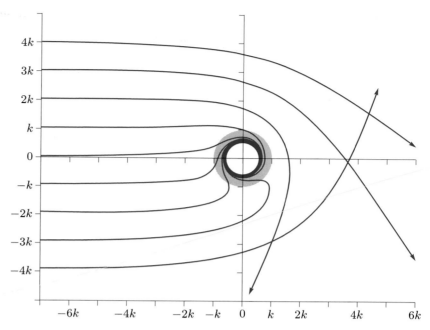

Figure 13   The paths of light rays, starting with differing impact parameters, as they approach a clockwise rotating black hole. The ergosphere is the shaded annulus between $r = k$ and the event horizon at $r = k/2$.

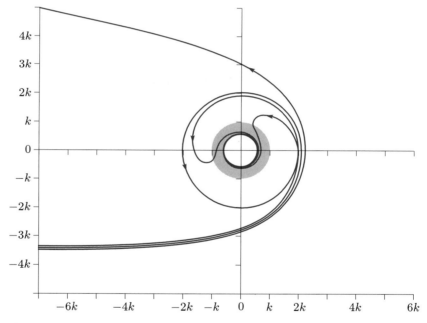

Figure 14   Three critical light rays approaching a clockwise rotating black hole. Although their impact parameters differ only slightly, the outer ray escapes the black hole, the middle one circles the black hole before spiralling in, and the inner ray spirals in without orbiting the black hole.

A dramatic illustration of the dragging of spacetime around a rotating black hole is afforded by computer calculations of light rays sent past the black hole with various impact parameters. These are shown in Figure 13 and Figure 14 for a black hole of maximum permissable angular momentum. The light paths shown all lie in the 'equatorial plane' and can be directly compared with the paths calculated in a similar way which you have seen for non-rotating black holes, cf. Figure 8. The rotation of spacetime has the effect that when a light ray enters the ergosphere, it must move in the sense of rotation of the black hole, even if it was originally circling the black hole in the sense opposite to its rotation.

Objective 9   **SAQ 16**   Consider the representation of a rotating black hole shown in Figure 15. The path of a spacecraft approaching the static limit is shown as a dashed line. (a) Explain why this cannot be the path of an observer in free fall. (b) Is it possible for the spacecraft to follow the dashed path? Explain. (c) Is it possible for a spacecraft to follow the dotted path in Figure 15? Explain.

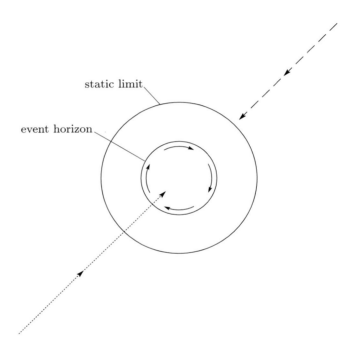

Figure 15   Illustration for SAQ 16.

We cannot go beyond a qualitative description of the effects of rotation, but, even so, we have covered all the principal features of the spacetime exterior to black holes. It turns out that the *only* quantities that can label a black hole are its mass, m, its angular momentum, J and its electrical charge Q. (Any electric charge, which is not so strong that it is immediately neutralized, leads to a negligible change in the properties of a black hole.) *All* the other information contained in whatever material falls into the black hole is *lost, forever*. This situation inspired Wheeler's colourful saying: 'A black hole has no hair'.

One aspect of this is that one cannot have black holes of arbitrary shape. In the same way that the Birkhoff theorem tells us that the spacetime exterior to any spherically symmetric matter distribution is described by the Schwarzschild metric, a more recent theorem due to Israel, Carter, Hawking and Robinson has shown that, regardless of the initial distribution of matter that begins to spiral in to form a rotating black hole, the final form of the spacetime exterior to the in-falling matter is that given by the Kerr metric. If by some freak process we were able to set up a large enough, or dense enough, initial matter distribution in the shape of a cube, or of the Eiffel Tower, in rapid rotation, the spacetime exterior of this in-falling matter would soon lose any 'memory' of its interesting shape and become the simple, axially symmetric spacetime described by the Kerr metric. The fact that black holes are sinks where information disappears irrecoverably is thought by some to be related to the direction of time in the universe. It is also related to the thermodynamic properties of black holes according to which black holes can be assigned temperature and 'entropy' proportional to their surface area, as found by Bekenstein and Hawking.

4 Quantum gravity, mini black holes and Hawking radiation

For many years, theoretical physicists have striven to combine the two great twentieth century theories, quantum mechanics and general relativity. That is to say, to construct a consistent theory of 'quantum gravity.' One of the reasons for intense interest in black holes is that the singularity at the centre predicted by general relativity presents a huge challenge. A full solution will presumably require a consistent theory of quantum gravity. To have such a theory is important for at least two reasons:

1 It is obviously unsatisfactory that our two basic theories of physics are not yet combined consistently — it was, after all, Einstein's realization of the inconsistency between Maxwellian and Newtonian theories that led to relativity.

2 A theory of quantum gravity is vital for cosmology because it is essential for an understanding of the first stages (before 10^{-43} s) of the big bang (see next Block), the very first singularity.

Quantum gravity is required for the explanation of gravitational effects on a length scale determined by a constant, with dimensions of length, that can be constructed from G, c and Planck's constant h. This length (called the Planck length) is

$$\left(\frac{hG}{2\pi c^3} \right)^{1/2} = 1.6 \times 10^{-35} \text{ m}. \tag{21}$$

It is evidently much smaller than any other length scale we know of, but even if the quantum effects of gravity can come into operation only at such small distances they may nevertheless be of crucial importance in providing some process that avoids infinite density. This is why a theory of quantum gravity is required for a solution to the problem of the apparent singularity at the centre of a black hole.

Note that it is the combination of quantum theory and *general* relativity which is the unsolved problem. The combination of *special* relativity and quantum theory has long been established and is the basis of all modern theories of the constituents of matter.

While we cannot discuss quantum gravity (you might have heard of 'superstring theory' which is widely regarded as promising), quantum theory has been successfully applied in a specific situation where general relativity is also required. We now give a brief account.

There is a quantum effect that takes place at the event horizon of a black hole. In relativistic quantum mechanics (the synthesis of *special* relativity and quantum mechanics, see marginal note), the vacuum is not the static, featureless, void of classical physics, but is a fluctuating sea in which particle–antiparticle pairs continuously form and recombine. In quantum theory, energy conservation in some local inertial frame can be violated by an amount ΔE, but just over intervals of time Δt less than about $h/\Delta E$ (this is another consequence of Heisenberg's uncertainty principle). Of course, energy must *finally* be conserved; no system can permanently transform into a state of different total energy. But the possibility of briefly 'borrowing' energy to form a particle–antiparticle pair, for example, is important where extremely short times (and therefore short distances) are involved.

The unique feature of a *small* black hole is that the extreme spacetime curvature (and hence large tidal effect) *near its event horizon* can cause the world-lines of adjacent particles to separate very quickly. Now consider a particle–antiparticle pair being spontaneously produced in this environment. Here, the spacetime curvature (or tidal force) can separate the pair in the short time $h/\Delta E$ that it is allowed to exist by quantum theory. It then becomes possible for one component of the pair to cross the event horizon and fall into the black hole while the other escapes outwards. The same argument applies to pairs of photons.

The consequence is that 'a black hole is *not* black' — quantum theory allows it to radiate photons and hence decrease its mass! In 1974, Hawking showed that a black hole, in complete *isolation*, should produce a *thermal* spectrum of radiation, with exactly the same shape as that inside an oven. The temperature T characterizing this radiation is inversely proportional to the mass, m, of the black hole.

Specifically, Hawking showed that an isolated, spherically symmetric black hole of mass m radiates electromagnetic energy in precisely the same fashion as does a black body of surface area $4\pi r^2$ and temperature T, where r is the radial Schwarzschild coordinate of the event horizon and

$$T = 6.18 \times 10^{-8} \left(\frac{M_\odot}{m} \right) \text{K}.$$

Thus a black hole of mass $M_\odot$ is very faint since the temperature associated with the Hawking radiation is less than 10^{-7} K above absolute zero. But the inverse dependence on the mass has, as we shall see, a startling consequence.

In general, for any object to lose energy by radiation to its surroundings, it must be at a higher temperature than its surroundings. Thus for a black hole of mass $\sim M_\odot$, this quantum radiation is not important. The associated temperature is so tiny compared with the 2.73 K cosmic background which fills interstellar space that the loss of mass from 'quantum radiance' is far outweighed by the increase in mass from absorption of radiation (from the background), and in-falling matter. That is, the surroundings radiate *into* stellar-mass black holes. But for a very small black hole, the situation can be quite different. Already for m less than 4×10^{22} kg, the temperature is greater than that of the cosmic background. A black hole of small mass might therefore lose more energy from radiation by the Hawking process than it gains from absorption. Its mass gets smaller and, as a consequence, its temperature increases. It then radiates even faster; this process of increasing temperature and increasing radiation accelerates so that a small black hole finally explodes. It can be shown that a black hole of mass m, which is destroying itself by giving off thermal radiation, has a time proportional to m^3 before disappearing.

This follows from (i) the fact that the surface area A of the black hole is proportional to k^2, where k is the Schwarzschild radius, itself proportional to m, and (ii) the thermodynamic fact that a black body of surface area A and temperature T loses energy at a rate proportional to AT^4. Noting that $k = 2Gm/c^2$, we thus have:

$$A \propto k^2 \propto m^2 \quad \text{and} \quad T \propto 1/m.$$

Thus the rate of production of electromagnetic energy by the Hawking process is

$$\frac{dE}{dt} \propto AT^4 \propto m^2 \times \left(\frac{1}{m} \right)^4 = m^{-2}.$$

To an outside observer, an appearance of energy ΔE is compensated by a decrease of $-\Delta m = \Delta E/c^2$ in the mass of the black hole. Thus

$$-\frac{dm}{dt} \propto \frac{dE}{dt} \propto m^{-2}.$$

Thermal radiation is discussed in the next Unit.

The 2.73 K cosmic microwave background radiation is discussed at length in Unit 13.

Non-assessable ▼
optional text

The solution of this differential equation implies that a black hole of current mass m has a remaining lifetime proportional to m^3. Note that the above deals only with the emission of photons (electromagnetic radiation). We have thus neglected the production of electrons and positrons, but this does not affect the dependence on mass, only the constant of proportionality.

End of optional text ▲

One can calculate the rate at which a black hole loses mass when it radiates photons and neutrinos. If these were the only particles produced, the lifetime τ of a black hole of mass $m < 10^{22}$ kg would be given by

$$\left(\frac{\tau}{2 \times 10^{10} \text{ years}} \right) \approx \left(\frac{m}{2 \times 10^{11} \text{ kg}} \right)^3 .$$

Hence a black hole of mass 2×10^{11} kg formed during the big bang might now be in its death throes. In fact, mini black holes with $m < 10^{15}$ kg will also produce electrons and positrons giving an even shorter lifetime.

Objective 11   **SAQ 17**   Why would the discovery of a mini black hole be important for physics? (You have seen that the Schwarzschild radius for an object with the mass of the Earth would be a couple of centimetres.)

Note that the Hawking radiation from a stellar or galactic-centre black hole is so slight that it can be neglected in the context of a 'search for black holes', the subject of the next section.

5   The search for black holes

It is apparent that direct observation of black holes must be nearly impossible. They are, after all, objects from which no light can escape. Moreover, stellar black holes, presumably at typical stellar distances, are much smaller than stars, and galactic-centre black holes are certainly much smaller than galaxies. The various phenomena which we now believe give away the presence of black holes all rely in some way on the very strong gravitational effect which is exerted from a very small region. Naturally, the details will be rather different for stellar and galactic-centre black holes.

5.1   Looking for stellar black holes

We seek effects that could be produced by an object of mass greater than $3M_\odot$ and of very small radius. A black hole of mass $3M_\odot$ has a Schwarzschild radius of about 9 km which is actually comparable with the radius of a neutron star near the Chandrasekhar limit. We could not eliminate the possibility of any candidate being a neutron star by direct observation since such dimensions are not resolvable by any telescope unless the object were within the Solar System (which we would certainly know about!)

Fortunately for black hole seekers, stars frequently occur in pairs: binary stars. It is also fortunate that if one of the pair of stars undergoes the supernova transition to become a neutron star, they often continue their mutual orbiting about their common centre of mass. This is also expected to be true if one star of the pair goes all the way to become a black hole. The observational signature would be a star whose radiation is periodically Doppler-shifted. This suggests the presence of an unseen partner which is not observed, the two stars being in orbit about their mutual centre of mass. The unseen partner *may* then be a black hole. The analysis of the size and period of the orbit of such a binary system can give us a good estimate of the mass of this unseen partner.

But the wobble of the non-candidate partner is just part of the story. In binary star systems, material from the atmosphere of one of the stars can sometimes be transferred across to its companion. This is particularly likely if one of the stars is a red giant, with an enormously distended atmosphere. If the other star were a black hole, then the material from the red giant would be likely to form a swirling flattish 'accretion disk' as it spirals into the black hole. The in-falling matter is heated by friction and turbulence to temperatures where X-ray emission occurs, before it crosses the event horizon. The production of X-rays by turbulent in-falling matter is due to the tidal effects we saw in Section 2.6. The gravitational influence of a massive, compact object on a collection of falling particles varies rapidly with distance when the matter reaches a small radius. To show this, we can first consider the Newtonian description of the process and then make the corresponding general relativistic argument.

In Section 2.6, we showed on the basis of Newtonian physics that the quantity $2Gm/r^3$ is the *relative* acceleration of two particles, a metre apart, and a distance r from a mass m. If these two particles belong to a collection of in-falling atoms, such variations of gravitational influence cause turbulent relative motion between atoms, which can result in copious X-ray emission. The energy and intensity of X-rays would be greater the larger the value of $2Gm/r^3$.

General relativity leads to a similar prediction, but now the quantity $2Gm/r^3$ has a much more immediate physical interpretation — it is a measure of the Riemann curvature of space at radius r

$$\mathscr{K}_r = \frac{2Gm}{r^3}.$$

Spacetime requires not 1 but 20 numbers to specify the Riemann curvature; $\mathscr{K}_r$ is the curvature of the two-dimensional *space* defined by all values of r and ϕ and fixed $\theta = \pi/2$, i.e. the equatorial 'plane', outside the mass.

At the event horizon of a black hole of mass $3M_\odot$, this turns out to be $1.1 \times 10^9\,\mathrm{s}^{-2}$. Compare this with the spatial curvature at the surface of the Earth or the Sun, respectively, $3 \times 10^{-6}\,\mathrm{s}^{-2}$ and $8 \times 10^{-7}\,\mathrm{s}^{-2}$. This difference reflects the fact that m/r^3 is essentially the mean density; the mean density of the Earth exceeds that of the Sun.

One important point that we have space only to mention is the very high efficiency with which matter falling into a black hole can be converted to radiated energy. This is almost 10% — huge compared to the less than 1% of the mass of hydrogen which is converted to radiated energy all the way through the stellar life cycle from primordial hydrogen to white dwarf or neutron star.

5.1.1   The current state of evidence for stellar black holes

The first candidate for recognition as a black hole was the rapidly fluctuating X-ray source known as Cygnus X-1, first observed in 1962. It is the invisible component associated with a visible star with spectroscopic properties characteristic of stars found in binary systems. The measured parameters of this system suggest that the mass of the X-ray source cannot be less than $7M_\odot$, far above the maximum mass of a neutron star. Furthermore, the rapidity of the intensity fluctuations of the X-rays indicates that they originate in a very small source, almost certainly a collapsed star. If we accept that the X-ray source Cygnus X-1 is a collapsed star with mass considerably greater than $3.5M_\odot$, then it must be a black hole. Indeed, black holes are seen as nicely explaining what is otherwise inexplicable behaviour. (Of course many models not involving black holes have been discussed, but none seem to work.)

X-ray transient:
a star which is a source of unpredictably fluctuating X-rays

Other examples of binary systems that seem to contain a black hole are LMC X-3 and A 0620 - 00. The mass of the two stars of the latter 'X-ray transient' were measured in 1993 to be $10M_\odot$ and $0.6M_\odot$, so the first is pretty certainly a black hole. (The paper reporting it was confidently entitled 'The mass of the black hole in A 0620 - 00'.) For a good account of the search for stellar black holes, the book by Luminet cited earlier is recommended.

Where do we stand? At the time of writing (1996) it is widely believed that there is indeed a stellar black hole in Cygnus X-1 and probably also in many other binary systems.

5.2   Looking for galactic-centre black holes

It has been thought likely for some time that the class of objects called 'quasars' or (quasi-stellar radio sources) are the sites of galactic-centre black holes. Quasars are objects that at first sight look like stars on a photograph in that they have point-like images without the fuzziness or visible size and structure that normally identifies a galaxy. But on examining the spectrum one finds a large redshift, which means that the object is far too distant to be a normal star, and so it is called a quasar.

The redshift–distance relationship is discussed in Unit 13. See 'Hubble's law' in the glossary.

Quasars are therefore galaxies (or more likely, the active central regions of galaxies) at great distances but disproportionately bright to a staggering degree, having a vast source of energy at their centre. Since they are distant, the light from them has taken so long to reach us that we are seeing galaxies in the early stages of their evolution (this will become clearer in the cosmology block).

The process which gives rise to the enormous energy release of a quasar is a vastly scaled-up version of what occurs in binary stars. Stars are attracted to the black hole, orbiting around it and eventually becoming captured with the radiation of perhaps 10% of their mass as energy. As the process continues, the black hole gets more massive, and its event horizon expands. As it does so, the curvature of space at the event horizon becomes weaker so the heating of in-falling matter is reduced. The quasar therefore gets dimmer with age and eventually switches off. This dimming effect is accentuated by the fact that the black hole will tend to run out of in-falling matter. We may expect the switch-off to occur when the mass reaches some tens or hundreds of millions of solar masses. The reason we do not see nearby quasars may then be that they are old enough to have switched off. Indeed, we do see many galaxies which are sufficiently active (see discussion on M87 below) to be possible quasars which have not quite switched off.

Perhaps, then, some galaxies have at their centre the relatively quiescent remains of quasar-furnaces. Maybe galactic-centre black holes with masses in the range 10^7–$10^9 M_\odot$ are common features of galaxies. How could we tell? First, the orbital speeds of stars around the galaxy should be consistent with the existence of such a large mass at its centre. Second, and more revealingly, the switch-off will never be quite complete and any residual in-falling matter will show as a faint, but very compact, source of relatively low temperature radiation. Such tiny faint centres could be detected only in nearby galaxies. In fact, it may turn out that we need go no further than our own Galaxy to find such a case. Our own galaxy emits infrared and radio radiation from an extremely compact core at its very centre of mass of a few times $10^6 M_\odot$.

Recall that the Schwarzschild radius is proportional to mass.

5.2.1   The evidence for galactic-centre black holes

1   Existence of quasars

The first evidence is indirect but now widely accepted: quasars exist, and no mechanism other than black hole formation has ever come near to explaining the enormous output of energy.

2   Rotating gas and stars

There is also more direct evidence for galactic-centre black holes. Recent advances in astronomical techniques provide two complementary ways to identify galactic-centre black holes: one method uses X-ray observations and the other optical and radio frequency observations.

2a The X-ray method comes closest of all methods to 'seeing' black holes. It utilizes the details of the spectrum of X-rays emitted as the accreting stellar material (probably gas from tidally destroyed stars) approaches to within 3 to 10 times the Schwarzschild radius. As the gas approaches such radii, its velocity will be near the speed of light, leading to characteristic relativistic effects on the X-ray spectrum including a gravitational redshift. These constitute a clear signal of proximity to a black hole. This signal was seen for the first time in 1995 by Tanaka and colleagues in the active galaxy known as MCG-6-30-15 using the Japan/US ASCA X-ray satellite. In this case, the black hole has a mass of 'only' $10^7 M_\odot$.

maser
Microwave Amplification by Stimulated Emission of Radiation. Predecessor of laser (Microwave → Light). Masers have been known in outer space since the 1960s.

2b The optical and radio observation method involves the observation of the rotation of stars and interstellar gas over regions some 10^2 light years across in the central regions of galaxies, in particular non-active nearby galaxies like the Andromeda galaxy. From observations of the Doppler shift of light from stars and gas at particular distances from the centre, one can infer the rotational speeds at those distances. From the speed/distance relationship one finds masses in the range 10^7–$10^{10} M_\odot$. Observations using the Hubble Space Telescope and also radio observations of *maser* emissions (which have exceedingly good angular resolution) have revealed galaxies in which masses in this range exist within a radius of no more than a light year. (Just how large a density this implies can be seen by noting that the nearest star to the Sun is about 4 light years away.) The actual radiation from this central region is typically hundreds of times less that from the number of suns which would make up this mass. It is probably due to stars still spiralling in, though clearly at a rate which is much less than when the central black hole was first forming. There is no way such masses with so little light radiated can exist other than as a black hole; a black hole is far less implausible that 10^9 neutron stars confined to such a volume. By early 1996, the record mass for a black hole in a mature, non-active galaxy was $2 \times 10^9 M_\odot$, held by a galaxy known as NGC 3115 — but this record is sure to be broken during the life of this course, and more massive black holes are known in active galaxies, as we now explain.

3   Jets from active galaxies

Some of the most powerful (and hence earliest discovered) astronomical sources of radio waves (going under such names as Cygnus A, Virgo A ...) have been identified with galaxies which put on a very specific and striking display of activity. The common feature is one or two* enormous jets issuing from the active galactic centre. The jets extend far beyond the galaxy and a key observation is that the outflow of matter and energy must have been precisely fixed in direction for millions of years in order for them to have formed.

A famous example is the galaxy known as NGC4486 (alias M87, alias Virgo A) see Figure 16.

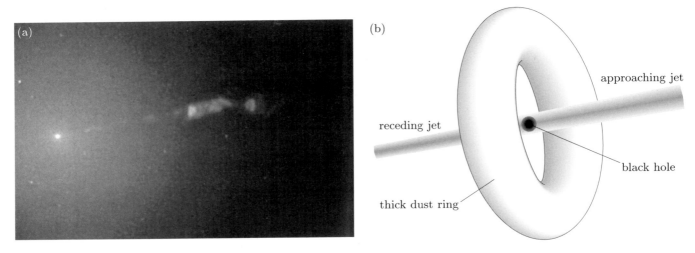

Figure 16   (a) A jet emerging from M87. (b) A schematic view of the jets emerging from an active galaxy.

*Where there is a second, it will be directed in the opposite direction to the first.

The source of this jet is almost certainly a black hole at the galactic centre. It is believed that the jet emerges along the axis of an accretion disk, a swirling flat doughnut of matter centred on the black hole. The inner edge of the hole of the doughnut, where the in-falling stars rotate most violently is the source of the energy powering the jet. The angular momentum of the swirling material keeps the jet oriented in its direction for the millions of years required for it to become the dramatic feature that we now see. The key observation is that the central region has a mass of $2.4 \pm 0.7 \times 10^9 M_\odot$ within a 60 light-year radius (the black hole itself would be much smaller, say one light-hour across, but this could not be resolved from Earth.) But the luminosity of this region is less by a factor of 170 than one would expect for that number of suns. The theory of how the jets are formed has been studied for many years, and there is no known mechanism that does not involve a black hole. Moreover, the measurement of the central mass based on the orbital motion of stars is consistent with the jet models.

The record mass for a black hole in an active galaxy was, in the early 1990s, about $50 \times 10^9 M_\odot$ in galaxy NGC 6240.

Objectives 12, 13   **SAQ 18**   Jot down notes for a short essay on the subject 'The evidence for the existence of black holes.' Indicate how you would structure the essay, and note the key points for inclusion.

5.3   The search for primordial (mini) black holes

We cannot predict the details of the final explosive disappearance of a mini black hole, but it has been estimated that as much energy is liberated from the *last* million kilograms of mass, during the last tenth of a second, as is radiated by the Sun in that time. Since a black hole of mass 10^6 kg has a Schwarzschild radius of only 10^{-21} m (10^{30} times smaller than the radius of the Sun) it is clear that a mini black hole does not die with a whimper!

Any primordial black hole that was formed with a mass less than $\sim 10^{11}$ kg would have probably exploded at some time in the 10^{10} years since its creation. Those more massive than $\sim 10^{22}$ kg would still be accreting matter and radiation and will certainly long outlast us. Those which had an initial mass of approximately 10^{11} kg might even now be in their terminal gallop to extinction; they are presumably rare and, since we do not know where to look for them, it will be hard to observe even so spectacular an event as the sudden appearance and extinction, within a tenth of a second, of something as luminous as the Sun.

Of course, if such an event happened close to the Solar System it would be unmistakable.

The high temperature of a black hole in its last moments opens one possibility for the detection of mini black holes dying in distant galaxies. The radiation corresponding to temperatures of hundreds of millions of kelvins is not visible, but lies in the X-ray or gamma ray part of the spectrum. A gamma ray telescope sees the sky as mostly dark, with just a few sources. A number of intense cosmic gamma ray flashes have been observed, the so-called 'cosmic ray bursters'. Their origin is a mystery. At one time it was considered possible that they were indeed dying mini black holes, but they do not seem to have the right characteristics. Currently (1997), mini black holes are not thought to be the origin of cosmic ray bursters.

There is at present no evidence for the actual existence of mini black holes.

Objective 11 **SAQ 19** The planet Pluto was discovered after its existence had been predicted on the basis of perturbations of the orbit of the planet Neptune. Suppose it had been suggested at that time that the disturbance to Neptune was caused by an otherwise undetected black hole of mass 6×10^{23} kg $(3 \times 10^{-7} M_{\odot})$. What evidence would you need to argue *against* such an interpretation in the light of the subsequent discovery of a visible planet?

6 Further applications of general relativity

6.1 Gravitational lenses

The verification by Eddington of Einstein's prediction of the bending of light by the Sun first brought general relativity into the public arena (see Section 14 of Unit 10 & 11). The same physical process underlies a recent remarkable astronomical discovery which is at once an interesting consequence of general relativity and a potentially useful source of cosmological information. The discovery in question is 'gravitational lensing' or, perhaps, for reasons we shall explain, 'so-called gravitational lensing'.

Galactic redshifts and how they indicate distance will be discussed in Unit 13.

In 1979, Walsh and colleagues noticed that two quasars (Q0957+561 A and B; we shall refer to them simply as A and B) had identical optical and radio spectra. They were evidently at the same distance because they had the same 'redshifts'. The best interpretation was that A and B were two images of a *single* quasar. Indeed, it is now accepted that the light from a single quasar had come by two different paths around a galaxy located between the quasar and us. The galaxy was faint (as distant galaxies are, compared to quasars) but was subsequently identified. This was the first example of a gravitational lens.

A gravitational lens is not a true lens. In Figure 17,

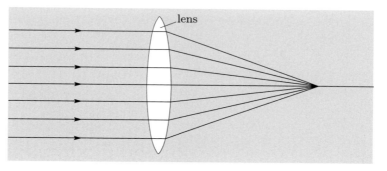

Figure 17   In an optical converging lens, the focusing effect relies on a greater deflection of light farther from the axis of the lens.

we see the action of a converging lens on parallel light, i.e. light from a source at effectively an infinite distance. Now, consider parallel light passing a gravitating body like the Sun. The distance from the central axis is, once more, the impact parameter b. We see that the larger b is, the lesser the angle θ of deflection (which was why Eddington exploited a solar eclipse so he could study the deflection of starlight which was as close to grazing the Sun as possible.) In fact, $\theta = 4Gm/c^2b$ for small θ where m is the mass of the gravitating body (see Figure 18). For small θ, the distance D at which the light crosses the axis is $D \sim b/\theta = c^2b^2/4Gm$.

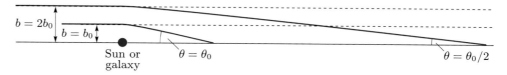

Figure 18   The angle of deflection, θ, of light by an object of mass M is inversely proportional to the impact parameter b.

It is evident that the theory of gravitational lenses, as they are (dubiously, you might think) called is quite different from that of ordinary lenses, and real images of extended objects are never seen. For point-like objects like quasars, an intervening galaxy must give, it can be shown, an *odd* number of images, including that in which the light has passed through the galaxy. In practice, there are usually missing images, and the original double image of A and B is not exceptional. Figure 19 shows a picture taken by the Hubble Space Telescope of an object known as the 'Einstein-cross'.

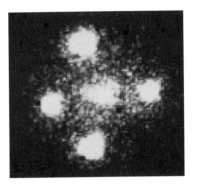

Figure 19   The four outer spots are images of a distant quasar and the fainter central image is the deflecting galaxy.

We cannot say much more about gravitational lensing here other than to make three points:

1 All aspects of the great variety of gravitational lens phenomena which have now been observed add up to additional firm support for Einstein's theory of general relativity.

2 Gravitational lenses show promise of yielding important cosmological information. For example, in Block 4 the 'missing mass problem' will be important. One aspect of this is that the galaxies must have more mass than one would guess from what is actually shining. The gravitational deflection of light by a galaxy is determined by the way the total mass of the galaxy, visible and invisible, is distributed. It is hoped that one can work back from the multiple images to an understanding of the actual distribution of mass within the deflecting galaxy.

3 For the A and B case, fluctuations in intensity of the quasar allow one to deduce that the two light paths to the Earth represent a difference in transit time of about 540 days. It is hoped that an analysis of this will eventually lead to a measure of the 'Hubble' parameter, discussed in the next Unit. The Hubble parameter is a key parameter for determining the age of the universe.

Objective 14, revision **SAQ 20**   Verify that the expression for the bending of light given above yields the 1.75 seconds of arc that Eddington measured for light bent by the Sun.

6.2 Gravitational waves

In Unit 10 & 11, we drew attention to the analogy between Maxwell's equations and Einstein's field equations. In each case, complicated differentials of certain fields were set equal to certain source terms. In the case of Maxwell's equations, the fields were the electric and magnetic fields **E** and **B** and the sources were charges and currents. In the case of Einstein's equations, the source term was the 'energy–momentum tensor' i.e. in effect, masses and currents of masses. The fields in this case were the components of the metric tensor, g_{ij}, which defined the local behaviour of spacetime through the metric

$$(\Delta\tau)^2 = \sum g_{ij}(\Delta x^i)(\Delta x^j). \tag{22}$$

If spacetime were the flat Minkowski space of special relativity, then, using Cartesian coordinates, $g_{00} = 1/c^2$ and $g_{11} = g_{22} = g_{33} = -1/c^2$ and all the rest are zero. But spacetime becomes distorted near a mass. The Schwarzschild metric is an example, the distortion falling off with distance from the mass just as electric fields fall off with distance from a charge.

In Unit 4, we mentioned that a dramatic confirmation of Maxwell's theory came with the detection by Hertz of the waves that Maxwell found to be solutions of his equations. Are there such wave solutions to Einstein's equations, representing oscillations in the metric coefficients g_{ij} spreading through space? If so, can they be detected? The answer to the first question is that indeed, Einstein's equations *do* have wave solutions representing spreading ripples in spacetime travelling at the speed of light. The answer to the second question might well be amended during the lifetime of this course. At present (1997), the situation is this: laboratory gravitational wave detectors have been under development since the early sixties, but have not yet succeeded in detecting waves. However, in 1993 the Nobel prize in physics went to Hulse and Taylor for their very convincing demonstration that a particular binary star consisting of a pair of neutron stars (one being a pulsar) lost energy at a rate and in a manner which could only be accounted for in terms of energy being emitted as gravitational waves.

Why are gravitational waves so hard to detect? Well, it turns out that spacetime is 'stiff'. For any object vibrating with a given energy, the stiffer it is, the less the amplitude of the vibration. In the case of those gravitational waves which might be expected from a supernova explosion in our Galaxy, the local change in the metric coefficients would be one part in 10^{18}. Laboratory-scale distances would be perturbed by the passage of such waves to the extent of something like a hundredth of the width of an atomic nucleus! But, like all waves, the energy density is subject to an inverse square law, so perhaps we could generate gravitational waves in the laboratory, just as Hertz generated electromagnetic waves? Presumably masses in motion would generate ripples around them? In fact, detailed calculations show that the power emitted by an oscillating mass is roughly:

$$P_0 \left(\frac{k}{R}\right)^2 \left(\frac{v}{c}\right)^6 \tag{23}$$

where P_0 is a constant. The good news is that P_0 is about 10^{52} W, but the bad news is that k is the Schwarzschild radius of the body and R is its actual dimensions, while v/c is the ratio of the velocity of the body to that of light. It turns out if one rotates a bar of steel weighing several tons to the point where it is about to split under centrifugal forces, one still only radiates some 10^{-30} W! So, one looks elsewhere for a source — supernovae, perhaps?

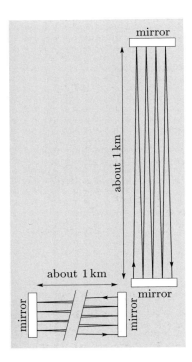

Figure 20 Highly schematic view of an interferometer set-up for detecting gravitational waves. The optimum path length for detecting 1 kHz waves is 150 km, so the proposed detectors will use mirrors to achieve 150 passes through a mirror–detector distance of 1 km.

Modern gravitational wave detectors resemble magnified versions of the Michelson–Morley apparatus described in Block 2. Light is split into two paths, see Figure 20, reflected back through each path and allowed to interfere. A gravitational wave passing through such a detector in the right direction would minutely stretch one of the paths and simultaneously compress the other, leading (one hopes) to a detectable change in the interference pattern at the point where the two light paths recombine. The detection of gravitational waves is described in the video that goes with this Unit.

Gravitational waves and black holes. A possible source of gravitational waves would involve two black holes in orbit about each other. Such an orbiting pair would steadily emit gravitational radiation eventually culminating in a huge burst as they fused into a single black hole. While the final black hole would, by virtue of its 'hairlessness' (see page 28) be indistinguishable from any other black hole of the same mass and angular momentum, the outgoing ripples in spacetime would have encoded in them an account of the process in which they were emitted. This would be a very distinctive signal for the existence of black holes.

Gravitational waves and cosmology. Cosmology is the subject of the next Block, so all we can say here is that gravitational waves of a wide spectrum of frequencies are expected from the 'quantum fluctuations' in the metric of spacetime that occurred during the 'big bang'. This will mean more after you have studied the next Block, but the observation should throw light on a central problem of modern cosmology: the origin of the density fluctuations which eventually led to a lumpy universe (i.e. one containing galaxies) rather than a uniform universe.

Gravitational waves and supernovae. One of the expected sources of gravitational waves is supernova explosions in neighbouring galaxies. (Supernovae in our own Galaxy are sufficiently infrequent to make their search by gravitational waves detectors unattractive to funding agencies.) Indeed, it is with this in mind that the target sensitivities of detectors have been set. A supernova explosion in a galaxy in the Virgo cluster of galaxies would make a change of something like 1 part in 10^{21} in lengths on Earth, and this is the sensitivity target of the detectors discussed in Band 4 of VC3. It is important to note that if the collapse of the star to a black hole in a supernova is spherically symmetric, there will be no gravitational radiation as a result of Birkhoff's theorem. However, it is thought that supernovae, particularly in binary systems, are asymmetric.

6.3   Frame dragging, geodetic effect, 'Gravity Probe B' and all that

Few things have stretched the concepts of space and time further from the Newtonian ideas of Block 1 quite as much as the dragging around of spacetime by a rotating black hole. We have seen that the extreme bending of light by black holes has a more modest version nearer home: the bending of light by the Sun as first measured by Eddington and friends. Is there also a counterpart to the 'frame dragging' by rotating black holes that can be measured on Earth? The answer is 'yes' although key elements of the experiment would have to be carried out using Earth satellites. The effect, which is named after Lense and Thirring, is exactly such a frame dragging effect, and is the subject of one of the most heroic experiments ever planned. First proposed in 1960 by Schiff, the 'Gravity

Lense–Thirring effect

Probe B' experiment should finally be launched in 1999 after nearly 40 years of development.* The experiment is intended to detect and measure the dragging around of spacetime by the rotation of the Earth. It will do this by observing the precession of the axis of a gyroscope in polar orbit some 650 km above the Earth. The expected precession is tiny: 0.042 arcsec per year.

One of the characteristic features of curved spacetime complicates the detection of the Lense–Thirring effect in a most interesting fashion. To understand it, consider one of the phenomena which would reveal that we are living on the curved surface of a planet. If you carry a pointer with you over the surface of the Earth, always taking care that as you turn, the pointer stays pointing in the same direction, then, in general, after completing a closed circuit, the pointer will be found not to point in the same direction as it did when you set out.

> *A specific example*: walk east along the equator a quarter of the way around the Earth holding a pointer pointing due north. With the pointer still pointing due north, turn and walk to the North Pole. Again, keeping the pointer's direction fixed, turn through 90° and set off down the meridian so as to reach your starting point. The pointer will now point due west.

Now this sort of thing would not happen if the Earth were flat, so it is a signature of a curved space. It can be shown that if a gyroscope is flown around the Earth in a satellite, then as a result of the curvature of spacetime, a small precession of the gyroscope will result. This so-called *geodetic* precession (about 6.7 arcsec per year) is actually over a hundred times greater than the Lense–Thirring effect we are trying to measure. However, it takes place in a different direction.

The difficulty of doing the experiment is extreme, and pushes technology to the limit. The gyroscope itself is a superconducting ball so smooth that on the scale of the Earth, the irregularities would be only a metre high. This is because tidal effects would cause spurious precession in a more irregular sphere. Indeed, this is a case where our discussion in Unit 9 of 'local' in the context of 'local inertial frames' becomes real: even a ball a few centimetres across, in free fall 650 km above the Earth, sees tidal effects when measurements of the precision required in this experiment are made.

We cannot say more about Gravity Probe B here but, with luck, it will be front page news within the lifetime of this course.

---

*But don't start holding your breath at the beginning of 1999. One finds in one's library various references to a launch of Gravity Probe B 'in the mid 80s' ...

7 Summary

1 A black hole is a closed spatial region within which the world-lines of all material particles or light rays have radial coordinates that decrease as the time (or x^0) coordinate increases. The closed spatial surface that is the boundary of this region is called the 'event horizon'.

2 For a spherical (spinless) black hole, there exists a mass m within the volume of space bounded everywhere by the radial coordinate $r = k = 2Gm/c^2$. The sphere at $r = k$ is the event horizon and $2Gm/c^2$ is the Schwarzschild radius corresponding to mass m.

3 The existence of a black hole depends on mass m being within the corresponding Schwarzschild radius k.

4 Time intervals ticked on a clock stationary at radial coordinate $r \geqslant k$ outside a black hole of mass m are related to time intervals ticked on a clock at a large (in principle infinite) distance from the black hole by the formula

$$\Delta\tau = \left(1 - \frac{k}{r}\right)^{1/2} \Delta t_\infty \tag{24}$$

where the time intervals at infinity, Δt_∞, are effectively the intervals of coordinate time Δt. Equation 24 implies large redshifts for radiation reaching $r = \infty$, having been emitted at radial coordinate $r \approx k$, the redshift becoming infinite as r falls to approach k.

5 Observers falling into a black hole will not observe any discontinuous increase in the effects of spacetime curvature as they cross the event horizon. They will hit the central singularity a finite time after crossing the event horizon according to a clock they carry with them.

6 Observers stationary at infinity watching the progress of a freely falling object towards a black hole will not in a finite time observe its arrival at the event horizon.

7 A spherically symmetric black hole traps all light sent towards it with 'impact parameter' less than $2.6k$. The critical light ray, with impact parameter $2.6k$, circles the black hole indefinitely at radial coordinate $r = 1.5k$. The sphere at $r = 1.5k$ is called the 'photon-sphere'.

8 For a spherically symmetric matter distribution that is in-falling or pulsating, Birkhoff's theorem implies that the spacetime exterior to the matter distribution is described by the Schwarzschild metric.

9 Spacetime around a rotating black hole is described by the Kerr metric, not the Schwarzschild metric. This spacetime is dragged around, imparting a strong tendency on light or any approaching body to rotate about the black hole. The event horizon moves to a smaller radius and is surrounded by an oblate region, the ergosphere, within which rotation in the same sense as the black holes's angular momentum is obligatory. The boundary of this region is the 'static limit'.

10 The singularity at the centre of black holes presents a particular challenge to science. Complete understanding will only come with the development of a theory of quantum gravity.

11 Stellar black holes might be created in the final stages of evolution of a massive star. Lower mass stars can achieve a stable configuration supported by electron degeneracy pressure (as in white dwarf stars) or neutron degeneracy pressure (as in neutron stars). Likely candidates have been found in binary stars, Cygnus X-1 being the first. The evidence is based on rapidly fluctuating X-rays from a small source, together with mass measurements obtained from the dynamics of the binary system.

12 Galactic-centre black holes are believed to form in the centres of galaxies. Several candidates, such as M87, have been identified. Black hole formation in the early stages of the evolution of galaxies is believed to explain the phenomenon of quasars.

13 Mini black holes are speculative primordial by-products of the 'big bang' in which the Universe came into being. There is at present no evidence for them. They would be interesting since a black hole much smaller than a stellar black hole might exhibit measurable Hawking radiation, a prediction of one of the first successful attempts to combine general relativity with quantum theory.

14 General relativity predicts: (i) frame dragging by rotating bodies that might be measured experimentally (the Gravity Probe B experiment), (ii) gravitational lenses, which have been found and which might prove a valuable source of cosmological information, and (iii) gravitational waves, the existence of which has been deduced from the properties of a binary star, and which should within the coming decade become directly detectable on Earth, thereby forming the basis of a new kind of astronomy.

Objectives 3, 6, 11 **SAQ 21** Explain why it is justified to call a black hole 'black', to call it a 'hole', and what qualifications on these terms arise as a result of quantum mechanics. How can we ever detect a black hole if it is truly black?

Band 8 of AC3 comments on this Unit.

Acknowledgements

Grateful acknowledgement is made to the following sources for material used in this Unit.

Figure 11 Adapted from Figure 37, p. 155 of 'Black holes' by J-P Luminet, Cambridge University Press (1995); *Figures 8, 13, 14* Taken from H. Cohn in *Am. J. Physics*, **45**, No. 3, p. 240 (1977); *Figure 19* NASA/ESA.

Self-assessment questions — answers and comments

SAQ 1 (a) The interval of proper time τ between two events is the time recorded on a clock moving between the two events.

(b) The coordinate time, t, corresponds to time intervals as measured on clocks at great distances (where $r/k \to \infty$ and the metric $\to$ the flat metric of empty space).

SAQ 2 Light always travels on geodesics for which *any* interval of proper time is *zero*. Such geodesics are called null geodesics. (This important property of light is often vital for understanding what is going on in curved spacetime.)

SAQ 3 (a) $\Delta\tau = (1 - k/r)^{1/2}\Delta t$.

(b) $(\Delta\tau)^2 = -\dfrac{(\Delta r)^2}{c^2(1 - k/r)}$.
The interval is space-like.

(c) If $m = 0$ then $k = 0$, and one way to write the metric is

$$(\Delta\tau)^2 = (\Delta t)^2 - \frac{1}{c^2}[(\Delta r)^2 + r^2(\Delta\theta)^2 + r^2\sin^2\theta(\Delta\phi)^2].$$

This is the metric of flat Minkowski spacetime, undistorted by the presence of mass. In Cartesian coordinates, it is simply

$$(\Delta\tau)^2 = (\Delta t)^2 - \frac{1}{c^2}[(\Delta x^1)^2 + (\Delta x^2)^2 + (\Delta x^3)^2].$$

SAQ 4 We need to evaluate $2mG/c^2$ for three values of m. Let's calculate $2G/c^2$. In SI units, it is numerically 1.48×10^{-27}. Taking $M_\odot = 1.99 \times 10^{30}$ kg and the mass of the Earth as 5.98×10^{24} kg, we get Schwarzschild radii for the three cases of $2\,950$ m, 8.85×10^{-3} m and 1.48×10^{-26} m, respectively. [Note that the Schwarzschild radius corresponding to the mass of the Earth is just less than 1 cm, so the Earth would have to be compressed into roughly the volume of a golf ball to become a black hole. A corresponding exemplar for the size of the 10 kg mass we leave to your imagination.]

SAQ 5 Exploiting the value for $2G/c^2$ evaluated in SAQ 4, we find 2.95×10^9 km. Since the radius of the Earth's orbit is 1.5×10^8 km, this works out at 20 times the radius of Earth's orbit around the Sun. (It is in fact about equal to the radius of the orbit of Uranus around the Sun. Very roughly, such a galactic-centre black hole has an event horizon of comparable radius to the Solar System.)

SAQ 6 You should attempt to make a list of the salient points without looking at Section 2.2 and then check it against that section.

SAQ 7 Shapiro's experiment, described in Unit 10 & 11, involved the time delay of radar signals passing close to the Sun.

SAQ 8 Setting $r = 0$ and $R = k$ in Equation 6, we get a proper time interval of $\pi k/2c$. From SAQ 4, k for a $1M_\odot$ black hole is about $3\,000$ m and so will be $15\,000$ m for a $5M_\odot$ black hole. Evaluating $\pi k/2c$, we find 7.85×10^{-5} s. For a $10^9 M_\odot$ galactic-centre black hole, the time is a factor of 2×10^8 greater, i.e. 1.57×10^4 s, or a proper time of just under four and a half hours (262 minutes).

SAQ 9 Setting $\Delta r = \Delta\theta = \Delta\phi = 0$ in the Schwarzschild metric, we readily find

$$\frac{dt}{d\tau} = \frac{1}{(1 - k/r)^{1/2}}.$$

The rest of the solution will be found in the text immediately after the SAQ.

SAQ 10 The answer to this SAQ is contained in the main text immediately following the question.

SAQ 11 The two values of circumference correspond to $r_1 = nk$ and $r_2 = (n + 1)k$ respectively. Hence,

$$L_{12} = k(\sqrt{n(n+1)} - \sqrt{n(n-1)}) + k\ln\frac{\sqrt{n+1} + \sqrt{n}}{\sqrt{n} + \sqrt{n-1}}$$

which for $n = 10$ gives $1.051k$ and for $n = 20$ give $1.0253k$. Of course, in flat space, the distance between two concentric circles which differ in r by k would be just k, and this value is clearly more closely approached for $n = 20$ than for $n = 10$.

SAQ 12 As we saw in Unit 7, an interval connecting the crossing point of a light cone to a point outside the cone is space-like, whereas an interval to a point within the cone is time-like (and can therefore be connected by a possible world-line of a particle.)

SAQ 13 Progressively narrower light cones indicate progressively smaller increments of radial coordinate r (in either inward or outwards directions) for given increments of coordinate time, t. It is in this sense that we can speak of a reduced speed of light. In a freely falling local inertial frame, light would still, in principle, be measured to have speed c.

SAQ 14 The answer to this SAQ is contained in the main text immediately following the question.

SAQ 15 When $J = Gm^2/c$, then $\rho = J/mc = Gm/c^2 = k/2$. Inserting this into Equation 19, the second term vanishes and we find $r_- = k/2$, i.e. half the Schwarzschild radius for a non-rotating black hole. When $J = 0$, then $\rho = 0$ and $r_- = k$, as we would expect.

SAQ 16 (a) The path shown by the dashed line in Figure 17 shows no change in angle as it approaches the static limit. Space outside the static limit is also dragged around, even though rotation is no longer compulsory. However, a particle in free fall must be affected by this dragging, and so a particle in free fall could not fall in on the dashed line. The path of free fall would have to curve in the direction of rotation of the black hole.

(b) It is possible to follow the dashed path, but the spacecraft would have to exert thrust to counteract the effects of the spacetime curvature of the rotating black hole that make the paths of free fall have a decreasing angular coordinate.

(c) The dotted path represents an impossible trip for the spacecraft. Inside the ergosphere no amount of thrust in the anticlockwise direction can make the spacecraft maintain a constant angular coordinate while decreasing the radial coordinate.

SAQ 17 The discovery of a mini black hole:

(a) would imply that conditions during the big bang were such as to lead to the production of mini black holes. This would be immensely important for cosmology.

(b) would open up the possibility of confirming the existence of Hawking radiation, thus giving attempts to weld together quantum theory and general relativity some experimental support.

SAQ 18 A natural structure for such an essay would be to discuss first the evidence for stellar black holes and then the evidence for galactic-centre black holes. Common underlying features, such as the fact that one seeks a very strong gravitational effect from a small volume should probably go in the introductory part. (For exam purposes, you would not be expected to remember elaborate star and galaxy identifiers, though you would probably be able to recall 'Cygnus X-1' and M87, or at least something identifiable about them even if the name is not given.) Your essay should convey the basic principles underlying the different arguments for galactic-centre and stellar black holes. You should now check the list you made against the contents of Sections 5.1 and 5.2 (and subsections).

SAQ 19 The radial Schwarzschild coordinate of the event horizon of a black hole of mass $m = 6 \times 10^{23}$ kg is

$$
\begin{aligned}
r &= \frac{2Gm}{c^2} \\
&= \frac{2\left(6.67 \times 10^{-11}\,\mathrm{m^3\,kg^{-1}\,s^{-2}}\right)\left(6 \times 10^{23}\,\mathrm{kg}\right)}{\left(3 \times 10^8\,\mathrm{m\,s^{-1}}\right)^2} \\
&\sim 10^{-3}\,\mathrm{m}.
\end{aligned}
$$

In general, black holes might be observed in two ways: (a) from the radiation emitted by the Hawking process, or (b) from the radiation emitted by turbulent matter falling in towards the event horizon.

(a) Hawking's arguments suggest that a black hole of mass $3 \times 10^{-7} M_\odot$ will behave like a black body of surface area $4\pi r^2 \approx 4\pi \times 10^{-6}\,\mathrm{m^2} \approx 10^{-5}\,\mathrm{m^2}$ and temperature

$$
T = \frac{6.18 \times 10^{-8}}{3 \times 10^{-7}}\,\mathrm{K} = 0.2\,\mathrm{K}.
$$

It is clear that such a black hole would have insufficient 'quantum radiance' to be detectable.

(b) However, there does not exist in interplanetary space sufficient gas and debris to form a source of X-rays by falling in towards the event horizon.

Thus, the facts that Pluto has been seen, and that the radiation from it consists largely of visible light, suggest that it is not a black hole. Pictures of the surface showing that it has a radial coordinate of more than a millimetre are even more direct evidence!

SAQ 20 The key point is to recognize that for light from a distant star grazing the Sun, the impact parameter b is simply the radius of the Sun. Evaluating $\theta = 4Gm/c^2 b$ yields 8.48×10^{-6} radians which is 1.75 seconds of arc.

SAQ 21 A black hole is black because of the trapping of light within the photon-sphere, the infinite redshift at the event horizon and the fact that no light can come out through the event horizon. The black hole is a hole because anything that falls through the event horizon soon inevitably reaches the central singularity. All particular properties of the in-falling material are lost and the black hole is characterized only by its mass, angular momentum and electric charge (which is likely to be near zero). The qualification arises from the fact that the quantum phenomenon of Hawking radiation means that all black holes radiate, albeit *very* slightly, corresponding to very low thermal temperatures for stellar and galactic-centre black holes. Mini black holes, however, if sufficiently 'mini', would radiate observably. The possibility of detecting black holes at astronomical distance is due to the intense gravitational field exerted from a relatively small volume.